CU00925416

ALBRIGHT & WILSON

THE LAST 50 YEARS

ALBRIGHT & WILSON

THE LAST 50 YEARS

*The story of the growth, struggles and
disintegration of a long-established member
of the international chemical industry*

HUGH PODGER

BREWIN BOOKS

First published by
Brewin Books Ltd, 56 Alcester Road,
Studley, Warwickshire B80 7LG in 2002
www.brewinbooks.com

© Hugh Podger 2002

All rights reserved.

ISBN 1 85858 223 7

The moral right of the author has been asserted.

A Cataloguing in Publication Record
for this title is available from the British Library.

Typeset in Times
Printed in Great Britain by
Warwick Printing Company Limited.

ACKNOWLEDGEMENTS

This book has been based on extensive Company records and contributions from many people. An appendix lists, with brief biographies, the nearly 60 staff of the Albright & Wilson Group and of Tenneco who have helped through interviews or written accounts. Sadly, some have died during the years that it has taken to complete this book and so will not be able to see the work to which they have contributed. Out of all the contributions I should like to single out those by Michael Peard, who died in March 2001, Jim Medves (who also died in 2001) and Lloyd Lillico, who all took much trouble to give their recollections.

I have had access to a very large quantity of written material - annual reports, Board minutes and files covering the whole period. I am indebted to Corinne Alliston who sorted the archives held at Knightsbridge before the Company's Head Office was moved to Warley - a task of many months. At one time, a warehouse in Blackheath was rented for the storage of the bulk of the archives, comprising over 300 boxes of files. A particularly valuable source of information has been the Company's house journal, which started in 1953 and continued until the final submergence of A&W; while the last five years contained little useful information, up to then there was an excellent balance of news of developments, staff movements and articles on current affairs beyond the Company.

I have benefited from the material collected by David Livingstone, who had envisaged the publication of volume 2 of the Company's history, having been largely responsible for the first volume, 'The Story of 100 Years of Phosphorus Making'. He had offered to assist in the production of this volume but died in March 1994, when I was about to begin the task. I am grateful to Jenny for making David's collection of papers available.

The writing of this book was commissioned in 1994 by Robin Paul, at that time Managing Director of Albright & Wilson Ltd. I thank him for his initiative. The work resulting from that has spread over a much longer period than he and I had expected, because of the size of the task and other commitments on my time, but it has been an enjoyable task, recalling events and people known to me.

I am grateful to Harriet Sharkey for her editing. Apart from the direct result of her work, it has been encouraging to have the reactions of someone not concerned in the affairs of the Company, to a work of much detail in a somewhat specialised field. I also want to convey thanks to Brewin Books for valuable assistance in the printing and publication of this book.

Finally, my thanks to the numerous employees and ex-employees who have been patiently enquiring from time to time over the years how the work has been progressing and expressing keenness to see the result one day. I hope that they will not be disappointed with this account of the last 50 years of a venerable but vulnerable enterprise.

Hugh Podger - March 2002

CONTENTS

LIST OF ILLUSTRATIONS

Charts

FOREWORD

by Dr R.C. Paul, CBE, Chief Executive of Albright & Wilson from 1986 to 1997

Why write the history of a company at all? There seem to me to be two very good reasons. First, the history of an individual company is a microcosm of our wider social and industrial history. The reader will obtain a compelling involvement with the company's leaders, understanding their pressures and sharing in their triumphs and disasters, all of which will provide a much better insight into the reality of industrial life than could be obtained from regular reading of the business pages in the newspapers or from a whole series of television documentaries.

Secondly, for a company, unlike the history of science or religion or even a whole nation, the scoresheet can be ruthlessly exposed chapter by chapter. Brave words all too often turn into rotten figures. Great men, on the other hand, leave their imprint on the balance sheet long after they have ceased to be personally involved.

Albright & Wilson is in many ways an ideal company for such a story. It was a truly international British based company. It had a highly eventful 150 year history, from creation to extinction. This volume takes up the story in 1951 and covers events through to the acquisition of the company by Rhodia in 2000. The first volume, "The Story of 100 Years of Phosphorus Making 1851-1951", written to coincide with that centenary, cast the achievements of the company in a somewhat overgenerous light, perhaps inevitably because it was a kind of celebration book. Hugh Podger has studiously avoided that temptation. Indeed if the independent reader were to lose confidence that the story was being told objectively and without 'spin', the value of his work would be greatly diminished. Only in the Epilogue does he permit himself some personal comment and reflection.

For many people the name of Albright & Wilson will be associated with the disaster of Long Harbour. In his book "Making It Happen" John Harvey-Jones makes only one reference to Albright & Wilson - their "really big mistake in building their phosphorus plant in Newfoundland". But what actually happened in the saga of Long Harbour? For the first time, it is set out here in all its gripping detail, a cocktail of human vanities and frailties, more akin to a process of water torture than to a big bang calamity. For this chapter alone Hugh Podger's carefully researched account makes this a book of lasting importance.

Speaking for myself, I wish I had had the early chapters to read before I joined the company in 1986. I believe this very human story will be of great value to all those who want to know what the chemical industry is really like inside.

Robin Paul

INTRODUCTION

This is the second and last volume of the history of Albright & Wilson. It follows 'The Story of 100 Years of Phosphorus Making 1851 - 1951' (published 1952), which began at the point when Arthur Albright, a partner in the firm of John & Edmund Sturge, first made phosphorus. He separated from Sturge in 1854 and took John Edward Wilson into partnership in 1856, when the firm of Albright & Wilson came into existence.

The author of the centenary history was Richard (Richie) Threlfall, son of Sir Richard Threlfall (Director of Research from 1899 to 1932), who became a non-executive Director in 1949. Four thousand copies of the history were printed and distributed and Richie was thanked by the Board "for having assumed, on behalf of the Company, the labours and perils of authorship and for having leavened with a little judicious levity the results of hours of toil and consultation of authorities". This volume, although covering fewer years, examines in more detail a changing pattern of growth, diversification, decline and eventual submergence, and encompasses much material that would not otherwise have been available to the public.

There were earlier suggestions for a second volume. In April 1965, Richie wrote to Sir Sydney Barratt, then the Chairman of the Company, to say that the Deputy Chairman, Bryan Topley, had suggested that "as since 1951 the group had undergone a certain expansion it might now perhaps be the time to write up a modest Vol. II of the A&W history with special reference to the acquired fractions". Sir Sydney's response is not known, but it seems that he was too occupied, or the period was deemed to be too short for a worthy successor to Volume 1.

Ten years later, in November 1975, David Livingstone (by then Managing Director) wrote to Bryan Topley, who had retired in 1967, to invite him to write Volume II. He replied "Tempted, I read through the set of Annual Reports 1948/74, which impressed upon me how much I should have to ferret out from people who are busy enough already, doubtless especially for the period '67-'75. Too much work and travel. The fact is, I'm lazy".

It is perhaps appropriate that, although overdue, this second volume has been able to review the performance of Albright & Wilson through a period of great interest and also to cover the Company's final days. When I agreed in 1994 to tackle the task of writing Volume II, Albright & Wilson was wholly owned by Tenneco (based in Houston, Texas). The period to be covered was extended, first to the company's return to the stockmarket in 1995 and then to its absorption into Rhodia in 2000. Volume II thus turned out to be truly the story of the last 50 years of Albright & Wilson.

The background to the Company events was a period of immense changes in the world scene which included:

- a general reduction in tariffs, the ending of Imperial Preference and the creation of the European free trade grouping
- inflation of an order never previously experienced: UK retail prices, which post-war were not much higher than at the time of the Napoleonic Wars and lower than at the end of the first World War, rose between the end of 1951 and the end of 1999 by a factor of nearly 20, while average earnings rose even more
- very large movements in exchange rates, reflecting different rates of growth in the major economies, notably Germany and East Asia, especially Japan: in 1951 the £ bought 1000 yen and 12 deutschemarks while the rate against the US$ was pegged at 2.80 for the next 16 years but by 2000 was in the range 1.4-1.6
- a steep growth in the value of equities (measured by the FT30 index): in the UK, between the end of 1951 and the end of 1999, the equity index rose by a factor of 14, while fixed interest stocks languished; in real terms, however, the value of UK equities fell by nearly one-fifth
- the computer revolution, in factory, office, shop and home
- the reversal of the process of nationalisation
- the growth of awareness of health, safety and the environment, with particular reference to the chemical industry
- the development of the European Union, with political as well as economic influence
- a cycle of mergers and de-mergers in business.

In assessing the performance of an industrial company such as Albright & Wilson, heed must obviously be paid to this background. Probably the hardest aspect to put into perspective is the value of money; there are many companies whose apparent progress is illusory when adjusted for inflation and such adjustments show some of Albright & Wilson's past results in a perhaps unexpected light (see Appendix I).

In reviewing the closing years of Albright & Wilson, a question that arises is: what criteria should be applied in judging success or failure, progress or decline, for an industrial company? Is the most important aim survival? Or is it a mark of success that the company survived for 150 years despite difficult times and tremendous changes, and that it achieved much in that time? That leads on to the question of whether eventual submergence was unavoidable. That is considered in the Epilogue, where conclusions and judgments are made, with much benefit of hindsight. I hope that the objective presentation of the facts in the first eight chapters will enable readers to draw their own conclusions, whether they be similar or otherwise.

Hugh Podger
April 2002

Chapter 1

BUILDING FOUNDATIONS

1951-1955

"In general, it is true that American chemical industry expects and seems to get, in spite of its belief in tempestuous competition and our own predilection towards a quiet little monopoly, a much higher return on turnover"
(Sydney Barratt 1952)

The Background to 1951

At the dawn of the 1950s, Albright & Wilson Ltd still gave the appearance of a family company: it was run by descendants of the founders and had dominant family shareholdings. Kenneth Wilson, grandson of the founding John Edward Wilson, joined the Board in 1910 at the age of 25 and became Chairman in 1932, remaining in service until 1958. Beside him was W.B. (Bill) Albright, Grandson of Arthur Albright, who had joined the company in 1931, became a Director in 1937, served as Managing Director from 1942 until 1955 and remained on the Board until 1978. Kenneth Wilson's younger brother, J.C. (Christopher) Wilson, came to Oldbury in 1919 and became a Director in 1921 and Secretary in 1932; he remained on the Board until 1963. His son, Nevil Wilson, became Secretary in 1955 and remained in that office until the end of 1988.

In 1951, the Albright & Wilson group comprised Albright & Wilson Ltd, the parent company and main UK operating company, and subsidiaries in England, Ireland, Canada, the USA and Australia. There were about 4,000 employees of whom 2,250 were in the UK. The changes since the beginning of the century had been relatively small: A&W had expanded into Ireland and Australia and in the UK had acquired some small subsidiaries and a second manufacturing site. Two wars and the recession between them had resulted in fewer changes than might have been expected, and far fewer than were to come in the next ten years.

The Korean War stimulated world trade, making 1951 a boom year when A&W's sales reached nearly £14 million (£247 million in 2000 money), a figure over one-third higher than the previous year, with a pretax profit of nearly £2.25 million. The capital employed, excluding cash balances, had a book value of £8 million of which about half was in England. Profit margins were good, averaging over 16% (profit on sales before interest and tax). Most of the sales were in products derived from phosphorus, the main exceptions being 25,000 tons of sodium chlorate produced in Canada and the USA (where A&W held a leading position), carbon tetrachloride produced at Widnes, a miscellany of fine chemicals by Thomas Tyrer (£1 million) and strontium compounds by Bristol Mineral & Land Co.. A&W's market position in phosphorus and phosphates was relatively weak in the USA but strong in the UK, Canada and Australia, where it was the only local producer, protected by high tariffs. Its technology in phosphorus was not strong though it was better in phosphorus-derived ("thermal") phosphoric acid and phosphates.

UK

A&W had two main operating sites in England: at Oldbury, a town in the industrialised Black Country between Birmingham and Wolverhampton in the West

Kenneth Wilson, Chairman until January 1958, with his successor, Sydney Barratt.

Yellow phosphorus, sold as wedges kept under water because it flames when dry.

Amorphous (red) phosphorus, used in matches, being drilled out from baking tanks.
[photo: Caters News Agency Ltd]

Ferric ammonium citrate scales, for use in tonics, made at Stratford (East London) in 1962, by painting solution onto glass plates.

Midlands; and at Widnes, a Lancashire (now Cheshire) town on the Mersey near Liverpool which was one of the main areas of chemical industry in the UK.

The **Oldbury** site, birthplace of Albright & Wilson, had been extended between 1851 and 1950 to a total area of 50 acres. It was the headquarters and the research and engineering centre as well as the most important production site. It included a phosphorus plant and plants for the manufacture of phosphoric acid (by burning phosphorus), food and detergent phosphates, phosphates for water treatment, phosphorus oxychloride, hypophosphites, and other derivatives of phosphorus. Match phosphorus materials, the oldest of A&W's products, were produced by Albright & Wilson Match Phosphorus Company Ltd, a company which had been formed jointly with British Match Corporation. Phosphides for marine flares were manufactured for sale by Holmes' Marine Life Protection Association Ltd, a small company acquired by A&W in 1919. Oil additives (organic phosphorus derivatives) were made by A&W under licence from Lubrizol Corporation, of Ohio, and marketed by Anglamol Ltd (owned by A&W, Lubrizol and Dalton & Co).

The buildings at Oldbury were mainly old, brick-built (and therefore inflexible) and congested. The works had a reputation for fumes and smells, especially those emitted by the phosphorus furnaces and from phosphorus-sulphur compounds produced in the oil additives plant and the Malathion insecticide plant. Working conditions were uncomfortable, and safety precautions minimal. Operations were labour-intensive, with nearly 1,000 hourly-paid employees and over 400 staff. Traditions of paternalism and long-service, however, remained strong. There were good recreational, medical and dental facilities, a funeral fund and above-average pension schemes, although there were large variations between "works" and "staff" in most aspects of employment. Married works pensioners received £8 per month, which may be compared with the labourer's basic rate equivalent to about £24 per month (the salary for a newly-graduated staff entrant was around £400 pa).

The 11.5 acre site at Ann Street, **Widnes**, was leased from ICI in 1933 for the production of phosphorus on the understanding that A&W's interest in industrial and fine chemicals would not impinge on ICI's fertiliser interests. In the early 1930s, plants were added for alkali phosphates and later for food phosphates. In 1934 a carbon tetrachloride (CTC) plant was built, taking advantage of the chlorine and carbon bisulphide available from ICI next door, and replaced during the war at the request of the Ministry of Supply. After the war, the CTC plant was refurbished, capacity for phosphoric acid was expanded and a sodium phosphate crystals plant was built. Many years, however, were to elapse before there was any substantial capital investment in expansion or modernisation. In 1951, there were 400 works employees and 120 staff at Ann Street; the number declined slightly in the following three years and then stabilised, until plants were added in the 1970s.

Elsewhere in the UK, the largest of A&W's other interests was Thomas Tyrer

& Co. Ltd, acquired in 1942, with sites in Stratford (London) and Barking (Essex) making and merchanting hundreds of fine chemicals, mostly in very small quantities. Bristol Mineral & Land Co Ltd, mining strontium sulphate near Bristol, had become a subsidiary in 1941. Clifford Christopherson & Co Ltd, originally A&W's sales agent, was acquired in 1932 and became a merchanting arm, based at A&W's sales office in London. These subsidiaries had no significant effect on the Company's profits - between them in 1951, a peak year, they contributed a little over £100,000 to pretax profits.

Ireland

Albright & Wilson Ireland had been formed in 1935, with premises at Dun Laoghaire, Dublin, to manufacture acid calcium phosphate, a leavening agent for bread, with the protection of a tariff granted to encourage local manufacture. Semi-finished product was supplied from England and local manufacture consisted only of milling and packing. Initially there were only 20 employees. The range of industrial phosphates was then broadened and extended into branded products for the consumer market. In 1947, Goodbody Ltd was formed to market consumer products, following which a number of major international companies appointed A&W Ireland to distribute their products, some of which were also packaged in Dublin. Meanwhile, to meet a promise made to the Irish Government when the company was formed, the Albright & Wilson Ltd holding was reduced to 47.5% in 1945; 21 years later, when the tariff situation had changed, A&W Ireland once again became a subsidiary. In 1951, the main significance of the company was as a minor outlet for phosphates from Widnes and Oldbury.

North America

The two North American subsidiaries - The Electric Reduction Company (Erco) in Canada and Oldbury Electro-Chemical Company (OECCo) in the USA - were well established. They had combined sales not far short of those of the parent company but were not closely linked to the Board and headquarters at Oldbury. At a time when travel by air was not common and a transatlantic telephone call had to be booked a day in advance, this relative isolation was hardly surprising.

Erco was established at Buckingham, Quebec, where it could take advantage of hydroelectric power available from the adjacent Lievre River. Initially, Erco produced potassium chlorate, but when the plant was destroyed by fire in 1896 manufacture switched to phosphorus. The export of phosphorus from Buckingham to Europe at low prices led to a patent suit by Albright & Wilson, which lasted from 1899 to 1902, when Erco had come to the end of its resources; A&W took 60% of

Erco's share capital, acquiring the balance from the Erco directors over the next twelve years. From 1902 Erco's only product, apart from temporary manufacture of ferrochromium and chlorates, was phosphorus, some of which was shipped to Oldbury. Later, phosphoric acid was made and then in 1933, when the Widnes phosphorus plant began to supply Oldbury, Erco's product range was broadened into phosphates and chlorates. In the early 1950s the growth of detergent phosphates led to a major expansion in Erco's phosphate capacity and to the building of a phosphorus plant at a new site. Sales by Erco in 1951, at CAD 6.4 million (£2.3 million) accounted for about 15% of the A&W total; pretax profit of £0.2 million was less than 10% of the total.

OECCo, the Company's longest-established subsidiary, was set up in 1896 with a factory making phosphorus by an electric furnace operation at Niagara Falls where power was in constant supply. Until then, most of the phosphorus used in the USA had been imported from Oldbury. The next products were potassium chlorate and sodium chlorate, and match phosphorus chemicals. In 1927, OECCo took over The Phosphorus Compounds Company, a company partly owned by A&W, which had been formed in 1903 to manufacture products using OECCo's phosphorus; it thereby broadened its product range to include phosphoric acid, hypophosphites, phosphorus chlorides and sulphides. It had also become the sole remaining producer of sodium chlorate in the USA. In 1951 the sales of OECCo were $9.3m (£3.3m.); while up by nearly 50% on the previous year and more than a fifth of the total of the A&W group, they were small in the US chemical industry. Pretax profit was USD 2.1 million (£0.76m.), three times the profit in 1950 and a peak not matched in any later year.

Australia

Albright & Wilson (Australia) was founded in October 1939 as a joint venture between Albright & Wilson Ltd (60%) and ICIANZ (40%). A&W had begun exporting to Australia in the early 1930s using Brunner Mond & Co.(Australasia), then a part of ICIANZ, as its selling agent. Responding to the desire to increase sales and the threat of isolation through war, a company was formed with an initial capital of £100,000 and local manufacture commenced. The agreement between the two companies listed phosphorus and industrial phosphates, chlorates and carbon bisulphide as products reserved for the joint venture. ICIANZ offered 4.88 acres of land on deep water at Yarraville, on the outskirts of Melbourne, at a cost of £2,000 per acre; three acres were bought then and another acre later.

From the end of 1940, phosphoric acid and phosphates were made from phosphorus imported from Erco, an inconvenient arrangement that was inevitably replaced by phosphorus manufacture in Australia; a furnace with a capacity of 1,000 tons pa was commissioned in 1943. The process developed for the manufacture of phosphoric acid was adopted by Erco and A&W UK. Named the Maunsell process after its inventor, it avoided the need for ever-larger towers, which had become a distinguishing feature of the Oldbury skyline. From 1946, Calgon (sodium hexametaphosphate) was also manufactured. The right to make sodium chlorate in Australia was ceded to ICIANZ in 1948 and carbon bisulphide was never made.

Not surprisingly, communications between the parent company and its Australian subsidiary in its first 10-15 years were even poorer than those across the Atlantic because of the distance and the smallness of the operation, although there were invitations to directors from the UK. In 1951, the Australian company's sales were AUD 600,000 (less than £½ million) and its trading profit less than £100,000.

Phosphorus manufacture

The element of phosphorus is said to have been isolated in 1669 by Hennig Brandt, an alchemist in Hamburg, from phosphates contained in urine. A process for its manufacture from bone ash was developed in Sweden in 1785 and there was small-scale industrial manufacture in France from about 1838. The white form of phosphorus then being produced was used in the early Lucifer matches. White phosphorus, however, is poisonous and ignites when exposed to air. In 1845 the Viennese Anton von Schrotter developed a process for heating white phosphorus to produce a stable and non-poisonous form of the element, red or amorphous phosphorus. In 1849 Arthur Albright met Schrotter to acquire the rights to his process and improved upon it by eliminating the tendency to explosions. Red phosphorus, used mostly in matches, became Albright & Wilson's main product, almost until the close of the nineteenth century, and was the foundation of its prosperity.

The method used by Arthur Albright for the production of phosphorus at Oldbury from 1851 was the "retort" process. That involved heating phosphoric acid, produced by the action of sulphuric acid on calcium phosphate (from bones or mineral phosphate), with carbon in a clay retort; phosphorus vapour was then condensed to form solid white phosphorus.

In 1888 patents were granted in England – but not to A&W – for the manufacture of phosphorus by the electric furnace method, which made continuous production possible and rendered the historic retort process obsolete. The owners of the patents formed The Phosphorus Company in 1890 and built a plant at Wednesfield in Staffordshire, not far from Oldbury. That crucial threat to A&W's business was quickly removed by A&W's acquisition of the company, plant and patents. A&W then built a plant at Oldbury with a capacity of 200 tpa. It started up in 1893; the Wednesfield plant closed soon after.

In the next 25 years, larger furnaces were built and by 1918 the output had risen to 2,700 tons. The reduction in demand for war purposes, however, together with the loss of markets through the growth of competition (phosphorus plants were by 1918 operating in Japan, Russia, Italy, France, Germany, Sweden and Norway) and the relatively high cost of electricity in England, led to the closure of the Oldbury furnaces in 1919 and the cessation of UK phosphorus production. More than 20 years passed before Oldbury again produced phosphorus, this time from a plant built by the Ministry of Supply for its wartime requirements. In 1942 the plant was converted to produce ferrosilicon, because of the shortage of phosphate rock, but recommenced phosphorus manufacture when A&W purchased it in 1947. In 1951 its output was expanded to 10,300 tons pa.

PHOSPHORUS MANUFACTURE BY THE ELECTRIC FURNACE METHOD

A chemically proportioned mixture of phosphate rock (calcium phosphate), carbon and silica (the "furnace burden") is smelted in a closed furnace heated electrically by electrodes passing through the roof, arcing with the carbon-lined body. The products resulting from this electro-thermal reaction are a gas consisting mainly of carbon monoxide with phosphorus vapour, carried away from the top of the furnace, and a molten calcium silicate slag, removed from the base of the furnace. The chemical reaction may be expressed as:

$$2Ca_3P_2O_8 + 6SiO_2 + 10C = 6CaSiO_3 + 10CO + P_4$$

phosphate rock + silica + carbon = Calcium silicate + carbon monoxide + phosphorus

The gases are typically passed through electrostatic precipitators to remove dust and then to a condensing train, where the phosphorus is collected and the carbon monoxide gas passed through for burning. The molten slag, at a temperature of approximately 1,500°C, is removed from the furnace either periodically or continuously, depending on the furnace load and operating characteristic. Any dust entrained in the gas offtake that is not collected in the electrostatic precipitators passes into the condensers, forming a phosphorus mud that requires secondary processing to release the phosphorus.

The material input to the furnace, particularly the size and thermal characteristics of the phosphate rock, is critical, as is the silica/lime ratio of the slag. Incorrect materials can give rise to sintering (i.e. coalescing), leading to arching of the burden and subsequent falls, which can cause breakages of the electrodes and excessive gas offtake temperatures, with resulting high dust carry-over and mud make. Furnace parameters such as diameter, depth, electrode spacing and the configuration of feed chutes and tap-holes are extremely important features. The suspension of the electrodes must provide a combination of flexibility (movement up and down) and rigidity (vertical alignment). The electrical system must allow a range of variation in the current load (the amps/volts ratio), which will affect the furnace temperature and the rate of smelting.

It has frequently been said that successful operation of a phosphorus furnace is an art rather than a science, because of the number of variables involved. Undoubtedly experience among operating staff is valuable. More important, however, is the design; the plant should be built without compromise and, for the most part, should employ well-developed components.

The Canadian phosphorus plant of Erco at Buckingham was smaller than Oldbury's but had the advantage of cheap power, which had led the A&W Board as early as 1909 to consider concentrating production there. Phosphorus was shipped from Buckingham to Oldbury intermittently from 1905 and then from 1919 it became Oldbury's source of the material. While Erco's capacity was increased at that time, it was still only 2,000 tons pa, less than that of the closed Oldbury furnaces. The growth in demand for food and other alkali phosphates in the UK from 1923 led eventually to the building of furnaces at Widnes and the cessation of imports from Canada. Two additional phosphorus furnaces, larger than any previously built by A&W, were built at Buckingham in the 1939-45 war but were closed after the war was over.

In the United States, OECCo started making phosphorus in electric furnaces in 1897. Up to that time, a very small amount of phosphorus had been made in the USA by chemical methods but the material was largely imported from England. OECCo's output grew slowly in the next 20 years until the entry of the USA into the 1914-18 war, when its capacity was increased to meet the demands of the US Government, for which it was the principal supplier of phosphorus.

Following the war, things did not go so well for OECCo. Early in the century, the management declined an opportunity to buy the Swann Corporation, of Birmingham, Alabama; in 1939, Swann was acquired by Monsanto, which went on to become a major manufacturer of phosphorus. OECCo also failed to embark on the manufacture of alkali phosphates, which became the major outlet for phosphorus in North America. In 1933, OECCo acquired the major interest in Pembroke Chemical Corporation, which had a plant in Florida designed to make phosphorus from accumulated phosphate fines; the only sales, however, were of the fines and some mined phosphate and in 1949, after depletion of the phosphate deposits, the company was liquidated. In 1951, Niagara Alkali Company made an approach for merger, which would have improved OECCo's position in phosphorus;

although the move was favoured by the management of OECCo it was called off because the Niagara Alkali management believed that their shareholders would object to British control.

The only significant development in A&W's phosphorus-making technology in the twentieth century came in 1930 when OECCo introduced a three-phase furnace (i.e. with three electrodes in place of one), and a new design of vertical condenser for the phosphorus vapour. Even so, it took two years before the development was adopted by other plants in A&W. It is clear that the story of phosphorus for A&W is one of missed opportunities. At the beginning of the 20th century, once know-how had been taken on board, OECCo formed and Erco acquired, Albright & Wilson had become a leader in phosphorus. It then failed to capitalise on its position.

In 1939, Widnes was producing about 4,600 tons pa of phosphorus, Buckingham 3,800 tpa and Niagara 2,200 tpa. By then, however, the total US production was about 40,000 tons and there were several plants in continental Europe. Although A&W's capacity grew during the 1939-45 war the Company remained a second-rank player in the international phosphorus scene. (See the chart of phosphorus production by A&W world-wide from 1903 to 1952, over the page.)

The relative decline was most marked in the USA, where OECCo's initially strong stance had been eroded. By 1951, the estimated capacity of the seven US producers of phosphorus totalled 192,500 short tons; OECCo's capacity was only 8,000 tpa, or about 4% of the total, down from about 5.5% in 1939. The industry's capacity had grown rapidly, from about 10,000 tpa in 1930 to 40,000 tpa in 1939 and 80,000 tpa in 1945, and it more than doubled in the next five years. The major producers were Monsanto, Victor (later Stauffer), Food Machinery & Chemical Corporation (FMC) and the Tennessee Valley Authority (TVA), with Virginia Carolina Chemical Co also larger than OECCo.

This expansion followed technical development work between 1918 and 1922 by the US Department of Agriculture on the production of phosphorus and phosphoric acid, initially through the Federal Phosphorus Company and later through TVA, Monsanto and Victor. TVA's furnace design, for which the plans were freely available, was adopted by A&W in 1951 for Erco's new phosphorus plant at Varennes (see p.13). The plans were purchased for $5. The capacity of the typical TVA furnace was greater than the total output of OECCo.

The decline in A&W's relative position in the manufacture of phosphorus was not dwelt on in the Company's centenary history. It is understandable that the celebration of 100 years of operation was an occasion for optimism and for satisfaction that the company had weathered storms to emerge into an era of recovery and expansion. There was, however, an element of hubris, a belief that the company was a leader in its business, with knowledge based on long experience. A&W's monopoly in the manufacture of phosphorus and its derivatives in Britain,

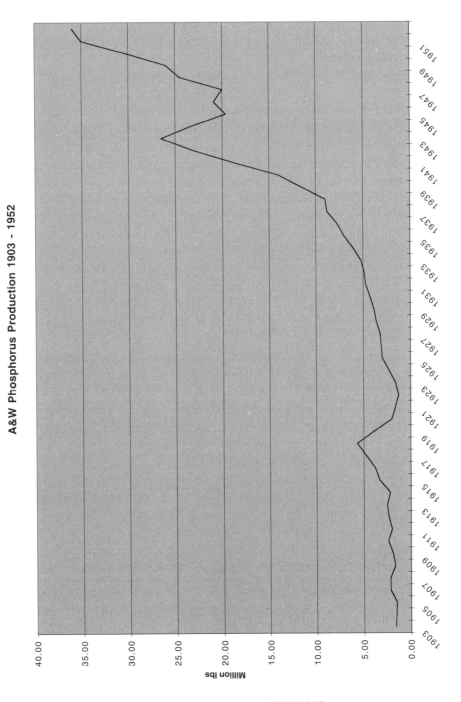

Phosphorus production 1903-1952

Canada and Australia bred complacency and presumptive confidence in the company's technical expertise. It was not long before that confidence was to be tested and found wanting.

Looking at A&W's decline retrospectively, it seems inevitable: the family-owned company was long on history but short on financial resources. It had been affected by the slump in the 1920s and 1930s, but cushioned by a monopolistic position in its home market and protected by duties on imports into the UK (especially Key Industry Duty of 33.3%), so seeking new business was not a priority. It was oriented towards British Empire markets by inclination and by Imperial Preference (the system of differential duties favouring trade between the countries of the British Empire). The lack of modern communications and fast travel also hindered the exploitation of international markets and despite a long-established subsidiary in the USA, some senior management in England were very apprehensive of becoming too involved with America and the Americans. Thus A&W was slow to develop in the fastest-growing and most innovative market across the Atlantic.

Another inhibiting factor was long service among senior managers on both sides of the Atlantic. For example, F.A. Lidbury joined the Board of OECCo in 1914, was President from 1923 and did not retire until 1947. His predecessor served as President from the formation of the company in 1896 until 1923 and his successor Walter Wallace, although President for only three years, had served as Vice-President since 1923 and was 69 when he retired at the end of 1949. Relations between the US and Canadian companies were perhaps too close: Erco was under the direction of Lidbury and Wallace from 1914 to 1944.

After the 1914-18 war the dominance of the Albright and Wilson families lessened, although it was still influential in 1951. This tradition of long service was mirrored at all levels among employees, leading to conservatism. Recruitment of new staff looking for change and expansion was limited not only by a low turnover but also by a shortage of graduates wishing to enter industry. Soon, however, the pace of change in A&W was to accelerate in line with the world at large.

The beginnings of change

Many significant changes were taking place at the time of the centenary celebrations. After the 1939-45 war, a period of major expansion for Albright & Wilson had begun. The production of materials for munitions ceased and the former carpet factories that had been taken over for that purpose were no longer required. Thoughts then turned to new products, which originated principally from America. Major capital expenditure laid the foundations for expansion in products that were to be important for the Company for many years to come. The two most significant were detergent phosphates and silicones.

Developments in phosphates

Polyphosphates – tetrasodium pyrophosphate and sodium tripolyphosphate (STPP) - were being considered for use in detergents before the 1939-45 war; patents for their production were published from 1937 onwards, mainly in Germany and the United States. Initially they were used as builders in soap products, for their water-softening and emulsifying properties. From around 1948 they were applied as builders in synthetic detergent powders (based on dodecyl benzene sulphonate, etc). STPP, the generally preferred builder, became the single most important factor in the expansion of Albright & Wilson in the 1950s and remained the Company's leading product for the next 30 years.

A&W's first STPP plant was built at **Oldbury** in 1948/9, with an intended output of 15,000 tons pa. At about the same time, the No.4 phosphoric acid plant was built at Oldbury, to supply the requirements for STPP, Calgon and other products; its four large towers, which remained a landmark for over 40 years, were a major scale-up of the similar No. 3 acid plant, itself the third stage in a scaling-up evolution, which demonstrated that expansion without a leap in technology could be very successful.

Before long a larger plant for STPP was needed. The site selected was **Kirkby**, a new town between Widnes and Liverpool, well placed to supply the two main customers, Lever Bros at Warrington and Thomas Hedley in Newcastle-upon-Tyne. Since at that time steel was in short supply, a disused seaplane hanger on the shore of Lake Windermere was purchased and moved to Kirkby to house the plant. Essentially a scaling-up of the Oldbury plant, the new STTP plant was authorised in September 1950 and came on stream in April 1953.

It was, of course, necessary to install capacity for phosphoric acid for the increased output of STPP. Since 1950, there had been two distinct camps in A&W. Bill Albright supported the production of phosphoric acid by A&W's practised method known as "thermal acid"(burning of phosphorus). Bryan Topley, the Research Director, supported the alternative method, that is the application of sulphuric acid to phosphate rock, known as "wet acid". Topley presented a paper on wet acid to the A&W Board in 1946; the Board decided to adhere to the thermal method since the quality of wet acid was suitable for STPP but not for food phosphates, soft drinks and other applications. In 1950, the Board again voted for thermal acid. Consequently, thermal acid units were installed at Kirkby, combining steam-raising units based on the Oldbury design and others of the Maunsell design (see p.6). The total cost of the Kirkby STPP and acid plants was £1.7 million.

Additional phosphorus capacity was also needed. There had been a serious proposal in 1947 to locate a new site in the North of Scotland, but power was not available at less than 0.6d. per kwh. Instead, **Portishead** near Bristol was chosen in

1950. It had the advantage of a dock for the receipt of phosphate rock shipments and an adjacent power station and rail connection for the transport of phosphorus to Kirkby.

The initial design was for six 7.5 megawatt (MW) furnaces, giving a total loading of 45 megawatts (1 MW is equivalent to about 1 million lbs, or 450 tons of phosphorus pa) and a theoretical capacity of 20,000 tons pa. That was a scaling-up of the Oldbury plant, which then consisted of six furnaces with a total loading of 30 MW. The output of the Oldbury plant in 1949 was about 6,000 tons, raised by 1951 to more than 10,000 tons and subsequently to more than 12,000 tons, close to their theoretical capacity. The first of the Portishead furnaces came on stream in February 1954, the capital cost of the plant being £4 million. The original design for Portishead provided for duplication of the initial plant on the 20-acre site, but that was never attempted.

In **Canada**, similar expansions were taking place to meet the demand for detergent phosphates. New plants were built at Buckingham for phosphoric acid and phosphates but phosphorus production was not expanded because of the limitation on hydro power and difficulties bringing in large quantities of phosphate rock and other raw materials. In April 1951 the Board agreed to buy a 120-acre site at Varennes on the St Lawrence river near Montreal, for location of a phosphorus furnace to replace Buckingham's (9,000 short tons, against 8,000 at Buckingham) at a cost estimated at CAD 2.5 million. Two months later the Canadian Government offered a loan for a second furnace to provide phosphorus for munitions. Built from TVA plans, the rectangular furnaces with three in-line electrodes were different from all other A&W furnaces. They came on stream in November 1953, at a total cost of CAD 5 million. There was no parallel development by OECCo; the possibility does not appear to have been considered by the A&W Board.

At the end of 1949, however, the Board did approve the building of a second phosphorus furnace in **Australia**, after a lengthy shutdown of the first furnace had demonstrated the vulnerability of a single-furnace operation. Economic review caused delay and consideration was given to locating the furnace in Tasmania, where power was cheaper. Eventually, in 1951, a new plant came on stream in Yarraville (Melbourne) in November 1954. Its capacity, 1,750 tons pa, was enough at the time to meet all requirements and to allow the original furnace to be put on stand-by.

Although enquiries for polyphosphates for detergents were received by A&W (Australia) in 1950 and some polyphosphates were imported from Germany in 1951, demand did not take off until 1955. Polyphosphate manufacture finally started at Yarraville in 1956. The phosphoric acid plant that had been built in 1949 was intended primarily to meet the growing demand for food phosphates and for Calgon (sodium hexametaphosphate) for the domestic consumer as well as for industrial uses including boiler water treatment.

Silicones

The second stream of development in the immediate post-war period was provided by silicones. Before the 1939-45 war, Albright & Wilson developed ethyl silicates and marketed them under the name of Silicon Esters, forming a company (Silicaseal Ltd) for the purpose. Their application was in the hardening of stone, bonding of inert fillers and as a medium in fresco and secco painting. A&W's interest in silicon chemistry originated during the 1914-18 war through work on the production of smoke by silicon tetrachloride (which was found to be inferior to phosphorus in that respect). Silicones, silicon-carbon compounds with insulating, coating, lubricating and heat-resisting properties, were developed by Corning Glass Works of the USA, which joined with Dow Chemical Company in 1943 to form Dow Corning Corporation, the world leader in the field.

Towards the end of the war, the Ministry of Supply invited Dow Corning to send a representative to the UK to discuss the development of silicones with British industry. In December 1945 Dr Shailer Bass of Dow Corning met A&W. As a result, Bill Albright, Sydney Barratt and Bryan Topley visited Midland, Michigan, at the beginning of 1946. Dow Corning offered to supply the technical information for A&W to manufacture as part of a joint company in which A&W would subscribe £125,000 for a 52% share; A&W's holding would be increased to 70% after five years through the investment of a further £200,000. The A&W Board rejected the offer.

In September 1946, Dow Corning agreed to grant A&W the sales agency for its silicones in the UK. Two years later, the A&W Board again considered but decided against the manufacture of silicones. In March 1950 there were further inconclusive discussions with Dow Corning. ICI then announced its intention to make silicones under licence from General Electric of the USA; the A&W Board considered joint manufacture with ICI but opted in April 1950 to manufacture under licence from Dow Corning. Five months later, Midland Silicones Ltd was formed as a joint venture between the two companies. A&W bought a 26-acre site at Barry, in South Wales, which was extended in 1951 and 1952. When production started in 1954, the plant was sold to the joint venture and A&W became the holder of 60% of Midland Silicones Ltd. There were two non-silicone operations at Barry: the manufacture of thioglycollic acid (for home perms) and the recovery of nickel catalyst from residues produced in the manufacture of margarine (an operation originally at Thomas Tyrer & Co., Stratford). Both operations remained wholly-owned by A&W.

Sodium Chlorate

Although **OECCo** was not participating in the expansion of phosphorus and phosphates production, it was engaged in a significant expansion in sodium chlorate. Potassium chlorate had been made by Albright & Wilson from its very beginning in 1851, as an important ingredient in the manufacture of matches[1]. As with phosphorus, the price of power is a key factor in the cost of chlorates. For that reason, manufacture was transferred from Oldbury to Niagara Falls in 1899, and an improved electrolytic cell developed by Sir Richard Threlfall was installed. Three years later, production of potassium chlorate ceased in the face of US competition, and production of sodium chlorate (used as a herbicide) commenced, with gradually increasing capacity and successive improvements in the cells. In 1912 the development of an all-graphite cell significantly reduced production costs. By 1926, as a result of competition from Europe, the other US manufacturers of potassium chlorate went out of production. OECCo was then the only manufacturer of sodium chlorate in the USA. Seven years later OECCo resumed production of potassium chlorate in response to US match manufacturers' wishes for domestic supply.

Meanwhile in **Canada**, the success of the graphite cell led to the building of a potassium chlorate plant at Buckingham (1913). Soon after start-up, sodium chlorate was also produced. In 1922, however, competitive imports led to the end of chlorates manufacture until 1932 when the growing demand for weedkiller encouraged production once again. In 1951, the rapid growth in demand for sodium chlorate for pulp bleaching prompted expansion in both Canada and the USA, increasing Buckingham's capacity from 6,000 to 9,300 tons and Niagara Falls' capacity to 19,000 tons, which was still 5,000 tons short of demand. To meet the shortfall, a new site was selected at Columbus, Mississippi. Treasury and Bank of England consent was given for $4.5 million to be borrowed for the plant, which came on stream in June 1954.

Other developments

Among several other developments undertaken at the beginning of the 1950s, the research laboratory at Oldbury is notable. A contract for £126,000 was placed in March 1951 and the building was occupied in early 1952, attracting a full complement of graduates. In 1951 a Central Engineering Department was formed to handle the major programme of expansion and the first international conference of the Albright & Wilson Group was held.

---

[1] Safety matches typically contain 37% of potassium chlorate on the head and about 50% of amorphous phosphorus on the side of the box; strike anywhere matches contain 20% of potassium chlorate and 9% of phosphorus sesquisulphide.

Financial Assessment – 1951

1951 was clearly a year of high activity and commitment to expansion. To assist in financing this expansion, the Company arranged loans in Britain, the USA and Canada, introducing an element of gearing in the capital structure, previously negligible; at the end of 1951, however, cash balances still exceeded borrowing. On sales of £14 million, pretax profit was £2.3 million. Ordinary dividends were covered nearly four times.

Progress from 1948, when the first accounts were published, is shown in the following figures (values in £ million):-

Progress 1948 - 1951

	1948	1949	1950	1951
Sales				
UK companies	4.5	4.8	5.9	7.8
Overseas companies	3.1	3.2	4.2	6.1
Total	**7.6**	**8.0**	**10.1**	**13.9**
Profit (before interest & tax)				
UK companies	0.72	0.75	0.99	1.27
Overseas companies	0.35	0.29	0.47	1.01
Other income	0.02	0.02	0.01	0.03
Total	**1.09**	**1.06**	**1.47**	**2.31**
Capital employed				
UK companies	1.8	2.0	4.7	7.2
Overseas companies	2.3	3.1	3.3	4.9
Other net assets	0.5	0.2	0.1	0.7
Total	**4.6**	**5.3**	**8.1**	**12.8**
Capital Expenditure Total	0.8	1.0	1.0	2.1

Although the major expansion projects described were under way in 1951, they had no impact on sales and profits in that year; the substantial rise in trading results in 1951 was due partly to the boom conditions (a decline was experienced in 1952) and partly to the earlier, smaller-scale, developments in STPP and sodium chlorate. The marked growth in capital employed in 1951 was due largely to the loans of nearly £3.5 million arranged during the year, which were reflected in cash and investments at the end of the year totalling nearly £5 million (three-quarters held by the parent company), in anticipation of the £7.5 million capital expenditure that was to take place in the next two years. If the cash and investments are excluded, the profit earned in 1951 shows a return of over 25% on capital.

In all respects, A&W's financial position was strong and its path to expansion well marked.

Management

The need for capital for these developments led the Board to decide in 1947 to convert Albright & Wilson into a public company, which occurred in March 1948. The original intention to increase capital by issuing additional shares was postponed to 1950 (due to unfavourable market conditions), when £2 million was raised through an issue of Preference stock. The family began to reduce its holdings, starting with sales of 20% of the Ordinary shares to institutions. The Register of Directors' shareholdings shows that at the beginning of 1953 nearly 30% of the Ordinary share capital was owned or controlled by the Directors. Their share had fallen to less than 12% by the end of 1955 and to 8% at the end of 1959.

The influence of the families was fading and a new style of management was emerging. The main person responsible for the transition to a more professional style was Sydney Barratt, one of the outstanding figures in the history of the Company. He was the driving force behind expansion and the originator of planning for the future. Born in 1898, SB (as he was generally known) read chemistry at Oxford and then taught at Leeds and University College, London. At UCL his pursuits included work on a submarine signalling device and on a torpedo recovery light, for which phosphine was required. That led him to Oldbury, where similar research was taking place at the request of the Admiralty. From collaboration on that research came an invitation to join the company. In 1932 he joined A&W as Assistant Director of Research and very soon after became Director of Research in succession to Sir Richard Threlfall, who died in that year.

SB's excellence shone through. In 1936 he became Director of Development and by 1938 had joined the Board. By 1951 he was effectively the Financial Director and indeed bore the title for a time in 1955, as well as taking on the office of Company Secretary in the short gap between Christopher and Nevil Wilson. He succeeded Bill Albright as Managing Director in 1955 and became the first non-family Chairman on Kenneth Wilson's retirement in 1958. His study of the company and vision for the future in 1952/3 are reviewed next.

The Sydney Barratt papers

In a series of five papers, issued between March 1952 and January 1953, Sydney Barratt, then acting as Financial Director, analysed the Company's position and general business management. These papers were noteworthy for the time, when management treatises were not common, and were unique within the Company, where pragmatism rather than philosophy was the rule.

Paper I: An Essay on Growth and Decay (March 1952)

In the first of his papers SB opened by declaring his intention "to provide some basis for further thought about our future as a company and for that coherent discussion of it which we must achieve". He based this on the thesis that any commodity moves through four stages: *accommodation to novelty; general acceptance; full usage; decay.*

In the case of Albright & Wilson, he took phosphorus usage as the index of growth, and showed that from 1903 to 1922, when most of sales were to the match industry, the business was in the third or "soporific" stage, with virtually no growth (about 2% per annum). From 1922 to 1951, the introduction of food phosphates and then phosphates for water treatment led to growth of about 12.5% pa compound, representing the second stage and bringing opportunities and responsibilities. The enhanced rate of growth was then expected to continue for a while because of the introduction of sodium tripolyphosphate in detergents.

SB was concerned at the implications of the faster rate of growth in terms of investment. Up to 1946, he said, Albright & Wilson was under-investing and accumulating reserves; the flow was then reversed and he expected the Company to reach the limit of its borrowing power by 1953 or 1954. He did not favour issuing Ordinary shares for cash because of the earnings required to pay dividends with adequate cover. (Indeed, in the whole of its existence as a public company, until the reflotation in 1995, Albright & Wilson issued Ordinary shares for cash only once, in 1955, primarily to finance the acquisition of Marchon, described on p.45.)

It would therefore be necessary to restrict capital expenditure and concentrate research and development on fast-maturing projects until the cash flow from current expansion provided new resources. SB calculated the limit on capital expenditure after 1955 to be £500,000 pa (in 1952 money), assuming that the Company would not use its borrowing powers to the full and would not still be achieving growth of as much as 12.5% per annum. All this represented the first attempt at forward planning in A&W, as far as is known, but it does now seem to have been over-cautious.

Capital expenditure in 1952-4, relative to the size of the Company, was, however, higher than in any subsequent three-year period: at nearly £11 million, it was 85% of the total capital employed at the end of 1951. There was indeed a breathing-space in 1955, when expenditure was only £1 million, lower than in any subsequent year in the Company's history. The higher future expenditure was caused partly by expansion through acquisitions, which were not considered in SB's calculations, and partly by the need to spend more simply to stay in business.

Paper II: On the preservation of capital values (May 1952)

Following on from the first paper, the second considered how much investment would be required to replace fixed assets and cope with inflation in working capital. SB argued that plants and premises had an average life of 25 years, based on both their physical life and the durability of the markets served; he calculated that at the time of writing the Company had to spend at least £500,000 pa (including inflation) simply to replace its fixed assets and a further £250,000 to keep pace with 7.5% annual inflation in working capital. Any expansion or new products would involve new share capital. So he had moved on from his first paper. He looked at ICI, which at that time had a practice of setting sums aside for obsolescence of fixed assets and for stock replacement, and concluded that they were working on similar lines.

In fact, A&W had set up an Obsolesence & Replacement Reserve several years earlier and had regularly been appropriating sums from profits for it. The reserve reached £1 million in 1954, when the first use of it was made to write down the value of obsolete plant. Thereafter the sums set aside were erratic, tending to reflect the amount of profit available - nothing was set aside in seven of the next fourteen years - until the reserve was quietly eliminated in 1968 and its £1.5 million total used to write down the value of obsolete plant and unproductive assets. Circumstances submerged theory.

Paper III: On Profits, Profitability and Prosperity (September 1952)

In his third paper SB compared profit in 1951 with the amounts required to service fixed assets, finance working capital and pay dividends at 2.5% net on shareholders' funds. "In general," SB observed, "it is true that American chemical industry expects and seems to get, in spite of its belief in tempestuous competition and our own predilection towards a little quiet monopoly, a much higher return on turnover" - 20-35% in USA against 15-20% in the UK. Albright & Wilson did not publish any sales figures until 1958, deeming it commercially imprudent to do so; its margin on sales in 1951 was 17%, giving a return on capital (profit before interest and tax on net capital employed) of nearly 19%.

For a company with a monopoly in the manufacture of its products within the UK and protection through Key Industry Duty of 33.3% on much of its product range, SB's description of A&W's return on capital in 1951 as "modest" seems appropriate. Moreover, many of the assets were relatively old, with a low book value and were working close to capacity pending heavy investment in new plants in the next two years. 1951 was also a boom year for the world economy; A&W's profit fell by 30% in 1952 and with the continuing investment the return on capital was reduced to less than 12%.

SB's main concern was that A&W was facing a prospect of falling profitability. His paper included the somewhat surprising words: "We are now at the beginning of our troubles. No amount of financial planning, any more than production or sales planning, can ensure success, which in the end also depends on our ultimate customers whose behaviour we can influence only in minor ways". The Company was embarking on major expansion, with the prospect of new plants which would not be fully employed for some years and were mainly for large tonnage products on which profit margins were expected to be below 15%. The margins on other products would also tend to shrink. SB thus highlighted a need for cost reductions and the introduction of new products with high margins.

Paper IV: On Research Policy (September 1952)

The fourth paper logically turned to the question of how to introduce new products with high margins, asserting that a "clearly understood and firmly maintained research policy is a basic necessity". At the time, the UK chemical industry spent 2.5% of its sales on research – more than in paints but less than in electrical engineering. The US chemical industry was forecast to grow fourfold by 1975, a compound rate of growth of just over 6% pa. SB suggested a target for A&W of 7.5% pa, which would require "products which are a surprise to the customer". He distinguished two kinds of research: the first, described as fire brigade, family doctor and plant replacement work, would need expenditure of around 1.5% of sales; the second, for progress, around 2.5%. On that basis, the current rate of expenditure was not enough.

A&W had had a good rate of growth despite research that had been "totally inadequate on any basis of computation". In the period from 1900 to 1925 research had provided several continuing products with good margins: sodium chlorate, food phosphates and phosphorus oxychloride. Other people's research had provided Calgon and oil additives. The whole chemical industry had grown rapidly but A&W's monopolies had meant that its growth tended to be within a relatively narrow compass. SB threw in a jovial warning (attributed to Lidbury): "the Lord looks after the Quakers, but then there are unfortunately so few of those left in the firm that one cannot really rely on this preferential treatment much longer!".

In support of his advice for increased research, SB quoted a statement by Monsanto (USA): "The growth of progressive chemical companies can be predicted with amazing accuracy from the size of their research budgets". Evidence came from Du Pont and Dow Chemical, both growing at well above the average for the industry: Du Pont's sales quadrupled in 10 years, while Dow's sales in 1951 were eleven times those of 1941. There was also a trend away from basic chemicals towards higher-priced specialities, even in the early 1950s. Regarding ICI's strong position in basic chemicals, SB commented that they "are determined now to divest themselves of what they thought to be a Magic Carpet but has turned out to be an Old Man of the Sea". He thus anticipated events by more than 40 years.

Based on the extent of A&W's activities overseas, SB thought that research could have a wide geographical application. A report presented to the Executive Board in 1951 indicated that only 0.3% of sales (£55,000) was being spent on innovative research. SB proposed expenditure of 2.5% of sales, including 1% on research for progress, which he believed would lead to long-term growth of 7.5% pa.

Just over a year before this proposal, a new research laboratory had been built at Oldbury (see p.15). The Director of Research at the time was Bryan Topley, who had succeeded Sydney Barratt in 1936 and became a Director of the Company in 1944, at the age of 43; he was appointed Deputy Chairman in 1960, and retired in 1967. He had been authorised in November 1945 to spend £50,000 over the next 5 years on long-range research, an activity of great interest to him, but one which produced few lasting benefits.[2] Bryan possessed phenomenal intelligence and great dialectical skill but was a professor manqué rather than a decisive man of business. When absorbed in a line of thought he appeared to lose all sense of time, to the discomfort of those working for him[3].

What unfolded was not the research-based progress SB sought. Links between research and commercial operations and production were weak, even though the main research laboratory was located at the Company's principal production site. Expenditure on research was budgeted at 2.5% of sales in the 1950s but the

[2] There was, for example, a scheme to make hydrogen peroxide and sodium phosphates by neutralising phosphoric acid with sodium peroxide, but at about that time the superior direct oxidation process for making hydrogen peroxide was introduced by Laporte. An X-ray crystallography section grew crystals of phosphorus in an attempt to define the crystal structure, but it proved too complex (and of no obvious commercial use). Much effort was diverted to government contract work, competently executed but with no commercial consequence. Work on organophosphorus chemistry led to some apparently interesting compounds, of which the outstanding example was phosphonitrilic chlorides of which it was said, "Possibly some derivatives may find widespread uses as pharmaceuticals, dyestuffs or insecticides". That never happened.
[3] Significantly, one of the chemists working for him, Noel Poynton, left and became responsible for the development of organophosphorus chemicals at the Avonmouth site of Butler chemicals acquired by A&W 20 years later.

percentage later declined to less than 2% and was further reduced when savings were required. Sydney Barratt's hopes and intentions for more innovative research leading to high-margin products were not fulfilled.

Paper V: The Fashion of the Times (January 1953)

SB's final paper was concerned with corporate organisation and what today would be called human resources. The Company was still changing from a private venture into a publicly owned managerial corporation and needed to be staffed and organised to cope with a threefold expansion by the mid-1960s.

To begin with, SB tackled the problem of replacing incentives hitherto prevailing in an owner-directed company operating in a time of under-employment. He concluded that motivation was required focusing on corporate pride and enthusiasm for an appreciated objective. Individuals should be able to perceive a clear organisation, know of the achievements and ambitions of the firm, be able to see a staff grading system and a path of advancement and be aware that their progress was being watched, with all posts open to talent. Beyond that, however, there was a need for a sense of companionship, proceeding from an infectious enthusiasm and teamwork of those in the high places of the organisation.

He went on to consider recruitment, stating "present staffing at high levels will be judged dangerously inadequate," and "intake of staff at anything but the beginner level must be evidence of a long term failure in policy, unless caused by an almost explosive and unpremeditated expansion". He believed that most staff positions should be filled by graduates, and technical training was essential for two-thirds or more of the senior posts. Sufficient numbers should be recruited to allow for losses to other employers and for discovered lack of ability (which should lead to departure).

It might be thought that SB was merely stating the obvious but what he wrote was indeed fresh thinking for his readers in the general circumstances of the early 1950s and the particular circumstances of a long-established family company that in the previous 25 years had appointed only 10 people to Board and Executive level. Nearly two years later, in a paper prepared for a discussion on staffing problems, he wrote "our staff is not large enough now, and may become cripplingly inadequate if our expansion (or diversification) policy succeeds". Progress, as might have been expected, was slow.

In 1952, a programme of recruitment of non-scientific graduates was introduced and several of those recruited in the following ten years rose in due course to some of the most senior positions. But there were few scientific graduates who attained senior management positions and only one (Dr Michael Peard) who started in the Oldbury Research Department and ended on the Board. In January 1971, Chemical

Age published an analysis of scientists and engineers on main and divisional Boards of UK chemical companies, which showed Albright & Wilson to have fewer than BP Chemicals, Fisons, Glaxo, ICI, Laporte and Shell Chemicals.

It later became clear that Sydney Barratt's attempts to improve the strength of management had had little success. As he noted, many of the problems faced from the mid-1960s were the consequence of inadequate staffing, in particular a shortage of scientifically trained staff. In a climate where the recruitment of mature expert staff from outside the Company seemed akin to an admission of failure, this is hardly surprising. There was also a reluctance to appoint non-executive directors with relevant outside experience: until 1965, the only external directors were the two sons of Sir Richard Threlfall, WB in 1921 and, on his retirement, Richie in 1949. When Marchon was acquired in 1955 (see p.44), Neil Peech, Chairman of Steetley, and Sir Henry Tizard, government-nominated Director of Marchon's subsidiary Solway, joined the A&W board.

In other aspects of staff management SB was more successful. A staff grading scheme was established, with a more rational pay structure, the line organisation and committee structure were defined, a central personnel department was established and internal communications improved, including the introduction of a very informative house journal.

Although only some of the ideas and proposals put forward by Sydney Barratt came to fruition, there is no doubt that his general outlook and enquiring mind had an important impact on Albright & Wilson's transition from family firm to public company. He became Managing Director in 1955 and was Chairman from 1957 to 1967, which meant that he was well placed to influence the conduct of the Company's affairs. Since, however, that also meant that he was fully occupied in the running of the Company, in circumstances that could not have been foreseen in 1952, it is not surprising that there were divergences between theory and practice.

Developments 1951-1955

The foundations for major expansion were being laid in 1951, where this history begins. In the next four years, new plants came into production and growth was organic, without acquisitions.

Economic and political background

*   the Festival of Britain in May 1951 marked the official ending of the war with Germany; the resulting dismantling of rationing and some controls under the Conservative government (elected in October 1951) marked a transition from the postwar recovery phase

- the Korean War ended in 1953
- the formation of the European Defence Community and Western European Union were preliminaries to the formation of the European Economic Community in 1958
- the £ remained at 2.80 US dollars (from September 1949), 11.75 deutsche-marks and around 1000 yen; the London foreign exchange market reopened in 1951 and the gold market in 1954 (both closed since 1939), but exchange controls, import controls and high tariffs continued in the UK
- Key Industries Duty of 33.3% continued to apply to phosphoric acid, phosphates and phosphorus chemicals (under the 1921 Safeguarding of Industries Act); phosphorus imports were subject to a 10% duty (under the 1932 Import Duties Act), despite the formulation of the General Agreement on Tariffs and Trade (GATT) in 1947
- the UK retail prices index rose between April 1951 and December 1955 by 28%, an average rate of inflation of 5.5% pa; average weekly earnings in manufacturing (males over 21) rose from £8.25 to £11.75, an average increase of about 7.75% pa
- the UK bank rate fell from 4% to 3%, while the yield on Treasury Bills rose from an average of 0.6% in 1951 to 3.75% in 1955 and the industrial ordinary share price index increased between 1951 and 1955 by over one-third; nevertheless, the yield on ordinary shares remained above that on long-dated government bonds until the end of 1959
- industrial production in the UK rose by 15% from 1951 to 1955 (with a small fall in 1952), while the rise in West Germany was over 50%, in France 25% and in Italy nearly 40%; the growth in gross domestic product in the UK was lower than other main European countries, USA and Canada
- unemployment in Britain remained low, at 1.2% of the work force in 1951 and 1955, with vacancies exceeding unemployment in both years; the recession in 1952 resulted in a temporary rise in employment to 2.0%

Progress

Major A&W plants under construction in 1951 came into operation:-

Kirkby STPP	April 1953
Varennes phosphorus	November 1953
Portishead phosphorus	February 1954
Barry silicones	June 1954
Columbus sodium chlorate	July 1954
Yarraville second furnace	November 1954

In June 1953 a house journal was started, under the title *Walbright News*, as a wall newspaper. In September, the journal contained the following statement:

"We shall pass from the building era into a period of consolidation. We have to produce and sell to earn money to pay for all the new plants that have been built ... at long last production will be able to prod sales and say with some justification 'Now it is your turn' ... the task now is to keep all our factories busy both in Great Britain and in countries overseas ... this is a position we have not been in since 1939".

Progress in the five years to 1955 in terms of profit was, however, unspectacular, as the burdens of depreciation and interest resulting from capital expenditure outweighed the income generated from the new facilities.

Progress 1950-1955[4]

(£ Million)		1950	1951	1952	1953	1954	1955
Sales							
UK companies		5.9	7.8	7.9	9.0	12.6	13.9
Overseas companies		4.2	6.1	5.7	6.4	6.9	8.0
	Total	**10.1**	**13.9**	**13.6**	**15.4**	**19.5**	**21.9**
Trading Profit							
UK companies		0.99	1.27	1.21	1.30	1.33	1.03
Overseas companies		0.49	1.01	0.30	0.63	0.87	1.08
Other income		0.01	0.03	0.05	0.04	0.06	0.05
	Total	**1.49**	**2.31**	**1.56**	**1.97**	**2.26**	**2.16**
Interest Payable		0.01	0.07	0.19	0.30	0.38	0.36
Pretax Profit		**1.48**	**2.24**	**1.37**	**1.67**	**1.88**	**1.80**
After depreciation of		0.36	0.53	0.68	0.78	1.28	1.40
Capital Expenditure		**1.0**	**2.1**	**4.0**	**4.8**	**2.1**	**1.0**
Net Capital employed (end of year)		**8.6**	**12.8**	**13.8**	**17.7**	**18.9**	**21.6**

[4] The figures exclude the Marchon group of companies, acquired towards the close of 1955; the exchange rates used are those applying in each year, which were constant for the US and Australian dollars but varying for the Canadian dollar.

With inflation in the UK averaging 5.5% pa between 1951 and 1955, performance in real terms was disappointing. While that is partly because 1951 was a boom year, which was followed by recession in 1952 and a slow recovery thereafter, an increase of nearly 60% in sales in the four years after 1951 was achieved. So what were the problems that prevented an increase in profit?

At the beginning of 1951, the Albright & Wilson group was virtually free of borrowing. The next two years were a period of heavy capital expenditure on plants that were not instantly productive. By the end of 1954, major plants came into operation, but there were problems. Borrowing had risen to over £7 million, or nearly 40% of the total capital employed, yet the growth in earnings for shareholders, which had been insignificant due to a lack of gearing (or leverage), was still not enhanced. Dividends did, however, double between 1951 and 1955 as the purse strings of the company were loosened.

One reason why profits did not advance as much as expected was the time taken by **Midland Silicones** to become profitable. Sales from the plant at Barry began in 1954 and by the end of the first full year were at a rate of more than £1 million pa. Operating and marketing costs, however, were high and a loss of £300,000 was made in 1955. Profit (even before interest) was not made until 1957.

The most severe problems were at the phosphorus plant at **Portishead** where the electric furnace method was used to manufacture phosphorus. The main problems arose from the raw material input. At Oldbury, pebble phosphate from Florida, a scarce and relatively expensive material, was used. The intention at Portishead was to use more variable grades of rock, agglomerated with clay and fed to the furnaces in the form of briquettes or pellets. For that a pug or rod mill and a high-temperature (550°C) oven, both expensive items, were necessary.

At the time the Portishead project was authorised in 1953 there were two distinct camps in the Company regarding routes for the production of phosphoric acid: as already mentioned, Bill Albright favoured "thermal acid" and Bryan Topley favoured "wet acid". Initial cost estimates indicated that the latter could be the winner. Thus the capital cost of the Portishead phosphorus plant was reduced through cutting back on the specification – there was no mill and a lower temperature oven (only 550°F, equivalent to 288°C), which was barely hotter than a dryer. The results were disastrous. The briquettes crumbled, there was sintering in the furnaces, high offtake temperatures and excessive dust, the precipitators could not cope, there was excessive mud make, operating conditions were very poor and furnace loading had to be reduced, resulting in lower output and additional operating problems.

After the failure of the briquettes, it was suggested that there should be a change to pellets, a smaller agglomeration, but the required money was not forthcoming. The raw material was then changed from Moroccan sand to Florida pebble

Electrode on Oldbury furnace top being tamped (sealed with sand).

Tapping slag (calcium silicate) from Portishead phosphorus furnace.

Tamping electrode on Varennes furnace top.

Varennes phosphorus plant, showing tapping from one of the two furnaces, with slag deposits in foreground.

phosphate but it was difficult to find adequate supplies of the most suitable rock. A pelletisation pan was installed in 1965 to deal with the phosphate fines but it did not have the capacity to treat more than a fraction of the total feed.

One of the furnaces was modified in 1961, and in 1963 £900,000 was spent on modifying four furnaces, upgrading them by moving from six 24-inch- to three 35-inch-electrodes. The first of the upgraded furnaces was switched on in July 1965. Another innovation was the use of hydraulically operated electrode suspension gear, intended to allow vertical movement without deviation. The changes proved to be a retrograde step leading to serious production difficulties: more sintering prevented the increased loading that had been intended and the electrode suspension system caused many electrode breakages. Problems also resulted from the use of anthracite rather than more expensive coke as the source of carbon (yet Varennes had experimented with anthracite, with results described as "terrible"). Also, furnaces were tapped according to an imposed schedule rather than when dictated by conditions, and the gas system clogged because of insufficient pressure.

The upshot was that the cost of Portishead's phosphorus was always higher than Oldbury's, even without the depreciation charge. The Portishead experience should have been valuable for any future phosphorus plant but the lessons were not taken on board. It is surprising that the problems at Portishead were not solved before A&W embarked on another phosphorus plant at Long Harbour where so many design aspects were similar and therefore problematic. These difficulties (see Chapter 4) proved to be almost fatal for the Company.

The phosphorus plant at **Varennes** in Canada, which started up three months before Portishead, was built to a design from the Tennessee Valley Authority (see p.12). The two furnaces here were rectangular with a shallow hearth and high dome and three electrodes in line, rather than circular with the electrodes in a ring. There were start-up problems: in the first year, output was less than half the designed capacity. Inexperience among operatives was one reason but there were sintering problems, leading to high temperatures, excessive dust and difficulties in the operation of the precipitators – much as at Portishead. As at Portishead, briquetting was attempted in 1954/5 but was not successful.

Most of the problems were, however, overcome at Varennes. The design of the furnaces and an increase in the electrical loading burnt through any sintering and kept the furnace burden mobile, and the precipitators were abandoned, which improved output (but led to increased mud production). Varennes proved to be a reliable source of phosphorus, eventually producing at nearly double the initial rated capacity, although with unpleasant operating conditions and much residual mud, which was stored in holes on the site.

Other developments

Alongside the main developments in building major plants, several significant steps were taken, some of which arose from the trawling for ideas from the United States. Keith Piercy was the leading fisherman.

In 1933, Keith had secured the development rights in Great Britain and the British Empire for Calgon from the Hagan Corporation, of Pittsburgh, and set up his own company to market the chemical. In 1935 Albright & Wilson acquired the patents and he joined the Company. He became Director of Development in 1953. Keith was outstanding in several respects. He was a mild entrepreneur and for most of his time with A&W was looking for opportunities to acquire products and processes. He had respect and affection for Sydney Barratt and Bryan Topley but for the most part preferred to keep his thoughts to himself rather than to drive forward aggressively. He was a gentle man as well as what is generally understood as a gentleman. He often gave the impression of being vague, which might reflect irresolution or a lack of involvement but could conceal a clear appreciation of a situation.

In 1951, Keith established a Market Research Department, the first (and last) such department in A&W, and appointed David Livingstone (see p.182) to run it. Over the next 5 years, the department produced around 20 slim volumes, covering areas of chemical business of potential interest to A&W, the economic environment and statistical methods. David's combination of an original intellectual approach and the ability to speak and write with great clarity, style and wit were outstanding qualities, shared with Sydney Barratt. It was not surprising that in 1956 he moved to become personal assistant to Sydney Barratt.

The next venture was in **insecticides**. Keith Piercy had read of a new insecticide, tetraethyl pyrophosphate, used to control aphids and red spider. After the Research Department had built a small plant at Oldbury around 1950, visits were made to fruit growers and spraying contractors and the product was advertised. A&W became a member of the Association of British Insecticide Manufacturers and set up a Crop Protection Group within the Society of Chemical Industry, with Keith Piercy as Secretary and later Chairman. In 1951, as a result of attending a meeting of the American Chemical Society in New York, Keith obtained from American Cyanamid the right to make Malathion, another organo-phosphorus insecticide that did not have the problems then becoming associated with DDT. Manufacture continued until the expiry of Cyanamid's patents, when competition made manufacture by A&W uneconomic.

Chemicals for **plastics**, first developed in the early 1950s, were also investigated. The possibility of manufacturing PVC was rejected – "one of the best negative decisions we took" said David some 20 years later – but A&W did manufacture phosphate plasticisers. In 1953, during a visit to Goodrich in Cleveland, Ohio, Keith Piercy was told that organotin stabilisers would soon be used in PVC. In Stratford, Dr Roff, Research Director of Thomas Tyrer, developed a process for their manufacture. This infringed on a patent held by the US company Metal & Thermit; A&W obtained a licence from it in 1955.

In the search for new products, it was natural that the Development Department should look at **metal finishing**, an activity in which A&W already had a toe-hold through the supply of phosphoric acid for phosphating, mainly of car bodies. Keith Piercy called on the US Government Research Laboratory in Columbus, Ohio, which had been working on the chemical polishing of metals in solutions containing phosphoric acid. The two chemists concerned with this research described the process and gave him a copy of the US patent, which had not yet been taken out in the UK. This led to Keith Piercy and John Christopherson setting up a department to handle the Phosbrite processes for polishing aluminium and copper as well as other metal finishing processes. A&W, lacking knowledge in the field, sought other processes to use under licence.

One of these was the Kanigen process for nickel plating without electricity ('electroless plating'), using sodium hypophosphite, which was made at Oldbury. The process was licensed from The General American Transportation Company of Chicago in 1955 with a downpayment of $100,000, and a small plant was built at Oldbury in 1956. Some sales of Kanigen plating were made, notably to the aerospace industry, where it was used for the Comet airliner. At the end of 1958 the plant was extended, despite losses. At the time of the Farnborough Air Show in 1960, the plant was running close to capacity, but that was not as great as had been hoped. Growth in sales was disappointing and losses continued. Selling the process to plating companies was not easy – the phosphorus content (5–6%) could have deleterious effects and the plating was much thicker than the usual electroplating. It looked different from electroplated nickel and was generally unacceptable to the conservative Birmingham platers. At the end of 1960 the Oldbury plant was closed and plating companies were invited to take over Kanigen plating as sub-licensees. Finally, in March 1961 Fescol Ltd took over manufacture.

While Kanigen had a short and unprofitable life, a number of other processes and products for metal treatment were acquired through licensing or developed by A&W and persisted, with modifications, over the years. These included chemical polishing solutions for aluminium, licensed from United Anodising in 1956, and Plusbrite, a process for bright nickel plating, licensed from Hanson-Van Winkle-Munning in 1958. In-house developments included Pyrobrite, a copper plating process using copper pyrophosphate. At the beginning of 1961 Electropol Ltd was acquired; it owned patents relating to the electropolishing of stainless steel. More than once, serious consideration was given to the possibility of acquiring Wm

Canning & Co. Ltd, one of the leading British companies with business in electroplating and the supply of materials and services in the field of metal treatment. A metal finishing department was formed at Oldbury in 1955, which later became a division of the Specialities business unit. Other lines were added over the years, including chrome plating and coloured finishes, and there was some expansion outside the UK. Yet metal finishing – later known as "surface technology" – remained a relatively small part of the Company's operations, generally profitable but with limited growth potential.

Of more long-term significance was the development of flame-retardant finishes for textiles. In 1953, Oldbury ElectroChemical Company (OECCo) reported some interesting conversations with the US Regional Research Laboratory in New Orleans. Keith Piercy set off once more, in the liner Queen Elizabeth (air travel was not usual in A&W at that time), to New York and thence to New Orleans. There he met two government chemists, Dr Reeves and Dr Guthrie, who had jointly invented a process for flameproofing cotton with THPC (tetrakis hydroxymethyl phosphonium chloride). Keith negotiated an agreement with the inventors (who under American law were free to exploit their invention outside the USA) for the rights to patent the invention outside the USA in return for royalties on sales. For knowledge of textile processing A&W approached The Bradford Dyers Association (BDA). The two companies set up a joint venture with the trademark **Proban**, registered in 1955, when a 50/50 company, Proban Ltd, was formed.

The Proban story is one of extraordinary persistence, a period of development unequalled in A&W and not often matched elsewhere. Eventually the process and the chemicals involved produced useful profits for A&W and led to other significant applications for the chemicals. A&W decided to license the process to selected textile manufacturers for royalties based on the yardage treated, with A&W deriving additional profit from the sale of THPC made in a plant at Oldbury. Proban was launched with a flourish at a press conference in London in 1955. Support was given by the Daily Mirror in a series of articles on the dangers of inflammable nightwear for children and by a demonstration on the television programme *Tonight*, compered by Cliff Michelmore. Unfortunately, the first version of the process applied to cotton fabrics such as winceyette produced cloth that was stiff and 'boardy', an apparent setback that BDA believed would be acceptable. It was not long before fears were realised: Marks & Spencer had placed large orders for nightdresses but soon stopped trying to sell them.

Early in 1956 the first licensees were appointed and the first royalties were received at the beginning of 1957. Early in 1957 a report to the A&W Board forecast royalties of £200,000 pa in 5 years' time (equivalent to more than £2.5 million pa in 2000 money). Later that year the number of licensees rose to 7. Yet there were still problems. In 1959 it was reported that Proban-treated cloth would still "burn casually". It was not until the middle of 1960 that the ammonia cure process was developed to overcome stiffness, and the product was re-launched as Proban X. Losses, however, continued.

From the middle of 1958 attempts were made to broaden the range of products for textiles. Among these were a shrink-proofing process for wool, a drip-dry crease-resistant treatment for cotton fabrics (Prystene), marketing a knot-counting machine (agreed in October 1958, abandoned in May 1959), and the Immacula crease-retention treatment (a Speakman patent, licensed from Marks & Spencer, launched in mid-1959 and sub-licensed to 19 finishers but killed off in 1962 by outside competition).

At the end of 1962 A&W agreed to run Proban on a break-even basis until mid-1963, after reducing staff to a bare minimum. At a review in mid-1963, although the budgeted volume of sales was not expected to be attained, once again A&W persisted. Prospects were greatly improved early in 1964, when there was a decision to ban inflammable nightdresses for children in the UK, prompting an advertising campaign for Proban. The ban came into force in October of that year and in six months 400,000 yards of cloth were treated, against 250,000 in the whole year 1963. From that time, there was steady but slow progress and within A&W the viability of Proban was accepted. The venture was, however, still unprofitable, but this proved beneficial for A&W – Viyella, which had acquired BDA in 1964, sold its holding in Proban Ltd to A&W for just £4,800.

In the previous year A&W had developed a new process for making phosphine, the principal intermediate for Proban. Together with full ownership this cleared the way for at last moving into a profitable position. In 1969 the US Congress took powers to prevent the sale of inflammable fabrics. At his retirement presentation at the end of 1970, Frank Howes – who had been a key figure in Proban since 1958 as general manager and then managing director – attributed the very slow growth in the business to opposition from the textile trade, caused partly by concern at the effect on sales of fabrics that were not flame-resistant, partly by the public's reluctance to pay more for treated fabrics and clothing. Certainly it took a long time for the general awareness of health and safety issues to reach a level where investment in flame-retardant textiles became regarded as prudent, with governmental support.

Development through the **licensing** of others' know-how, particularly from the USA, was at its height in the first 10 years after the 1939-45 war. From the mid nineteen-fifties there was increasing reluctance by American companies to grant licences, and growing ambition for direct investment in Europe. A&W was also increasingly preoccupied with new businesses arising from acquisitions. What might be described as the Piercy route to development for A&W thus effectively came to an end and the speciality sector of A&W remained largely within the boundaries set up in 1955. Eventually the aim became to achieve speciality status for the whole of A&W's operation.

Organisation & Management

In the period 1951-5, there were fewer changes in organisation than might have been expected, given the number of developments taking place. It was not until 1955 that Sydney Barratt became Managing Director and Bill Albright stepped aside into the position of Vice-Chairman. Kenneth Wilson continued as Chairman, despite reaching the age of 70 and his 45th year as a Director. Nevil Wilson became Secretary in 1955, a year after Christopher Wilson, his father, had retired; the office had been filled temporarily by Sydney Barratt, then Finance Director. Nevil was to remain as Secretary until December 1988, and was the last representative of the founding families.

Although by mid-1955 there were 3,000 shareholders, the character of the Company had changed little. There were, however, some moves towards greater professionalism. In mid-1955, after a review by Production Engineering (the first use of management consultants), a Personnel Department was set up. Maurice Antcliff, who had joined A&W in 1913 as a lab assistant at Oldbury and progressed through works management to general management, was put in charge of the new function. A professional in that field, Maurice Clement-Jones, was recruited to manage the department under him. The staff superannuation scheme for the UK, introduced in 1952, was ahead of common practice at the time. The house journal graduated in 1954 to become the *Albright News*, distributed to employees. It was a journal with a balance of news and social reporting; in the April 1955 issue ladies at the Chemical Institute of Canada dance are described as dressing in, "rainbow hues – Mrs Carew in sky-blue velvet; Mrs Karn in rose-champagne net; Mrs McMahon in light brown; Mrs Crane in fawn; and Al Bowler's date in aqua-puffin".

Marchon

The foundations for organic growth had thus been laid. The next phase involved growth through acquisitions. The first, and the one of greatest long-term significance, was the acquisition of Marchon at the end of 1955.

The founders

The history of Marchon prior to its acquisition by Albright & Wilson in 1955 is an impressive story of enterprise. The company was the creation of two men,

<u>Mar</u>zillier and <u>Schon</u>. Franz Schon, the dominant character, was born in May 1912 in Vienna. His father was a civil servant who in retirement built up a successful practice in transport law. Franz went to a grammar school in Vienna, where he came to know Bruno Kreisky, later Chancellor of Austria. At the age of 19 he joined the commercial side of a chemical business in Vienna, with a branch office in Prague. Its business included dealing in synthetic detergents for a German company, a pioneer in the field. In his spare time, Franz studied law externally with the universities of Vienna and Prague and went to Paris for a short period to study. He moved to the Prague office, where he became manager, and from there observed the Anschluss in Austria. On 15th March 1939 the German army invaded Czechoslovakia. Ten days later Franz escaped to England with his wife Trudi, whom he had married in 1936. They were briefly interned as enemy aliens in the Isle of Man; Frank (as he had by then become) said of that experience, "I did not suffer it as an indignity - I appreciated the kindness with which I was treated". Upon their release they moved to London, where Frank, then aged 27, went to work for a chemical company, Dr Ludwig Schon (unrelated).

Fred Marzillier, who had returned to England, his birthplace, after an upbringing in Germany, was already working for the company. He was 33 when Frank joined. Soon the two men went into business together; in December 1939 they registered Marchon Products Ltd as a chemical marketing and manufacturing company. They started with small premises at 4 Cullum Street, off Fenchurch Street, in the City of London, and capital of a few hundred pounds. Schon was the man of ideas and the salesman, while Marzillier was the businessman, later described as a financial wizard. Either would not have succeeded without the other.

Before long, they invited Otto Secher, brother of Frank's wife Trudi, to join them. Otto had been working for Intak, an import/export company, and had spent some time in Spain. At first he could not join Marchon because the company was not contributing to the war effort; instead he joined Kangol Ltd, manufacturing berets and uniforms in Cumberland. After 9 months, he received permission to work for Marchon, initially for no pay.

The move to Whitehaven

Otto has described how Frank was very nervous about staying in London, because of the bombing. At the suggestion of Jacques Spreiregen, founding Director of Kangol, he decided to look at Cumberland, being assured that it was far enough away from the Continent for bombers to be unable to make the return trip. He borrowed £10 from Otto and travelled to Whitehaven.

In 1940, Whitehaven was a depressed area. At the beginning of the 18th century, it had been second only to London in the tonnage of shipping using the port. It was, however, badly affected by the Industrial Revolution and the rise of Liverpool. The growth of coal mining in the nineteenth and early twentieth centuries brought brief respite with a new source of prosperity; at the peak, there were 33 mines in West Cumberland. The depression of the 1930s took its toll though, and by 1935 all the mines were closed. In response, the Cumberland Development Council was formed and two years later some pits were reopened. In 1939, Miki Sekers established a silk factory in the Hensingham area of Whitehaven – perhaps that provided Frank Schon with an example of what could be accomplished.

Marchon initially occupied a derelict property in Hensingham, provided by a sympathetic farmer who had once holidayed in Austria. Together with an adjacent garage serving as factory premises, the house provided an office, living quarters and work space. Two months later, three derelict cottages were acquired and turned into stores. The fear of being bombed in London proved to be justified – the Cullum Street premises were bombed, but apparently after Marchon had left them (references to Marchon's having been bombed out twice in London were denied by Otto and appear to be embellishments of the story of the early struggles).

According to Otto, a German woman (identity unknown) suggested that the firm should manufacture firelighters. Frank claimed that it was Fred's idea and that he himself was not keen on it. The firelighters consisted of sawdust, mixed with a hot liquid based (initially) on naphthalene, which on cooling held the structure together. Because it was classed as a munitions chemical, naphthalene was difficult to obtain. In its place, Fyrex, a waste wax from Shell, was used. Sawdust was bought by the bag from Mr Jackson, owner of a local sawmill; Otto told how Frank obtained "the largest bag ever seen on earth" and two days later came back with two such bags.

Firelighters proved profitable, and the business soon expanded into a British Legion hut in Swing Pump Lane in Whitehaven, employing 20 people. The firelighters were produced on a Heath Robinson type of machine built by an amateur inventor called Harry Roberts that mixed sawdust and liquid which was pressed into blocks and sold to wholesalers. Marchon's next acquisition was the Guinea former warehouse in the centre of Whitehaven. At this time tasks were clearly defined between the three men: Otto Secher oversaw sales, the firelighter operation was Fred Marzillier's baby and Frank Schon concentrated on chemicals. One story – either recalled or invented – suggests that some firelighters had a reputation as fire extinguishers: when the biggest co-operative warehouse in Coventry burnt down, 200 cases of firelighters remained intact (the logical, but less amusing reason, being a lack of oxygen).

Marchon's next move provided the basis for the whole of the future development of the company. Jack Adams, Secretary of the West Cumberland Development council, invited them to move to the site of the former Ladysmith Pit coke ovens at Kells, on the headland above the town of Whitehaven. Like the Marchon team, John Jackson Adams was enterprising and full of stamina. At the age of four he lost his father in a mine accident. Ten years later, he too became a miner. At 21 he was elected to his local Parish Council (Arcledon) which served as a launch pad for a career in local government and his significant role in the regeneration of West Cumberland. When the area was designated a "Special Area" in 1935, he was appointed General Manager of the West Cumberland Industrial Development Company. He has been described as "the principal architect of West Cumberland's Industrial Revolution", and was granted a peerage in 1949, eleven years before his death.

The Kells site (initially 7 acres) was a mess, with many large disused buildings that were gradually adapted. The first operation installed was the manufacture of firelighters, which was greatly expanded by the introduction of an automatic machine, designed by Bill Pickering (later Chief Engineer) and built by Wallace Murray. In 1944 there were 39 employees; two years later the workforce had quadrupled to 160, and by the end of 1951, 586 people were employed at Kells.

When the ordnance factory at Sellafield (the small town 12 miles South of Whitehaven, later known worldwide for its nuclear plants) was closed in 1946, Frank Schon bought two large buildings and a small laboratory and had them re-erected on the Kells site. At the time, steel was virtually unobtainable from normal sources. Also from Sellafield came some of the future key staff – Arthur Halfpenny (usually referred to as "Half"), who became Works Director, Alec Lindsay (Chief Engineer), Bob Dickie (Production), Bill Hampshire (Chemical Engineer) and Ken Coles – who together brought expertise in chemical development, production and engineering. Frank Schon regarded Half as the outstanding member of the team, and Otto described him as a brilliant, practical and inventive chemist and engineer who sometimes played a tricky hand. Bill Hampshire's assistant was a fitter named Tom Adams, a nephew of Jack Adams.

The move into detergents

While firelighters continued in production and provided a significant cash flow (in the severe winter of 1947 orders were ten times the capacity to produce), and trading in glycerine monostearate (described as "edible esters"), used in ice creams, proved to be very profitable (made for £1 per lb, sold for £7 or £8), the main business became the production and sale of synthetic detergents.

The origin of the synthetic detergent industry can be traced back to a German patent during the 1914-18 War describing the alkylation of naphthalene with isopropanol and its subsequent sulphonation; the products could be used in hard or soft water and were used as wetting agents in the textile industry. In 1929, a Dr Bertsch of Boehme Fettechemie GmbH at Chemnitz in Germany discovered that the mixed fatty alcohol derived from sperm whale oil could be converted into a soap-like detergent; soon after, another company in Chemnitz, Deutsche Hydrier-werke, developed a process for making detergent alcohols from other fats such as tallow and coconut. The products were initially used in the textile and leather industries but were soon applied to toiletries, especially shampoos, and later used in household products, mainly dishwashing liquids and light-duty laundry detergents. The work on the organic chemistry of surface active agents was done in Germany between the wars, while the physical chemistry was worked on mainly in Britain. Boehme Fettechemie established manufacture in a number of countries, including Australia, where a joint venture was formed in 1935 and given the name of Gardinol Chemical Company (its later history is described in Chapter 3; see p.99).

Frank Schon became familiar with the detergent industry in Germany in the 1930s and acquired a thorough knowledge of the production and use of synthetic detergents. "It was borne in upon me," he said, "that this was a field of very large possibilities indeed, and when I came to England in 1939 I had every intention of taking an active hand in its development". At that time in Britain such German developments were widely looked upon as 'ersatz', inferior substitutes for the real thing, but the advantages of synthetic detergents over soap were soon appreciated.

Early in 1941, Marchon began to market chemicals used as raw materials for detergents on a very limited scale. In May 1941 a well-known firm of toiletry manufacturers asked Marchon to make some of their products. Operations were then moved to Swing Pump Lane; the firelighter operations were transferred to a small disused varnish factory nearby. In 1942, Marchon started making a detergent (sulphonated fatty alcohol) paste using two old dough mixing machines: the smaller was lead lined, for handling acids, and termed the 'sulphonator'; the larger was called the 'neutraliser'. A lead-lined box was used to feed acids slowly into the sulphonator for mixing; next, the box was lowered below the sulphonator and filled from it, then hoisted above the neutraliser, which contained liquid fat, and its contents slowly emptied into it. Detergent powders were made by letting the paste from the neutraliser become hard, breaking it with wooden mallets, putting it through marble rollers and finally sieving it. Otto recalled girls on the top floor of the building hammering lumps, under the supervision of Hilda McAleese, Marchon's first employee, who had been hired in April 1941. There were also materials for shampoos and toothpastes, based on lauryl alcohol.

Frank later said of his approach to the commercial development of surface active chemistry: "I think it could be maintained that we coarse and commercial persons are a necessary link between the search for truth in the laboratory and the public, which now confidently expects to benefit from the efforts of the scientist ...

The search for truth is not, alas, entirely independent of financial considerations – the pursuit of wealth is, fortunately, not to be divorced from a foundation of scientific truth". By then (1962) he had been a millionaire for some years.

The strategy for Marchon was defined as the supply of detergent materials to the major manufacturers and marketers of finished detergents for the consumer market. From 1943, sales were made to Beecham, Bibby, Cheseborough, Colgate and others, and it was not long before exports started. Frank spoke of the strength of the competition between the 'soapers', as they were generally known. He recalled the attempt by Charles I to establish a monopoly in soap, and referred to public displays of 1640 when Bristol's soap boilers showed that their product washed whiter and brighter than the King's! Frank appreciated that it would be unprofitable to attempt to take market share from the established soap makers – Lever Bros., Thomas Hedley (later part of Procter & Gamble) and Colgate – with their long experience of selling to the public and strong marketing organisations. Much later, the rise of the supermarkets was to lead to the production of private label finished detergents, but even then the market share taken from the soapers was quite small.

The Marchon team made its way by working seven days a week, with only rare holidays, ploughing earnings back into new plant and buildings, managing to fulfil orders even when they had been accepted beyond the capacity of the plant. A story is told of the time when Frank told Otto that a plant was 100 tons short of sales and asked him to go into Europe to get orders for the 100 tons. There was no word from Otto for three weeks and then he returned to say: "Frank, I have sold the 500 tons that you wanted – it is now up to you". Frank protested that he had asked for orders for only 100 tons, only to receive the reply, "The 400 tons - that is your problem". And so a new plant was built.

All the staff were expected to spend some time on the plants, working shifts – a shock for newcomers but an experience of permanent value. In the early days, maintenance of the few small vessels was carried out by people who during the day worked for other businesses and came in the evening to give a hand. Schon and Marzillier worked seven days a week. Schon would be around the plant every day and might be on site at any time, while Marzillier was confined to the office. They were opposite personalities: Marzillier was introverted and always smiling, while Schon was steely-faced and serious, though he did take a keen interest in everyone's welfare. Pat Hughes, who joined as an engineer in 1944, recalls starting with a basic pay of £1 for a 5½ day week. At the end of the first week, Schon came up to him and said, "I have been watching you; you are a very good worker and will do well here", and gave him a rise of 25%. On another occasion, he sent Hughes to the dentist (having learnt of the need in some way).

The buildings acquired from Sellafield provided premises for commercial-scale plants as well as adequate offices. One of the first new plants was a small

Kestner spray drier for detergent powders, installed in the autumn of 1945. Ron Bristoe, who came to Whitehaven in 1944, remembers making trials at the Bradford Fertiliser factory in Cockermouth and described how he was lowered into the central ducting, with a rope round his waist, to check that the drier was spotless. After the drier had been installed at Whitehaven, Frank Schon would inspect the product at its base every day; if it was not in operation, operators would pour bags of finished powder into the top of the drier – it is unlikely that this deception fooled Frank.

In 1948 Frank went with Marzillier and Half on a whirlwind tour in the United States, where Frank's enthusiasm opened doors and established enduring relationships with the major detergent companies. One of the most important visits was to Mr Harry Theobald, who had information on a larger spray drier which Marchon acquired, leading to a contract with Colgate for the manufacture of Fab, a heavy duty domestic detergent powder. Colgate sent two large packing machines to Whitehaven to enable Marchon to produce the finished product, but they never worked well and Colgate eventually moved them to Ireland.

The range of materials was expanded to include fatty alcohol sulphates for shampoos, foaming agents for toothpastes and other toiletries, and sulphonates for liquid and powder detergents. Development was assisted by grants from the Cumberland Development Council, and vertical integration (i.e. manufacturing intermediates instead of purchasing them) led to greater self-sufficiency. In January 1949, the expanded manufacturing and office premises were officially opened by Sir Stafford Cripps, then Chancellor of the Exchequer. An engineering department, able to build some items of plant as well as maintaining all the plants, was created, and a chemical research group and control laboratory were also established.

The move into STPP

The most significant development for Marchon at that time, and indeed at any time after the foundation of the company, was the move into the manufacture of sodium tripolyphosphate. It was a logical step in the broadening of manufacture to include detergent materials of all kinds. Phosphates then accounted for about 40% of the content of finished heavy duty domestic powder detergents. Albright & Wilson was at about the same time embarking on the manufacture of sodium tripolyphosphate. Whereas A&W used thermal phosphoric acid, Frank Schon favoured wet acid.

Schon and Half visited Perry & Hope Ltd in Glasgow, a long-established wet acid producer. Although the Perry & Hope plant was old and small, what they saw led them to believe that manufacture of wet acid was simple. Marchon bought the company but shut it down. Marchon did not use its process, adopting instead the more usual filtration process in a plant termed the 'Filter House' (F1). First attempts produced acid that was not clean enough to use in making phosphates but in time adequate technical quality was achieved.

Marchon's first phosphate plant was commissioned in the latter part of 1952. The sodium tripolyphosphate was produced by what became known as the 'wet salts' method, using a relatively impure phosphoric acid with impurities filtered out and discharged to drain. The process was messy but product cost was less than A&W's product produced at Oldbury from thermal acid.

THE MANUFACTURE OF PHOSPHORIC ACID - THERMAL AND WET PROCESS

"Thermal" process
Phosphorus is burnt in air, to form phosphorus pentoxide which is then hydrated to give phosphoric acid:

$$P_4 + 5O_2 = 2P_2O_5$$
$$P_2O_5 + 3H_2O = 2H_3PO_4$$

"Wet" process
Phosphate rock is attacked with sulphuric acid:

$$Ca_3P_2O_8 + 3H_2SO_4 = 2H_3PO_4 + 3CaSO_4 \text{ (gypsum)}$$

More of the impurities in phosphate rock are retained in the wet acid than in thermal acid, so wet acid requires further stages in purification. Wet process acid can also be produced by the action of hydrochloric acid on phosphate rock, but that route has only rarely been followed.

Sulphuric acid

Marchon was already a substantial user of sulphuric acid for the production of alcohol sulphates and sulphonates. The move into phosphoric acid would involve much larger tonnages of sulphuric acid. The National Research & Development Council Bulletin (Summer 1979) recounts Schon's receipt of a large order for detergent material in America at the end of 1950. When he told Marzillier, he learnt that the supplies of sulphuric acid had dried up. A crisis had arisen – imported sulphur was scarce due to rationing imposed by the US and British governments at the time of the Korean war.

Frank at once flew back to Prestwick and took the sleeper train to London, to appeal to the Board of Trade for supplies for his export business. He was unable to obtain an assurance of supplies of sulphuric acid, or support for building a plant to manufacture the acid from sulphur, or from pyrites. He wished to manufacture at Whitehaven because of the high cost of transporting acid. As Frank was about to leave the office, Bill Onslow, an Assistant Secretary, said to him "there won't be any sulphuric acid unless you make it from anhydrite". Marchon was encouraged to go ahead with the anhydrite process (invented in Germany in the first world war), and was told that government support would be forthcoming. Anhydrite, anhydrous calcium sulphate, had been mined by ICI in a deep mine at Prudhoe, in Northumberland, and used to make sulphuric acid at Billingham since 1930. The ICI plant was expanded in the early 1950s and a second plant was built at Widnes, by the United Sulphuric Acid Corporation, a consortium of users in the area, using anhydrite brought by rail from Penrith, in Cumberland.

Frank Schon returned to Whitehaven and, over lunch in the canteen, told of his discussions in London. Among those present was Jack Adams who, to Frank's great surprise, revealed that he was *sitting* on anhydrite. There had been boreholes by the former B & A Collieries, searching for gypsum (another form of calcium sulphate), and there was a borehole near Sandwith, close to the Marchon site at Kells; the calcium sulphate content there was even higher than at Prudhoe. Frank Schon went back to London immediately to register his interest in obtaining government support for an anhydrite-based operation.

Jack Adams introduced Frank Schon to Andrew Millar, a mining expert and retired Director of United Steel, who confirmed that there were substantial deposits of anhydrite under the nearby St Bees Head, and laid down the basic principles for mining. Land surveys and boreholes proved its existence– there was an 80-foot-thick seam at St Bees Head, some 130 ft below sea level, which could be mined by sinking two drifts. Drifting started in August 1953 and anhydrite was reached in November 1954, half a mile from the drift mouth. The mine was officially opened in January 1955. Initial target output was 7,000 tons per week (working 40 hours) using the pillar and stall method to extract 60% of the available mineral. Half of the output was to be used to produce acid on site and half was to be supplied to ICI at Billingham; later, material was also supplied to USAC at Widnes. It was calculated that the deposits would last 400 years.

Frank Schon needed to find out how to produce sulphuric acid from the anhydrite, but was unwilling to pay a high price. Knowing that a firm at Linz in Austria was about to operate the process, Schon placed advertisements in the Linz papers offering "glorious technical opportunities" for chemists who knew the secrets. When he had received many replies, he telephoned the head of the firm to admit placing the advertisements. He said that he did not want to break up his team; if he could be told where to get details of the process he would throw away the replies. He was given the name of the inventor: in August 1951, he visited Dr H.H. Kuhne, former Chairman of Bayer and co-inventor of the Muller-Kuhne process for producing sulphuric acid from anhydrite, who not only arranged for the information to be provided, but also became a consultant to Marchon. The plant was the same size as the plant at Linz and the drawings were simply copied, with a fee of £50,000 (equivalent to about £1 million in 2000) payable to Bayer, Leverkusen.

Solway Chemicals Ltd

The initial sulphuric acid plant at Whitehaven was designed to produce 90,000 tons pa from two kilns. Anhydrite, with the addition of shale from a local quarry, was heated to produce sulphur dioxide (SO_2), converted to sulphur trioxide (SO_3) and then to sulphuric acid (H_2SO_4). An equal tonnage of cement clinker was to be produced and sold under a long-term contract to Associated Portland Cement Manufacturers. Because of the credit from sale of the cement clinker and the low raw material costs, the operating costs of the process were very low, but the capital investment in the massive plant was large.

The £2 million required for the acid plant and the £1 million for the mine were all but covered by the government loans – £2,350,000 from the Development Areas Treasury Advisory Committee and £600,000 from the Industrial & Commercial Finance Corporation. The project was sponsored by the Board of Trade, whose President up to October 1951, when the Conservative party returned to power, was Harold Wilson. On several occasions in the future Harold Wilson visited Whitehaven; he also played golf with Frank Schon. Solway Chemicals Ltd was formed as the vehicle for the sulphuric acid operation; and two Treasury representatives were appointed to the Board. The Whitehaven site was divided between Marchon and Solway. Many years later, long after the financial separation of the two companies had ended, the Eastern part of the site was still referred to as Solway.

The two kilns came on stream in mid-1955 and the plant was officially opened by the Duke of Edinburgh in November of that year. It was expanded by the addition of a third kiln in 1962 and then by the addition of two larger kilns in 1967; that final stage was inaugurated in May 1965 by Harold Wilson, by then in his first term as Prime Minister. From 1950 there was an enduring connection between Marchon and Labour Governments. Ministers stayed at Fleatham House, the company's guest house at St Bees, on a number of occasions. There were also visits by members of the Royal Family: the Duke of Edinburgh in 1955, the Princess Royal in March 1954, the Queen Mother in October 1964, and the Queen and the Duke of Edinburgh in March 1980.

More raw material manufacture

The move into the manufacture of sulphuric acid was not the only step taken in the 1950s to strengthen Marchon's raw material position. On the organic side of the detergents and toiletries operations, imported fatty alcohols formed a key group of materials: 90% of the shampoos sold in the UK were based on primary fatty alcohol derivatives, which were also used in textile, leather, pharmaceutical, plastics and synthetic rubber industries. For Marchon their potential was as organic anionic washing constituents in detergents. In the USA at that time, the constituent was provided both by alkyl aryl sulphonates – petroleum derivatives – and by primary fatty alcohol sulphates, the fatty component of which was derived from vegetable or animal oils. The UK did not have any advantage (in pre-North Sea oil times) in petroleum derivatives, but Frank argued that within the sterling area as a whole, and within the British Commonwealth in particular, there were ample supplies of vegetable and animal oils. He chose the natural alcohol rather than petroleum route for technical and commercial reasons. Later, the choice was supported by the environmental merits of natural alcohols, particularly in toiletries.

A loan of £600,000 from the Prudential Assurance Co financed a small plant (built at a cost of £500,000) with a capacity of 4,000 tons p.a. The plant was formally opened in June 1954 by Sir Henry Tizard, one of the two Treasury Directors appointed to the Solway Board. It was flexible in its raw material feed – vegetable oils, tallow, fatty acids or fatty acid esters – and in its output, which could include chemicals such as sorbitol or cyclohexanol. In practice, it was fully occupied in making fatty alcohols. The process consisted of the high-pressure hydrogenation of fatty acids etc., and involved making the catalyst, producing hydrogen electrolytically from caustic soda, making fatty acids, reacting them with hydrogen and finally distilling to produce the fatty alcohols.

In December 1955, Sir Henry was invited by Sydney Barratt to join the Board of Albright & Wilson Ltd. Then aged 69, he replied: "It is very kind of the Board to wish me to join them, but I do feel rather too old to be of any real use to the Company. It takes 2 or 3 years before a new Director can really pull any weight, and the fact that some directors of some Boards don't pull any, and don't want to, doesn't appeal to me as a good reason for me to do likewise. Still if there are special circumstances, as I think there may be, for you to want my help in the immediate future, I shall find it hard to say no!". He duly joined the Board of A&W in February 1956 as a non-executive director. During his time on the board, his "Socratic genius in asking questions" (Richard Threlfall) stimulated in the accounts department the sort of reaction produced by questions to Ministers in Parliament.

Marchon executive Board in 1950s: l. to r.: Peter Baines, Bernard Dugan, Frank Schon, Fred Marzillier, Arthur Halfpenny, Otto Secher.
[photo: Ivor Nicholas]

Marchon's Whitehaven employees in the late 1940s.

Hensingham garage occupied by Marchon in the early 1940s.

Frank Schon in the late 1950s.

Anhydrite mine below Whitehaven works.

HM Queen Elizabeth the Queen Mother at Whitehaven October 1964; l. to r.:
Sam Clayton, Her Majesty, Frank Schon, Otto Secher, Arthur Halfpenny, Alec
Lindsay, Alfred Koebner.

HRH the Duke of Edinburgh at Whitehaven with Frank Schon, for opening of
Solway anhydrite kilns 1955.
[photo: Cumbrian Newspapers Ltd]

Hugh Gaitskell (leader of the Labour Party) with Frank Schon at Whitehaven 1959.
[photo: Ivor Nicholas]

Sir Henry Tizard had a career of the greatest distinction. He joined the Department of Scientific and Industrial Research in 1920, became Rector of Imperial College in 1929, Chairman of the Aeronautical Research Committee in 1933 and in 1946 Chairman of the Defence Research Policy Committee and Advisory Council on Scientific Policy. During the 1939-45 war he supported the development of the Spitfire, radar and Sir Frank Whittle's invention of the jet engine. He was a Fellow of Oriel College (Oxford) and later President of Magdalen (Sydney Barratt and Bryan Topley remembered him as the only examiner they really feared). During the 1914-18 war he met Sir Richard Threlfall, then Research Director of Albright & Wilson, and in the years that followed Sir Henry became one of Sir Richard's closest friends.

A letter to Sydney Barratt in September 1956 illustrates Sir Henry's incisive approach. In it, he first points out that reporting of past results is of limited use – "the trouble is that the Board can never do anything about the past, and...I have a feeling that they might be informed without quite so much paper"; he goes on to ask for a forecast of expected sales, profit and capital expenditure for the next 6 months; next he says "I do think that at the Board we should have a statement of the more important developments that are ripening and for which the Board will have to make an early decision"; and finally he requests a six monthly report "on what is being done in the research department and why". His general approach was well ahead of its time, in the A&W context. Sadly, Sir Henry was on the A&W Board for little more than three years; he retired in May 1959 and died later that year.

The acquisition of Marchon by A&W

By the middle of 1955 Marchon had become an important member of the British chemical industry. The number of employees at Whitehaven had risen to 1,200. The company had a site of 250 acres, of which 75 had been developed, and operated competitive processes with the most important raw materials secured. One-third of the output of the works was exported. Of particular significance was the production of sodium tripolyphosphate, at a cost well below that of Albright & Wilson.

Until the emergence of Marchon as a producer of phosphates, A&W had enjoyed a monopoly in the UK as a producer of phosphorus and a near monopoly in industrial phosphoric acid and phosphates. Marchon's activities were therefore of much interest to A&W. John Christopherson, who had become a Director of A&W in 1942, came to know Frank Schon in 1950, when Marchon bought

Perry & Hope Ltd (p.38). When John joined A&W in 1932, he travelled round the mills in East Anglia, all of which were using acid calcium phosphate (ingredient of self-raising flour) from Perry & Hope, which had started manufacturing it before A&W began production in 1923. John persuaded all the mills to switch to the A&W product, because of its superior quality.

In the early 1950s John built up good personal relations with Frank Schon, whom he met from time to time to discuss commercial matters and sometimes to play golf. Although the market for STPP was growing rapidly at that time, the capacities of the plants at Whitehaven and Kirkby were together in excess of the UK market demand. Furthermore, Marchon was selling to the two main customers, Lever Bros and Thomas Hedley (later Procter & Gamble) at prices lower than A&W's, reflecting (A&W believed) lower costs.

Negotiations were opened by A&W in 1954, initially without any proposal for acquisition. The minutes of the December 1954 A&W Board meeting include the interesting sentence "A draft agreement is being prepared which will allow Marchon an agreed share of the polyphosphate market". Not surprisingly, nothing came of that idea. In June 1955, Thomas Hedley requested a reduction in the price of A&W's STPP; a response was deferred until October. John Christopherson suggested to Sydney Barratt (then Finance Director, A&W) that Marchon might consider a proposal for acquisition – the A&W Board agreed in August 1955 to re-enter into negotiations. Sydney Barratt then met Sir Henry Tizard at the Athenaeum, after which progress in negotiation was rapid. Terms were agreed in October, and the acquisition was announced to the Press on 4th November.

Why did Frank Schon and Fred Marzillier, after 15 years of conspicuously successful enterprise, surrender their independence? A statement issued by Marchon when the acquisition was announced read:

"For some time it had been apparent that, due to Marchon's rapid expansion, its ordinary share capital had become completely out of gear in relation to the total capital employed in the business. In the past it had been the practice to finance the expansion in Marchon mainly by ploughing back all profits, but the necessity arose to find additional capital in the form of loans, particularly for the completion of the Solway sulphuric acid-cement plant.... the capital needed for such further expansion could not be raised without enlarging the financial basis of Marchon-Solway. To attempt this by the issue of additional ordinary share capital presents difficulties for various reasons. In consequence, the method was adopted by incorporating Marchon-Solway into an existing organisation which had the facilities lacking in Marchon".

Local Press comment at the time was favourable, seeing the move as a means of ensuring the continued growth of a leading source of employment in the area. The Whitehaven News commented:

"To those who were close to the rapid developments associated with Marchon Products Limited it has become increasingly obvious that the very personal set-up, where a handful of experts led by Mr. Frank Schon were carrying the load, demanded a rapid and much broader basis of responsibility, if only for physical reasons...we have now an industrial combine which not only has the 'know how' in a highly competitive and technical industry, but can spread the burden of development and management which should make certain that the project in Whitehaven will readily find all that it needs in order to ensure its future success in all fields in which it is engaged".

Financial position of Marchon (and Solway) at the end of 1954

	Marchon	Solway	Total
Ordinary Shares	£350,000	£375,000	
	(book value 430,000)	(book value 375,000)	
Preference Shares	£350,000		
			£1,075,000
Loan Capital	£600,000	£1,925,000	**£2,525,000**

During 1955, as the Solway acid plant was completed and the Treasury loan was fully drawn down, borrowing rose to just under £3 million. The earlier borrowing from the Industrial and Commercial Finance Corporation (ICFC) had been partly repaid and the balance converted into 291,000 Preference shares in Marchon. Additionally, ICFC held 10% of the Ordinary shares in Marchon and 50% of the Ordinary shares in Solway (but only 15% of the voting shares). Thus Marchon was stretched financially. The profit situation was, however, healthy: profit before interest and tax in 1955 was £600,000 and the cash flow from net profit and depreciation was about £500,000.

The price paid by Albright & Wilson was £2.6 million, a premium of £1.3 million over the value of the assets acquired. In addition, the loans were taken over. To cover the cost of the acquisition and to provide funds for further expansion, A&W made a rights issue of Ordinary stock, raising £4.5 million. The rights not taken up were over-subscribed, with applications for 1.4 million shares chasing 37,000 shares on offer. Issue and acquisition were carried through speedily and very successfully.

Frank Schon, holder of a little over one-third of the combined equity of Marchon and Solway, received a little short of £900,000 (in 2000 money equal to about £15 million); until then, he had never had money, beyond what he had ploughed into the business. Fred Marzillier received £370,000. ICFC's share was over £500,000, senior staff £375,000, staff trusts £220,000 and Colgate Palmolive

Peat (one of Marchon's largest customers) £240,000. Frank Schon was appointed to the Board of Albright & Wilson Ltd (with Bill Albright, Managing Director at the time, dissenting). The Press release in November 1955 included the statement: "There is no intention of changing the present administration or direction of Marchon Products or Solway Chemicals. Mr F. Schon will continue to act as Chairman of those companies". Sir Henry Tizard, writing to Sydney Barratt in September 1955, told of his initial concern over whether Fred Marzillier would stay and whether Schon and his team "would put the same energy into the business if A&W took it over". He did establish, however, that Marzillier would stay and added, "after a talk with him (Schon) I don't think there need be any misgivings about this so long as A&W don't wish to exert too close a control!".

Expansion continued at Whitehaven. In 1955, prior to the acquisition, A&W was selling 40,000 tons of STPP a year, from a capacity of 53,000 tons, while Marchon was selling only 13,000 tons from a capacity of 25,000 tons. When the relative economics of the two sources of product were compared (£62 per ton at Kirkby against £47 at Whitehaven) it was clear that the Whitehaven route should be promoted. In 1956, a second phosphoric acid plant was built at Whitehaven and STPP capacity expanded to 50,000 tons pa. The first of two small phosphate rock carriers, the Marchon Trader, was launched in the following year and at the end of 1958 a 50% expansion of the Solway sulphuric acid plant was authorised.

Developments post-acquisition

In the next five years plants were built at Whitehaven for methyl esters and alklyolamides (thickening and foam-boosting agents in shampoos and detergents), for methacrylic monomers and polymers (used as viscosity control additives in lubricating oils) and for toluene and xylene sulphonates (used as catalysts in foundry moulds and as hydrotropes to make liquid detergents homogeneous). The number employed at Whitehaven grew from 1,200 at the end of 1954 to 1,750 at the end of 1959. Profit before interest and tax rose to over £700,000 in 1956 and over £1 million in 1957.

The promise of near-autonomy in this, the first acquisition made by Albright & Wilson since 1942, was to be repeated in acquisitions during the 1960s. This approach, federal rather than unitary, was consistent with the 'Oldbury' philosophy, which reflected the family, Quaker and very English background of the management. It was worlds away from the entrepreneurial style of Frank Schon and his team, several of whom were cosmopolitan in background (Marzillier, Secher, Baines, Abel, Koebner and later Fagandini). The whole team remained in place in a self-contained operation with its own research and engineering departments, strong relationships with customers and connections with government. The Marchon accounting was ingenious, in the ability to produce results on budget and with amoeba-like capital expenditure budgets whose shifting analysis defied attempts at control.

Frank Schon had not given up his ambitions when he surrendered ownership. In the first place, he was determined that Marchon should continue to grow, using the financial strength provided by A&W and wresting leadership in detergent phosphates from them (which indicates an 'us and them' attitude). He looked to extend the Marchon empire into the Continent of Europe (Marchon Italiana was formed in 1956 and a manufacturing plant was authorised three years later) whereas the main thrust of external expansion for A&W continued to follow the traditional line of investment in Commonwealth countries.

It is not so clear what Frank Schon's ambitions were regarding Albright & Wilson as a whole. There was always a suspicion in Oldbury (and later, Knightsbridge), held particularly by Sydney Barratt, Wilson Carter, Sir Owen Wansbrough-Jones and David Livingstone, that Frank wanted to become chief executive of A&W. To borrow a phrase used by Margaret Thatcher, they would have said that Frank was not "one of us". Frank frequently opposed the policies of the A&W Board, usually without support. He in turn must have been suspicious of what was going on at HQ, where he rarely was. The divide between Whitehaven and Oldbury persisted for a very long time, even after Frank Schon had left the company. Integration of the businesses and workforce did not happen until Whitehaven became a manufacturing site rather than a subsidiary headquarters, in 1987.

The acquisition of Marchon was said at the time to create a British chemical company second in size only to ICI. In the long term, however, the main consequences of the acquisition lay in the addition of organic detergent and toiletry materials to A&W's product range and, above all, in the incursion into the manufacture of wet phosphoric acid and phosphates based on it. Even so, many years were to elapse before the full effect of these developments was felt. In the nearer term the main developments were in growth by further acquisitions and investment in phosphorus manufacture.

Chapter 2

GROWING IN PROSPERITY

1956 - 1959

"We believe that, in common with other companies in the chemical industry, we are helped in trade recessions by the diversity of the markets which we serve"
(1997 Annual Report)

Overview

In the four years following the acquisition of Marchon, Albright & Wilson showed an unbroken growth in profit, reaping the harvest of investment in the preceding five years. The background to that achievement was stability in the world economic scene despite major political conflicts:

Political and Economic background

- in 1956, the Suez campaign and the Soviet crushing of the Hungarian uprising created international tensions not experienced since the Korean war
- one year after Colonel Nasser became President of Egypt (in June 1957), King Faisal of Iraq was assassinated and Iraq became a republic; six months later, in January 1959, Fidel Castro took power in Cuba from President Batista
- in 1958, De Gaulle became President of France, Nikita Khruschev became Prime Minister of the USSR and Mao Tse-tung announced his retirement as Chairman of the Chinese Republic
- in Britain Harold Macmillan succeeded Sir Anthony Eden as Prime Minister in January 1957 and at the General Election in October 1959 the Conservatives doubled their majority, to 100
- the treaties establishing the European Economic Community and Euratom came into force in January 1958
- Calder Hall,the world's first commercial atomic power station, began operating in 1956, and in 1959 the first sections of the M1 motorway from London and the St Lawrence Seaway were opened
- the Restrictive Practices Act was passed in 1956, outlawing collective price-fixing and other anti-competitive practices
- most exchange rates were stable in the period, with the £ worth 2.80 US dollars, 11.7 deutschemarks, 1,750 Italian lire and 1000 yen; the French franc, however, was devalued by De Gaulle at the end of 1958, from 9.8 to 13.8 to the £; the £ became partly convertible into the US dollar
- economic growth slowed in 1957; a developing recession in the USA affected the UK, particularly in 1958 when governmental anti-inflation measures took effect
- before growth resumed strongly in 1959, the growth in UK GNP from 1955 to 1959 averaged 2% pa and industrial production grew by an average of 1.5% pa, less than half that in West Germany, France, Italy, the USA and Canada
- the UK wholesale price index rose by 3% pa in 1956–7 but fell in the next two years; the retail price index followed a similar pattern, rising by 5% pa in 1956–7 but by only 1% pa in 1958–9
- UK equity prices fell by 20% in 1956–7, then more than doubled in the next 2 years

Albright & Wilson's results

The financial results of Albright & Wilson in this period did not reflect the economic environment. The Annual Report for 1957 included the statement, "We believe that, in common with other companies in the chemical industry, we are helped in trade recessions by the diversity of the markets which we serve". While there was some truth in that claim, progress owed more to the foundations laid in the first half of the 1950s.

Progress 1956-1959

		1955	1956	1957	1958	1959
Sales (£ millions)						
UK companies		14.5	22.6	24.7	24.9	26.2
Overseas companies		8.0	9.0	5.7	7.3	8.3
	Total	**22.5**	**31.6**	**30.4**	**32.2**	**34.5**
Trading Profit						
UK companies		1.03	1.77	2.44	2.33	3.17
Overseas companies		1.08	1.20	0.60	1.02	1.16
Other income		0.05	0.05	0.30	0.44	0.78
	Total	**2.16**	**3.02**	**3.34**	**3.79**	**5.11**
Interest Payable		0.36	0.43	0.44	0.46	0.45
Pretax Profit		**1.80**	**2.59**	**2.90**	**3.33**	**4.66**
After depreciation of		1.40	1.82	1.85	2.06	2.28
Capital Expenditure	**Total**	**1.0**	**2.9**	**2.0**	**3.1**	**2.5**
Net Capital employed (end of year)		**26.0**	**25.3**	**26.8**	**28.7**	**30.8**

There are two important factors affecting these figures: the acquisition of Marchon in December 1955 and the sale of Oldbury Electro-Chemical Company in November 1956. The capital employed at the end of 1955 reflects the full cost of the Marchon acquisition, which totalled about £4.5 million and did not yield any significant sales and profits until 1956.

In 1956 nearly a quarter of A&W's sales were from Marchon, which accounted for £730,000 of the 1956 overall trading profit – without it the increase would have been small. Sales from other A&W concerns rose in value by roughly 10%. In 1956, the Solway acid and cement plant was operating at 90% of its capacity; in 1957–9, when the plant was fully operating, Marchon contributed just over £1 million of the annual trading profit in each year.

The share capital of Albright & Wilson Ltd was increased in 1955 first by a 1 for 2 scrip ('bonus') issue and then by a 1 for 2 rights issue to finance the acquisition of Marchon. The rising trend of profits brought with it increasing dividend payments. The dividend for 1956 was at the same rate (18%) as paid for 1955 on the capital before the rights issue, thus costing 50% more. It was raised to 20% for 1957. In 1958 there was a 1 for 4 scrip issue and a dividend equivalent to 21.25% on the 1957 capital. Another 1 for 4 scrip issue was made in 1959 and the dividend paid was equivalent to 28.6%.

In the 1958 Annual Report for the first time A&W's sales were published, for that year and all the years from 1949. Up to that time, it had been thought that if sales were revealed it would be to A&W's commercial disadvantage, perhaps encouraging its main customers to press for lower prices. Trading profit as a percentage of sales was 16.7% in 1958, which was exceeded only by 1950 and 1951. For 1959 the figure rose to a peak of 21.4%. Perhaps partly because of the greater disclosure than practice prevailing at the time, the A&W Annual Report for 1959 received the 'Accountant' award for annual reports by large companies. (The information provided in the 32 pages of that report was slender indeed compared with that usual in company reports 40 years later.)

A&W's cash position was strong. At the end of 1959, out of a total capital employed of £30.8 million, borrowing amounted to only £8.7 million, against which there were cash and short-term investments of £4.7 million. In many respects, therefore, A&W entered the 1960s in good shape for further expansion.

Organisation

Sydney Barratt became Managing Director in November 1955, as the Marchon acquisition was nearing completion. One of his early concerns was to alter the organisation of the Albright & Wilson group. He had two reasons for wanting change: to make the organisation more appropriate to A&W's increasingly complex structure; and to facilitate further acquisitions or mergers.

SB saw "a dangerous source of administrative confusion" in the responsibility of the board of Albright & Wilson Ltd both to directly manage trading operations in the UK and to be responsible for subsidiaries in Canada and Australia and associated companies. So at the beginning of 1957 Albright & Wilson Ltd became a holding company, with UK trading operations being devolved to a new subsidiary, Albright & Wilson (Mfg), and to Marchon. Although there were significant tax advantages in the reorganisation, the primary motivation was the need for a more modern structure.

Linked with the change in organisation was the move of the Head Office from Oldbury to London. The London Sales Office of Albright & Wilson (Mfg) had moved in 1957 from Park Lane to 1 Knightsbridge Green, almost opposite Harrods, where it was joined by the Head Office departments during 1958. A lease was signed in March 1957 for a period of 35 years at a fixed rental of 15s.6d. per square foot. When the lease was arranged by David Christopherson, the Sales Administrator of Albright & Wilson (Mfg), he was apprehensive that he would be criticised for the commitment. Over the years, the lease proved, in the words of his brother John, to be the "best contract we ever signed". London was chosen for the Head Office because it was at the hub of communications and the financial and governmental centre, reasons which made it the target for an increasing number of relocated company headquarters. Many years later, the disadvantages of having a head office separate from the main commercial functions and service departments came to outweigh the earlier perceived advantages and the head office departments gradually moved back to Birmingham. The very low rental acted as a restraint on change until in October 1991, only a few months before the expiry of the lease, the last of the head office functions moved back to the Birmingham area.

On 22nd January 1958 Kenneth Wilson ceased to be Chairman and a Director, on the 50th anniversary of his joining the Company, and was given the honorific title of President. Sydney Barratt became executive Chairman, and the titles of Managing Director and Vice-Chairman were dropped. Wilson Carter, who had become Chairman of Albright & Wilson (Mfg), was appointed to the main Board. Also appointed, as a non-executive Director, was Neil Peech, Chairman of Steetly, a company manufacturing refractories based in England and with a Canadian subsidiary. Other Board changes in this period were the retirement of Sir Henry Tizard in March 1959 and the appointment in October 1959 of Sir Owen Wansbrough-Jones, KBE, CB, as Technical Director (p.102).

While the Company was expanding and becoming less paternalistic, there were still many features of the old private company. In August 1956 Kenneth Wilson at the Annual General Meeting said: "There was a time when I could have walked round our Works and known every man's Christian name, what he was doing and how well he was doing it, just as my father and grandfather had done before me. Those days are past, but much of the friendly atmosphere which created them has survived and gives our Company, I like to think, for all its growing size and complexity a spirit of which we may be proud". In that year, two Oldbury employees reached 50 years' service; in the following year another employee, Bill Skett, reached his 50 years and brought the total service of his family at Oldbury to over 250 years, with two other members still there. The average service of the members of the '25' club at Oldbury was over 40 years. In 1959 a third week's holiday was granted for hourly-paid employees with 25 years' service. Directors and senior salaried employees were more fortunate: they were granted four weeks' holiday, which was extended also to less senior salaried employees over 55 with 25 years' service. Other developments included the formation of a Personnel Department at Oldbury, the publication of accident statistics (but still without general wearing of protective clothing), the creation of a Company Medical Officer, the hiring of the first female apprentice and the creation of sports grounds at Oldbury and Whitehaven.

Developments

In this period, while there was expansion in Canada, the United Kingdom and Australia, Albright & Wilson disposed of its operations in the United States; thirty years were to elapse before the Company once again had a significant investment there.

United States

Oldbury Electro-Chemical Company (OECCo), A&W's oldest subsidiary and its only interest in the USA, in 1955 contributed one third of the total pretax profit of A&W and achieved a pretax profit ratio of 16% on sales. That followed an investment of $4.7 million in 1953–5 on capital additions, including the sodium chlorate plant at the new site at Columbus, Mississippi. At the end of 1955, OECCo held cash of $2.7 million.

In comparison with other US chemical manufacturers, however, OECCo was small, and it had neither sought nor grasped opportunities for expansion, such as the chance to buy Swann Chemicals (p.8). There does not appear to have been any attempt by the directors of Albright & Wilson to introduce new products, nor any local initiative to do so. There was no move to make sodium tripolyphosphate, the major avenue for expansion in the UK, Canada and Australia. Instead A&W focused overseas expansion primarily on Canada and secondarily on Australia, perhaps because of the tradition of concentrating on the British Empire and within the area of Imperial Preference. Many of the senior staff of Erco, including the President, were British expatriates, but that was not the case in OECCo which had a large measure of autonomy, very occasional inter-continental communication and only rare visits from the UK. Dividends from OECCo were small and infrequent: since 1947, the only dividend paid was $100,000 in 1952 (from cash balances of around $3 million). When money was borrowed locally for the Columbus project, it was agreed to restrict dividends to the parent company (though not to forego them entirely).

OECCo was a small minnow swimming gently in the large USA pond (unlike

Erco which was a big fish in the smaller Canadian pond). Sydney Barratt's ambitions for growth were directed towards the UK rather than the USA; indeed, he showed some antipathy towards the US way of doing business and the American lifestyle and his disinclination to invest there was supported by the A&W Board. The 1956 Annual Report recorded, "we had been conscious for some time of our vulnerability in markets dominated by much larger concerns, and of increasing difficulty in generating in the United States new funds commensurate with the opportunities for expansion. Plans for heavy capital investment in the United Kingdom and in Canada emphasised the need for some concentration of resources".

It is not clear where the initiative for divestment originated. The minutes of the A&W Board meeting in January 1956 record that Earl Whitford (President of OECCo) had held discussions with Hooker Electrochemical Company, OECCo's neighbours at Niagara Falls, concerning a possible merger of the two companies, perhaps together with Erco and the Lubrizol Corporation (p.3). Hooker was a US company with five factories in the USA and sales in 1956 of nearly $100 million (against $11 million by OECCo). The deal that emerged in June 1956 was for Hooker to acquire OECCo for 450,000 shares (equivalent to 6.5% of its enlarged share capital). A&W received 378,000 shares, worth $18.5 million (£6.6 million). The price was equivalent to about 10 times the pretax profit in 1956.

The remaining 72,000 shares (worth $3.5 million) were distributed to senior employees of OECCo, all of whom, including Earl Whitford (as a Vice-President), were taken on by Hooker. There had been a long-standing arrangement for shares to be held by some employees and repurchased at net book value in the event of termination of their employment (by death or otherwise) or change in control of OECCo. In 1956, that should have involved the payment of a total of $1 million, a figure including the price of shares sold to five employees in 1953 - they were in fact given four times the original share value. The Board's decision to pay more was urged by Bill Albright, on the grounds that it would secure the future goodwill of the employees concerned.

At the June 1956 meeting when the sale of OECCo was agreed, Frank Schon made clear that he opposed the loss of the company's US base; it was the first, but by no means the last, occasion on which his dissent from Board decisions was recorded. Later, John Christopherson described the decision as a great mistake. Keith Piercy, the most frequent visitor of the Directors to the USA, wrote of his regret but accepted that the sale was an inevitable consequence of the failure to expand earlier. With Bryan Topley, he negotiated an agreement with Hooker for the interchange of research, but this was later abandoned because of Hooker's fears of the possible effects of antitrust laws. Collaboration on chlorine dioxide generators (sold to users of sodium chlorate for pulp bleaching) did, however, last for many years.

There were several immediate financial consequences for A&W. First, its USA-based profits from 1957 onwards included only the dividends from Hooker; based on 1956, the pretax total was reduced by about £500,000 as a consequence. Second, A&W had the equivalent of a liquid asset, which in later years was first pledged as security for borrowing in Canada and then, between 1964 and 1968, sold for a dollar value about 10% up on its value at acquisition, representing a disappointing return.

One positive aspect of the deal was that A&W was relieved of the liabilities associated with a chemical site, particularly one producing phosphorus, which 30 or 40 years later were to become so important for A&W in its site rationalisation programme. The very serious problems encountered by Occidental Petroleum (which acquired Hooker in 1968) in the 1970s with the Love Canal adjoining Hooker's site at Niagara Falls highlighted the growing importance of the environment.

Canada

Canada was the primary focus of development in the period 1956–9, during which time CAD 14 million was invested in Erco's chlorate and phosphate operations. In the early 1950s the demand for whiter papers, involving bleaching with chlorine dioxide in addition to chlorine, created the growth in requirements for **sodium chlorate**. The two centres of the Canadian woodpulp industry were Quebec and British Columbia. Buckingham, well placed to serve the Quebec mills, expanded its capacity in 1952 by installing new cell lines with a capacity of around 9,500 tpa to replace the pre-war 6,000 tpa plant. In February 1956 the A&W Board agreed to build a plant at Vancouver, British Columbia, with a capacity of 12,000 tpa and facilities to expand output to 24,000 tpa; $1.5 million was remitted from the UK towards the $5 million cost with the balance being met by borrowing in Canada and Erco's generated funds. The plant came on stream in March 1957.

At that time, it was believed that the extraction of uranium from mined ore would provide a second major market for sodium chlorate. Erco forecast a demand for 28,000 tpa at Blind River, Ontario. Despite pressure from Frank Schon to obtain contracts from the uranium processors before pressing ahead, Erco decided in December 1957 to expand the Buckingham plant by 12,000 tpa and to increase the capacity at Vancouver by 50%. In the event, sales to the uranium mines never materialised at the level forecast – by April 1959 the market was in decline. By then, the expansions at Buckingham and Vancouver had come on stream, putting Erco's capacity about 30% ahead of demand. The uranium application for chlorate had virtually ceased by the end of 1961.

Competition was also increasing. In Western Canada, G.O. Westerland, one of Erco's employees, left and started up his own chlorate business under the name GOW Industries. In the East, competition came from Huron Chemicals, with a plant close to Blind River founded by G.J. Crane, a former Chief Engineer of Erco, who had been dismissed in July 1957 when a complete set of drawings for the Vancouver plant went missing. Erco obtained an injunction against the use of the alleged stolen documents and was then faced with a claim for wrongful dismissal. The case dragged on until mid-1961, when the judgment went against Erco; it appealed but eventually withdrew in February 1962. Meanwhile, Crane had become a consultant for American Potash, a US competitor with a plant close to the Columbus plant of Hooker. Hooker built a chlorate plant in Vancouver, where it had a chlorine/caustic plant next to the Erco site. Later, Krebs, which had modern technology for chlorate cells, went into production and some pulp mills invested in captive chlorate plants.

Erco was, however, still the largest manufacturer in the world. In November 1958 it strengthened its position by setting up a division, Erco Engineering Services, to design, construct, install and start up chlorine dioxide units at pulp mills – a profitable activity that was also to prove a powerful aid to the selling of sodium chlorate.

In the four years from 1955 to 1959, sodium chlorate sales rose from CAD 1.3 million to 5.9 million; profit before interest and tax rose from CAD 340,000 to 1,540,000, when it accounted for more than 10% of the total A&W profit. The investment required in that period to produce that result was CAD 9 million. Then, as later, sodium chlorate production was a capital-hungry operation requiring relatively large margins on sales to service the capital. It was also a business susceptible to wide fluctuations in selling-prices, reflecting imbalances between supply and demand. So in 1960, in the face of falling demand for chlorate in uranium extraction and the bringing in of new manufacturing capacity, profit collapsed to a break-even position. The 1959 level of profit was not reached again for more than a decade.

Progress in **phosphates** was directed chiefly to meeting the growth in demand for polyphosphates for detergents, which led to a search for a new site in preference to expanding at Buckingham. In February 1956 a proposal was put to the A&W Board for building a factory at Hamilton, an industrial city on Lake Ontario not far from Toronto, for the manufacture of industrial phosphates and possibly wet phosphoric acid and fertiliser grade materials too. A site for $250,000 was located and, to deter possible competitors, it was announced that a wet acid plant would be built. The project's estimated cost was $10 million. Within three months, however, plans for a wet acid plant were abandoned because of the difficulty of disposing of the gypsum by-product. In October 1956 a revised $2.5 million project for phosphates and a thermal phosphoric acid plant at Hamilton was approved.

At the same time, David Jones (President of Erco) reported that a site suitable for wet acid production had been found further South, at Port Maitland on Lake Erie, near Niagara Falls. An option on the site was taken in January 1957 and in April 1957 the Hamilton project was cancelled. The following month, a 200-acre site was bought from the Toronto, Hamilton and Buffalo Railway, near the mouth of the Grand River. Expectations that plants could be built and in operation within nine months were not met – extensive landfilling was required to overcome flooding and for the next two years the land was left to consolidate. So, in December 1957, contrary to earlier plans, expansion of phosphate production at Buckingham was given the go-ahead.

That left open the question of what to do with the Port Maitland site. In January 1958, undeterred by Erco's announcement in 1956 of its intention to build a wet phosphoric acid plant, US entrepreneur Errol Beker had formed Dominion Fertilizer Company to manufacture superphosphate on a site adjacent to Erco's site at Port Maitland. By September 1958 the single superphosphate plant was in production. Beker then asked Erco to supply phosphoric acid to enable him to make triple superphosphate but his price was too low for Erco to contemplate. Beker was also reported to be threatening to make tripolyphosphate, in conjunction with American Cyanamid (which would provide the know-how). That was the scenario that Erco had feared when deciding to go to Port Maitland.

In January 1959 the A&W Board agreed, subject to finance being available, to spend $11 million at Port Maitland for sulphuric acid, wet phosphoric acid and sodium tripolyphosphate plants, and to investigate the manufacture of 50,000 tons pa of triple superphosphate for fertilisers. The triple superphosphate would provide an outlet for the impure underflow of phosphoric acid produced by the wet acid plant, which could not be used for industrial phosphates. Sir Henry Tizard warned that if Erco wished to manufacture competitively large tonnages of low-cost products it would be necessary to invest further substantial sums in the years ahead. Frank Schon abstained from voting because the information provided was insufficient. A press release was nevertheless issued in February 1959 stating: "Erco are to build new plants to produce sulphuric and phosphoric acids, as well as sodium phosphates and other products, to fill the needs of industry and agriculture in Eastern Canada ... production should begin early in 1960".

In May 1959, to overcome the threat from Beker, Dominion Fertilisers Ltd was purchased for $2 million, including $400,000 for goodwill. Apart from the elimination of possible competition in industrial phosphates, the move fitted into the plan to establish an integrated operation in industrial and fertiliser phosphates. The underflow of impure phosphoric acid from the wet phosphoric acid plant on the Erco site would be used to make triple superphosphate in the Dominion Fertiliser plant while the purer acid was sold or used in industrial phosphates, mainly sodium tripolyphosphate. Being close to the border with the United States, the plants would be well placed to serve both the Canadian and US markets. Sulphuric acid was to be supplied as a by-product from the nearby zinc ore roasting plant of Matthiessen & Hegeler.

The concept appeared to have much to commend it. The Albright & Wilson Board therefore approved the building on the Dominion Fertilisers site of a triple superphosphate plant and a plant to make feed-grade dicalcium phosphate, for a total of $14 million. The plan to make sodium tripolyphosphate on the Erco site was deferred for two years, partly because of the need to do more work on making the material from wet phosphoric acid but mainly because of a shortage of money. Thus the original reason for acquiring a site at Port Maitland was sidelined and instead A&W entered into the manufacture of fertilisers, hitherto eschewed as a business in which A&W did not have an advantage.

Indeed, as a fertiliser manufacturing site Port Maitland had serious disadvantages. Its main raw material, phosphate rock, had to be transported by rail from Florida, whereas the main US producers were located at the source of rock. One of the reasons for entering into the manufacture of fertilisers was a forecast that large tonnages would be required by the "third world" to increase the output of food for the rapidly growing populations. Yet Port Maitland was badly placed for exports. Another problem was the cost of sulphuric acid. The long-term contract with Sherbrooke Metallurgical (the Matthiessen & Heggeler subsidiary) contained escalation clauses that were very disadvantageous to Erco and could increase the price to Erco by $7 for only $1 increase in Sherbrooke's costs. It was not until the late 1960s that the contract was renegotiated through the threat to purchase wet phosphoric acid from Texas Gulf, at a lower price and of a better quality than the phosphoric acid produced from the Sherbrooke sulphuric acid. (A further 20 years were to elapse before the joint venture with Texasgulf in purified phosphoric acid was to provide the foundation for a leading position by Albright & Wilson in phosphoric acid and phosphates in North America; the Sherbrooke plant, which was acquired by Erco in 1972, had closed by then.)

One of the ironies of the history of A&W's involvement in fertilisers in Canada was that within three years of the acquisition of Dominion Fertilisers the Canadian Combines Commission began an investigation of alleged uncompetitive practices. A very long drawn-out process was eventually brought to a close at the end of 1969 by A&W's decision to plead guilty to the charges. A fine was imposed and changes were made to the contracts for the sale of sodium tripolyphosphate. The last chapter in this story was the sale of the Port Maitland fertiliser business and assets to International Minerals & Chemicals early in 1974 at a price above the written-down value of the assets; that profit was the first recorded for the business in the nearly 15 years since the acquisition of Dominion Fertilisers. Meanwhile, the sodium tripolyphosphate plant at Port Maitland came on stream in 1968 but experienced troubles in using wet phosphoric acid. The feed was later switched to thermal acid and so remained until the use of purified wet acid in 1991.

The requirements for more funds for investment in Canada were a feature of the

1950s as for many years after. Between 1950 and the end of 1955, there was a cash shortfall of more than $4 million, and in the 4 years from 1956 to 1959 another $4 million was required. The purchase of Dominion Fertilisers and capital expenditure at Port Maitland led to a further requirement of $4 million in 1959–60. A further $3 million was needed in 1961 to cover Erco's collapse in profits. While Erco was able to borrow from its bankers, the Bank of Montreal and the International Development Bank, as its financial position deteriorated the banks pressed for money to be put in by Albright & Wilson Ltd and for guarantees from the parent company. Between 1953 and 1961, $10 million was remitted from the UK and guarantees were given for Erco's local borrowing.

In the 1950s UK exchange controls were still in force, which meant that it was necessary to obtain consent from the Bank of England not only for remittances and guarantees from the UK but also for local borrowing by overseas subsidiaries. In giving its consent, the expectation of the Bank of England was that two thirds of overseas profits would be remitted. However, apart from a $250,000 dividend on the Ordinary capital in 1951 and an annual $30,000 dividend on the Preference capital, no dividend was paid to the parent company in this period, or subsequently. The Bank of England exercised remarkable tolerance throughout, being persuaded that there was no alternative to riding A&W's stumbling horse, with the hope of a reversal of the cash flow before long.

Other developments

Although **Marchon** became a wholly-owned subsidiary of A&W at the end of 1955, it remained in some respects self-contained. Because of the Treasury loan to Solway the price of sulphuric acid from Solway to Marchon had to be on an arms' length basis; Board approval for an increase was sought in October 1957. The requirements of Marchon and Solway for cash, beyond that generated by profits, were met by loans from the parent company, of £500,000 in April 1956 and a further loan in February 1957, bringing the total to £950,000. In October 1957 £399,000 was lent to Marchon to enable Solway to pay a dividend. Salary policy for Marchon was also different from the rest of A&W in the UK, for some years after 1955, until it was reviewed in mid-1958.

The most obvious divide between Marchon and the rest of A&W in the UK was concerned with STPP and the manufacturing routes to it. Solway's first full year of production was 1956. In that year, approval was given for expansion of the STPP capacity at Whitehaven to 50,000 tpa and for a small sulphur-burning plant to bring the capacity for sulphuric acid up to the level required. In July 1957 a proposal to build a third kiln at Whitehaven, at a cost of £1.3 million, to raise capacity for acid and cement by 50%, was rejected because the return was inadequate.

A suggestion that APCM (Associated Portland Cement Manufacturers, the customer for the co-product cement from the existing two kilns) be offered equity in Solway in exchange for financing the kiln was also rejected. In December 1958 another proposal for a third kiln at a cost of £950,000 was put forward. After considerable discussion, the project was deferred by the board in June 1959 because there was opposition to selling sulphuric acid, which would have been necessary because the Board also then decided that no more STPP manufacture should be transferred from Kirkby to Whitehaven. The output at Kirkby had been reduced because Thomas Hedley (Procter & Gamble) had decided to take all its requirements from Whitehaven from the end of 1957. The Board supported the manufacture of STPP at Kirkby from thermal phosphoric acid, using phosphorus imported from Varennes. Frank Schon dissented from the decision, pointing out that STPP cost £63 per ton to make at Kirkby but only £40 at Whitehaven. Eventually in February 1960 the Board approved the building of a third kiln, at a cost of £1.15 million, and an extension to the wet phosphoric acid plant for £570,000, to provide Kirkby with acid to replace thermal acid. Later the whole of STPP production in the UK was transferred to Whitehaven, where the use of wet acid and spray dryers was more economic than the thermal acid and drum dryers used at Kirkby.

In this period, there was a project for construction of wet acid and STPP plants on a new site on the Thames, to supply the Procter & Gamble detergent factory at West Thurrock, Essex. A site for the plant was bought in August 1958 nearby at Mucking. In January 1959 600 acres were bought at Fobbing, also on the north bank of the Thames estuary, for dumping the gypsum waste from the wet acid plant. The projected return from the likely tonnage required was, however, inadequate and so there was no development. Many years later the sites were sold (p.250).

All **phosphate rock** for the UK was shipped from either Morocco (for Whitehaven) or Florida (for Portishead, Oldbury and Widnes). In 1957 the first of the Company's phosphate rock carriers, the *Marchon Trader*, was launched. Because of the limitations of Whitehaven harbour, its capacity was limited to 2,500 tons. That was followed by the *Marchon Venturer* and *Marchon Enterprise*, of the same size. The ships, however, were too small to be economic and later shipment was by bulk carriers anchoring offshore and being unloaded by the smaller ships or specially designed barge. In 1959 a vessel for transportation of rock from Florida, with a capacity of 10,000 tons and suitable for docking at Portishead, was purchased. The ship was given the name *Arthur Albright*, after the Company's founder. A&W (Overseas Developments) was registered in Bermuda to own the ship and to be the vehicle for know-how agreements, to take advantage of the more favourable tax regime there. Phosphate rock was transported by road from Portishead to Oldbury. Production of phosphorus at Widnes ceased in 1959 (the year when the Buckingham furnaces were also closed, after 60 years of production there).

In this period there were several lesser **developments in the UK**. The first licensees for the Proban process for flame retardancy in textiles were appointed in 1957. The introduction of Domestic Calgon and Micromet, for water-softening and scale prevention, in that year marked the Company's first venture into selling directly into the UK retail market; although the product range was subsequently extended, sales were never significant and the venture was consistently unprofitable. Of greater long-term importance were expansions in DCP (dicalcium phosphate, for toothpaste), organic phosphorus compounds, metal finishing processes, detergent oil additives and phosphorus pentasulphide (the principal intermediate for the additives). The oil additives plant and the plant producing Malathion (for systemic insecticides) became notorious for the smells generated by the sulphur compounds, including one termed the 'tom cat' smell; in 1957, the smell penetrated to the centre of Birmingham, giving rise to claims for the contamination of foodstuffs. At Whitehaven there was expansion in another type of oil additives, methacrylates used as viscosity index improvers, as well as continued growth in products for cosmetics and toiletries. In 1958 it was decided to double the size of the research laboratories at Oldbury.

There was also investment in expanded laboratories and pilot plant facilities for silicones at Barry. **Midland Silicones** was the largest producer of silicones outside the USA but was encountering competition from imports. In 1958 it successfully brought an anti-dumping action against silicone fluids imported from Rhone Poulenc, followed by an import duty on all silicone imports. A year later, the anti-dumping restriction was removed as a consequence of the devaluation of the French franc. MS's sales and profits in this period were growing rapidly. Sales passed the £1 million mark in 1956 and were over £2 million in 1959. The first profit was made in 1957 and in 1959 it amounted to nearly £500,000, a well-above average return on sales, which was to be maintained in the next few years; sales passed the £3 million mark in 1963, with profit over £700,000.

The sales of **Albright & Wilson (Australia)** more than doubled in this period, from less than £800,000 in 1955 to £1.8 million in 1959. Profits also grew but remained relatively low in relation to sales - less than 10% in 1959. Australia was a high-cost country for manufacture, with an exchange-rate tied to sterling at AUD1.25: £1. In 1955 A&W (Australia) had been successful in obtaining enhanced tariff protection for phosphates but that did not apply to STPP since at the time it was not being manufactured locally (detergent phosphates started late in Australia, when Levers test-marketed Surf in Tasmania in January 1955); it was not until 1961 that the tariff on other phosphates (20% from the UK, 37.5% other) was extended to polyphosphates. Polyphosphates accounted for more than half the increase in Australian sales between 1955 and 1959, during which, after production started in 1956, the new Maunsell process for manufacture (p.100) was being developed.

A further one-third of the increase came from 'agency products', i.e. materials not manufactured by A&W (Australia), which included imports from Whitehaven and Midland Silicones. The Marchon agency for organic detergents and toiletries was taken over in 1957, from the Australian company appointed before A&W's acquisition of Marchon in 1955. There was a proposal in 1957 for a sulphonation plant to be established in Sydney, because of the location of the principal customers, but at that time it could not be justified and so manufacture started at the Yarraville site at the end of 1958. (After the acquisition of Gardinol in 1966, production was moved to the Gardinol site at Box Hill, also in Melbourne, and a further 12 years elapsed before eventually there was manufacture in Sydney.)

Although a new phosphorus furnace was built at Yarraville in 1958, the main effort in basic phosphate development turned to the wet acid route to detergent phosphates. In April 1959 a proposal was put to the A&W Board for the purchase of a 200 acre site at Cockle Creek, 80 miles north of Sydney, for the manufacture of wet acid and STPP, using by-product sulphuric acid from the adjacent Conzinc plant. The project was estimated to cost just under AUD 1 million. In November 1959 the Board agreed the project and authorised the ordering of a Prayon filter, the main plant item. Shortly after, however, the project was put on hold because of uncertainty regarding sales to Levers and Colgate, the two main prospective customers. Following the abolition of import licensing in February 1960 it became necessary to reduce the price of STPP because of import competition; A&W (Australia)'s profit in 1960 was less than half that of 1959. A year later it was finally decided to abandon the project.

With the termination in September 1954 of ICIANZ's agency to sell A&W (Australia) products, responsibility for sales and administration passed to the Company. The staff engaged for the purpose were temporarily housed in a converted ICIANZ warehouse until in 1957 a villa in St Kilda Road (at that time primarily a residential area in Melbourne) was purchased. It became the Company's head office at the end of 1957. In 1965 the building was demolished and a purpose-built office erected on the site. In time the 3-storey building, on a large block, became overshadowed by the large office blocks built along St Kilda Road. More than 30 years later, the office was closed and the staff moved to Yarraville as a cost reduction move that made possible the realisation of the greatly increased value of the site.

The European Common Market

Soon after the end of the 1939–45 war the first moves were made towards a common market in Europe. The Organisation for European Economic Cooperation (OEEC) was founded in 1948 and in the same year Belgium, the Netherlands and

Luxembourg entered into a customs union, which became known as Benelux. Three years later, the Benelux countries, together with France, Italy and West Germany, set up the European Coal and Steel Community, in accordance with the Schuman Plan; they began negotiations in 1954 for a full customs union. The Spaak Report, published in 1956, led to the Treaty of Rome, signed in March 1957. It established the European Economic Community (EEC), with a programme for reducing tariffs between the participating countries ("The Six") from January 1959 until the establishment of free trade and common external tariffs, within 12–15 years. Key Industry Duty was ended and quotas were to be increased and eventually abolished.

The United Kingdom, with its extensive Commonwealth trade and imperial preferences, did not take part in moves to form the EEC; the proposed common external tariff was a stumbling block. There was also reluctance to be drawn into something that promised to become more than a customs union, notably by establishing a common agricultural policy and making moves towards the integration of some fiscal and monetary policies. There was, however, concern that UK trade would be affected by exclusion from a powerful free trade area. The West German Chancellor, Konrad Adenauer, wanted Europe to become a third force in the world. In July 1956 the OEEC set up a group to study the relationship between the Six and the other OEEC members, and the possibility of creating a free trade area to include them. There was a proposal to abolish tariffs between members while allowing them to set different external tariffs but that was abandoned after two years of discussion.

In November 1959, the European Free Trade Area (EFTA) was established by a Convention signed by seven countries – Austria, Denmark, Norway, Portugal, Sweden, Switzerland and the United Kingdom – with the intention of abolishing tariffs and quotas on industrial products between the Seven by the end of 1969. It was hoped that a bridge could be built between the Seven and the Six but the wish to preserve different external tariffs was a fundamental obstacle. So it was not long before the EFTA countries were seeking full membership or a form of association with the European Common Market. Britain's application for full membership, with some concessions for the less developed Commonwealth countries, was made in mid-1961 but vetoed by France in January 1963.

Within A&W, there was much apprehension concerning the effects of reductions in tariffs and quotas within Europe. The UK chemical industry, despite the protection of Key Industry Duty on most chemical imports and lower tariffs into all the countries of the Six, was importing more from those countries than it was exporting to them: in 1954 exports were £27 million and imports £38 million. The contrast was particularly marked with France and Germany: in 1954, exports of chemicals to those countries from the UK were only £10 million against imports of

£25 million. There was a fear that much of the home trade would be lost through competition. Home market prices were typically much higher than export prices, on which there was only a marginal profit. There was, however, protection through agreements or understandings between producers, which persisted (albeit through habit or enlightened self-interest) even after the provisions of Article 85 of the Treaty of Rome had made the existence of overt cartels no longer permissible. A report to the A&W Board by the Market Research Department in December 1956 expressed concern at the likely loss of home sales and profits and emphasised the need to investigate the comparative costs of production in the UK and elsewhere in Europe. In July 1962, however, a second report concluded that A&W's home trade would be surprisingly little affected if Britain entered the Common Market. That conclusion took into account both competition from imported chemicals and the possible effects on customer industries.

Development on the continent of Europe was obviously one way in which markets could be exploited by UK companies across tariff barriers. In November 1956, A&W's first subsidiary in continental Europe, Marchon Italiana, was formed to handle exports of surfactants from Whitehaven. Two and a half years later, in July 1959, the Board authorised a factory to be built at Castiglione delle Stiviere, in northern Italy, for the manufacture of some of the Marchon range of products at a cost, including working-capital, of £200,000. That was followed by manufacturing by Marchon France (1970), by a second Italian factory, at Frosinone, south of Rome (mid-1972) and Marchon Espanola (end of 1972).

There was no similar development of the phosphates business, for a variety of reasons. First, competition in phosphates was more orderly, with producers taking care not to compete in each others' home markets. Second, whereas the initial investment in surfactant production was relatively simple and inexpensive (blending, bottling, etc.) and the products also relatively low-priced and often had a large water content, the phosphates required more elaborate plant and were more economic to transport, and so more susceptible to economies of scale. As tariffs were reduced, that argument was strengthened. The Marchon management was more oriented towards continental Europe than the rest of A&W but a proposal in 1959 to make STPP in Italy was abandoned because of unfavourable economics. In 1963 a joint venture with Montecatini for the manufacture of dicalcium phosphate was proposed by Frank Schon but foundered for the same reason. Thirty years later, the lack of phosphates manufacturing subsidiaries in continental Europe was claimed to be a strength rather than a weakness, but ultimately the balance swung against manufacturers in the UK.

While the establishment of manufacture in continental Europe was very limited, exports from the UK grew. Before Marchon was acquired, Albright & Wilson was selling through a network of agents supported by a European Technical Service department – the first conference of the European agents was held in 1950. Marchon was strongly export-oriented and Marchon Italiana became A&W's first sales company in continental Europe. Albright & Wilson obtained its first Queen's Award for Exports in 1966, the same year that the next sales companies were set up, in Sweden and in Holland. Eventually, there were Overseas Marketing Companies covering the whole of Western Europe and also servicing the Eastern bloc.

Mergers

In September 1954 Bill Albright, prompted by Sydney Barratt, produced a paper entitled "Acquisition, Amalgamation & Submergence" pointing out that since the beginning of 1953 there had been 50 mergers/acquisitions in the USA and that all the large chemical companies except Dow had been formed by merger. Although there were pitfalls, acquisition was "the high road to industrial glory when compared to many of the slower methods of integrated development from within". Up to that time, Albright & Wilson had been fully engaged in bringing on stream major plants in the UK and Canada rather than concentrating on mergers or acquisitions. The acquisition of Marchon in 1955 could not be regarded as part of a general strategy of acquisition (it was primarily defensive and directly related to A&W's core business).

What SB wanted was to create a second major force in the British chemical industry. According to the 1954 census of production, the chemical and allied industries in the UK comprised 3,255 firms employing 338,000 people; of these, 58 firms, accounting for over one third of total output, employed more than 1,000 people. A&W's UK employees numbered around 2,900. At the end of 1955, amongst the UK chemical companies (excluding oil, pharmaceutical and other companics not wholly involved in chemicals), A&W was lying second to ICI in terms of capital employed, though not in sales or profit. The gap in capital between the two was, however, enormous – £463 million for ICI, £26 million for A&W. The combined capital employed in A&W, Borax, Fisons, Laporte and Monsanto (UK) was only £87 million, while the figure for Glaxo was only £23 million. In terms of profit in 1955, A&W lagged behind Fisons and Borax; by 1959, A&W had overtaken both those companies, but its profit was still only 6% of ICI's.

In 1957 the first attempted move towards amalgamations took place with Fisons following their request for A&W's cooperation in a world-wide survey of phosphate rock deposits. The Fisons action was prompted by a riot in the Moroccan phosphate rock operations early in 1956, resulting in loss of life among the French management of the OCP (Office Cherifien des Phosphates). A&W's phosphate rock requirements for Marchon for STPP were similar to those of Fisons for fertilisers. A&W seconded Dr Michael Peard (who had joined the Research Department at

Oldbury in 1952 and became a Director of Albright & Wilson Ltd in 1969) to help in the search, initially with the A&W Geologist, Dr R.J. Adie, at Oldbury, and later with the British Sulphur Corporation, a Fisons company, at the Fisons office in Charles Street, Mayfair.

That prompted A.S. Woodhams, the Commercial Director of Fisons, to suggest that the two companies should consider a joint venture for making wet phosphoric acid at a site on the Thames estuary. This was followed through by Fisons' MD, Avison Wormald, who was concerned about Fisons' dependence on fertilisers and pharmaceuticals, which were both subject to a degree of Government control. The prospect of a merger was put to Kenneth Wilson (A&W Chairman) by Sir Clavering Fison, Chairman of Fisons – the two had known one another since the sale of the Prentice Bros baking powder business to A&W in 1931.

After several visits by Sydney Barratt and Bryan Topley to Charles Street, a report was presented to the A&W Board in September 1957, comparing the commercial and financial positions of the two companies, and recommending the setting up of a negotiating committee, including Frank Schon, with a view to merger. A financial scheme had been drawn up by A&W's financial advisor. Since the market value of A&W was greater than that of Fisons, it was proposed to call the merged company Albright & Wilson Ltd.

Optimistic about the prospects for a merger, the A&W Board commissioned reports on the effects on Fisons of competition in fertilisers from the oil companies and on the effect of the European Common Market and the European Free Trade Area on both companies. The Board also asked for proposals on the composition of the merged Board and top organisation, and asked for a draft of a circular for sending to all A&W and Fisons shareholders.

It was hardly surprising that a month later Fisons rejected A&W's financial scheme and put forward an alternative produced by Price Waterhouse; that was unacceptable to A&W and both parties decided to terminate negotiations. Seven years were to pass before another attempt at merger was made. By then, A&W had made several acquisitions (described in chapter 3).

*****

So in the second half of the 1950s A&W prospered, building on the foundations laid in the first half of the decade. Acquisitions were contemplated but none of any significance was made. There were some clouds – difficulties at Portishead and growing competition through reduced tariffs – but life was relatively uncomplicated. The pace of change was to accelerate in the 1960s.

Chapter 3

THE ACQUISITIVE YEARS

1960 - 1965

"Last year the group kept its above-average trading record unsullied and the long-term prospects are good...the relatively high investment rating is justified" (Stock Exchange Gazette, March 1965)

Overview

The six years from 1960–65 were in several respects a period of outstanding growth and prosperity for Albright & Wilson. There was some turbulence globally, but stability in exchange rates, low unemployment and moderate inflation.

Economic and political background

- a large proportion of the countries in the British Empire became independent, notably in Africa, where in 1960 Harold Macmillan spoke of the "wind of change"; Nelson Mandela was imprisoned in 1964 and in 1965 Rhodesia made its unilateral declaration of independence (UDI)
- the Cuban missile crisis of 1962 was followed a year later by the assassination of President Kennedy, elected President of the USA in 1960
- the first space flights took place in 1961 and the first communications satellite was launched in the following year
- ICI's bid for Courtaulds was rebuffed, in 1962
- a National Incomes Commission was set up in 1962, succeeded at the end of 1964 by a Board for Prices and Incomes, and in 1965 the Monopolies and Mergers Act was passed
- Harold Macmillan was succeeded as British Prime Minister in 1963 by Sir Alec Douglas Home, who a year later lost to the Labour leader, Harold Wilson; he remained Prime Minister until June 1970
- the British rail network was substantially reduced in 1963 as a result of the Beeching Report
- BP struck oil in the North Sea in 1965
- the first US troops were sent to South Vietnam in 1965
- the Labour government created the Department of Economic Affairs soon after coming to power and in 1965 published "the National Plan", setting targets to increase industrial investment by 7% pa and exports by 5.6%
- UK industrial production grew by 4% pa from 1959 to 1965, while the UK's share of world exports fell from 17% in 1959 to 13% in 1965
- the UK suffered balance of payments crises in 1960/1 and 1964/5, leading to rises in interest rates, incomes policies, import surcharges and export rebates, tighter exchange controls and heavy borrowing from the International Monetary Fund, the European central banks and the US Federal Reserve
- the UK cost of living index rose by 3.3% pa between 1959 and 1965, while weekly earnings rose by 6% pa; unemployment was low and restrictive practices were rife
- prices of UK chemical output were stable in the period 1958–67

- Britain and Norway failed to join the European Common Market but there was an Anglo-French agreement on building a Channel rail tunnel
- the £ : USD rate remained at 2.80 throughout the period, and there were almost no changes in the other major exchange rates
- the prices of UK equities, which had risen sharply in 1959, plateaued and were lower at the end of 1965 than at the end of 1959.

Albright & Wilson's results

The results of Albright & Wilson in this period were heavily influenced by the acquisitions that are described below:

Progress 1959 - 1965

Sales (£millions)	1959	1960	1961	1962	1963	1964	1965
UK companies	26.2	26.3	27.5	28.2	29.4	34.2	34.8
Overseas companies	8.3	8.4	8.5	10.1	11.4	14.1	15.4
Acquisitions		7.8	17.0	16.7	17.8	23.1	40.1
Total	**34.5**	**42.5**	**53.0**	**55.0**	**58.6**	**71.4**	**90.3**
Trading Profit							
UK companies	3.17	4.21	3.79	3.84	4.01	5.66	4.67
Overseas companies	1.16	-0.03	-0.09	0.05	0.44	0.79	0.69
Other income	0.78	0.75	0.66	0.63	0.52	0.39	0.66
Acquisitions		0.58	1.24	0.81	1.31	1.21	1.95
Total	**5.11**	**5.51**	**5.60**	**5.33**	**6.28**	**8.05**	**7.97**
Interest Payable	0.45	0.47	0.55	0.54	0.48	0.48	0.61
Pretax Profit	**4.66**	**5.04**	**5.05**	**4.79**	**5.80**	**7.57**	**7.36**
After depreciation of	2.28	2.35	2.83	3.16	3.35	3.56	4.39
Capital Expenditure (excl. costs of acquisitions)	**2.5**	**3.6**	**8.0**	**3.5**	**4.7**	**6.0**	**9.6**
Net Capital employed (end of year)	**30.8**	**36.1**	**44.8**	**44.9**	**46.2**	**49.4**	**70.0**

The figures give some indication of the importance of the acquisitions in this period, in terms of their contribution to sales and profits. The 1965 figures may be summarised and compared with 1959 thus:-

The importance of acquisitions

	1959	1965	1965
	(without acquisitions)	*(without acquisitions)*	*(with acquisitions)*
Sales (£ million)	34.5	50.2	90.3
Profit before interest	5.11	6.02	7.97
& tax (£ million)			
Employees (thousands)	n.a.	7.4	15.0
Net Capital Employed			
(£ million)	30.8	n.a	70.0

Acquisitions

Most acquisitions were of companies that were less capital-intensive, more people-intensive and with lower profit-margins than the core A&W operations. While there was a wish to expand through acquisitions more rapidly than was thought possible through organic growth, there was no initial programme with defined targets. Thus A&W moved into some new business areas that had not been envisaged at the outset.

Boake Roberts

The first of the acquisitions in this period was Boake Roberts, a publicly quoted British company whose full name was A. Boake, Roberts & Co. (Holding) Ltd. By the late 1950s, the Board of Albright & Wilson was becoming increasingly concerned that an unduly large proportion of business rested in detergent materials, with sales dominated by two powerful customers, Unilever and Procter & Gamble. In 1957, detergent materials accounted for nearly half of the total sales of the Albright & Wilson Group. There was therefore an aim to broaden the business and move into products used in industries with healthy growth potential. One promising field was plastics, in which A&W had a toehold through its production of some phosphate plasticisers and organotin stabilisers.

Boake Roberts was the largest British maker of plasticisers – its products included phosphate plasticisers for which it purchased phosphorus oxychloride from A&W. Early in 1959, Keith Piercy approached Fred Pentecost, the Chairman of Boake Roberts, to buy its plasticiser business. The Boake Roberts response was that it might be prepared to sell the whole of the company but not a part of it. Thereafter negotiations were protracted, with delays by Boake Roberts. Meanwhile its profit figures were improving and its share price rising. The acquisition eventually took place in February 1960, for a price of around £4 million in A&W shares.

A history of Boake Roberts

In 1869 Arthur Boake, aged 25, moved from Dublin to Stratford, in East London, which had become a centre of chemical manufacture. He started by making chemicals for the brewing industry, among them preservatives (sulphur dioxide, sulphites and metabisulphites) and colourings; brewing chemicals continued to be a part of the business until 1956. In 1876 Arthur Boake invited an old college friend, F.G. Adair Roberts, to join him as a partner and in 1888 the name of the firm was changed to Boake, Roberts & Co. Arthur Boake then developed a product for clarifying white wine and established a base at Bordeaux. The product range was further expanded to include the distillation of essential oils and the production of essences for soft drinks; in 1890 Arthur's son, Edmond Johnson Boake, joined the firm to take charge of the new department. In 1897 Boake, Roberts & Co became a limited company.

The founders travelled widely. As early as 1889 Arthur Boake had been to Australia; in 1901 he went on a round-the-world tour, visiting Australia, New Zealand, China, Japan, Canada and the United States. By 1910 the company had agents in France, Italy, Portugal, Spain, Canada, the United States and Australia. F.G. Adair Roberts died in 1924, aged 82, and Arthur Boake in the following year, at the age of 81. By then, although the families still held most of the shares, the company was no longer under family management.

At the turn of the century, the range of chemicals was extended to include amyl acetate and other solvents for cellulose lacquers as well as some fine organic chemicals. It was a field dominated by German manufacturers. The 1914–8 war cut off supplies from Germany and marked the beginning of aerial warfare, which led to an increased demand for amyl acetate as a solvent for cellulose nitrate, applied to stiffen the canvas of aircraft wings.

A more important development was the replacement of camphor by triphenyl phosphate as a plasticiser for the nitrocellulose dopes used on aircraft fabrics to prevent cracking, from 1917. After the 1914–18 war, plastics gradually began to be regarded as universal, highly versatile materials.

Plasticisers were developed to confer flexibility to plastics; in polyvinyl chloride (PVC), for example, plasticisers may account for one-third or more of the plastic. Boake Roberts extended its range of phosphate plasticisers to include chemicals based on phenol, xylenol and cresol – tricresyl phosphate, for example, was used for belting in coal mines in place of rubber to overcome a fire hazard.

After the 1939–45 war, a process for making phosphate plasticisers was developed in the Boake Roberts laboratories under the direction of Ted Boake, grandson of the founder. A Cambridge science graduate, he became a Director in 1937 and ran production during the 1939–45 war. After the war, he set up a process development department headed by research chemist Ron Mason. Also involved in process development was John Dean, who joined the company in 1946. These last two both became Managing Directors of Bush Boake Allen, into which Boake Roberts was merged (p.87).

The Boake Roberts factory in Carpenter's Road, Stratford (London), consisted of three separate small pieces of land, constricted by a road and waterway and with an unconnected business occupying a site between two of the pieces. In 1949 a site was acquired at Rainham (Essex), on marshes near the Thames, for the production of phosphate plasticisers. The plant was the first in the world to make phosphate plasticisers on a continuous basis. It took 2½ years to run effectively. Jack Brod, Works Manager at the time and for many years after, said of the early days when conditions were appalling and staff were difficult to employ: "At one time this place was regarded as the Abrac[1] penal station, a sort of Devil's Island". Eventually, the plant became a tremendous asset to Boake Roberts, and was the foundation on which the company's finances rested.

Meanwhile, Boake Roberts had been expanding in other directions. In 1923, the company started manufacturing perfumery chemicals at Stratford, primarily by distillation of essential oils, for supply to compounders. Following the 1939–45 war a food shortage in Far Eastern countries, the main suppliers of the traditional citronella, bois de rose and lemongrass oils, meant that food crops displaced essential oils crops and pressure mounted to develop a synthetic process. Ted Boake believed the best route was via myrcene, derived from turpentine. He went to the USA, where he met Dave Stallcup, a Vice-President of Glidden, the leading manufacturer of chemicals from turpentine, with a view to forming a partnership. After visiting the main perfume compounding houses in Europe, Stallcup struck a deal with Boake Roberts. A joint patent licence and research agreement was concluded in 1957, which lasted until 1964, and Ted Boake obtained (on a handwritten sheet of paper) a description of the process for making myrcene. On close inspection, John Dean concluded that the process required more space than was available at Stratford. A pilot plant was built at Rainham, where there were two vacant storage sheds, and Glidden agreed that Boake Roberts would produce 100 tons per annum for markets outside America. Eventually, synthetic aromatics (the term generally used to describe perfumery products derived from turpentine) were to become the most important part of the Bush Boake Allen operations.

At Stratford, the product range was extended in the 1930s and during the 1939–45 war to include liquid and powdered flavours, essences, perfumery compounds, emulsifying agents and other products for cosmetics. In 1946, a 3-acre site was acquired at Walthamstow (Essex), not far from Stratford, for the expansion

---

[1] Abrac, derived from, the initials of A Boake Roberts and Company, was used as a trade name.

of the essence and perfumery departments and for natural fruit juices and juice concentrates. Six further acres were purchased in 1952. The site, in the Lea Valley, in an area of light industry and housing, was clearly more suitable for such products than the older more heavily industrialised location in Stratford. Another development was the acquisition of a factory at Letchworth (Hertfordshire) for the manufacture of foam compounds for fire extinguishers, a small venture with no obvious connection with the rest of the company's activities; the operation remained small until it was disposed of in 1975.

Overseas companies were also formed in the postwar expansion of Boake Roberts. In 1946, factories were established in Sydney and Capetown for the production of flavours and essences and in 1952 a company was set up in Madras to produce compound perfumes as well as flavours and essences. To accommodate the increased complexity of the organisation, a holding company with a UK manufacturing and trading subsidiary was formed in 1953 (four years before A&W took a similar step).

By the mid-1950s the company was prosperous and continuing to expand. It had a sound technical base and an enlightened approach to management and training; Ted Boake had set up a personnel department and developed relations with the Unions and most of the senior managers had attended courses in management at the Henley Administrative College. The courses were initiated by Bertram White, who had joined Boake Roberts in 1953, after working in the Federation (later Confederation) of British Industries. Bertram was appointed Managing Director of Boake Roberts on the advice of Urwick, Orr, management consultants who had been hired by the Chairman, Fred Pentecost, to advise on the modernisation of the company's organisation – another initiative ahead of the other UK chemical companies.

Boake Roberts then embarked on a development that brought the company to a crisis and led to its loss of independence. The range of products for plastics made at Stratford had grown over the years to include metallic stearates, epoxidised oils and esters and other chemicals produced in relatively small quantities. To these were added a major product group – phthalate plasticisers. Unfortunately, Boake Roberts had no special position in phthalates technology or raw material supplies – the major raw materials, alcohol and phthalic anhydride, were commodities bought from ICI – and margins were always under pressure. In 1958 it was decided to make phthalates on a large scale and a 100 acre site at Dan's Road, Widnes was acquired. The plant, designed to produce 12,000 tons p.a., was disproportionately large for a company with plant then standing in the books at under £0.5 million. The Chairman (Fred Pentecost) stated in the annual report for the year to March 1959: "The design and engineering work for the Widnes plant was executed under contract and the result has proved most disappointing ... I must be cautious in forecasting improvements".

In 1958 the company borrowed £600,000 through a short-term debenture stock. Even so, in the year to March 1959 its overdraft rose from £45,000 to £345,000. The company was sliding into insolvency and the Board of Boake Roberts accepted that a loss of independence was inevitable. A&W believed that Boake Roberts had talked with other companies, including Fisons, Courtaulds, Monsanto and Geigy (Boake Roberts' competitor in phosphate plasticisers). Albright & Wilson's anxiety to defend its sales of phosphorus oxychloride and its expansive ideas made it a likely purchaser.

The purchase, and its consequences

Through its purchase of Boake Roberts A&W acquired a strong technical and market position in phosphate plasticisers, a potentially important position in synthetic aromatics (with plans for a major development at Widnes) and an interesting diversification into flavours and fragrances. Boake Roberts' overstretching in phthalates, however, provided lessons that should have been heeded by its acquirer. Ten years later, Albright & Wilson experienced a similar problem on a grand scale, which also contributed to a loss of independence.

W.J. Bush & Co

When A&W acquired Boake Roberts, there were some who wanted to dispose of the flavours, fragrances and perfumery side. Bryan Topley and three of his senior technical staff (Alf Loveless, Tony Childs and Harold Coates), however, had looked into those operations, particularly the potentially large aromatic chemicals operation, and had concluded that they were well worth developing. This view was supported with enthusiasm by Sydney Barratt and Keith Piercy, who saw the opportunity to broaden the base of Albright & Wilson, "into a new world with the excitement and promise of novelty..." (to quote Keith Piercy). Boake Roberts, however, was too small in flavours and fragrances to be competitive with the larger companies in the field such as International Flavours & Fragrances (see p.84) and Givaudan (part of the Hoffman La Roche empire). The obvious choice for further expansion was W.J. Bush & Co, which was bigger than Boake Roberts and largely complementary, being stronger in flavours but not as strong in aromatic chemicals.

Bush had been concerned that it might not be able to preserve its independence without some enlargement, but it had been slow to take action. When A&W acquired Boake Roberts, Eric Bush, Chairman of W.J. Bush & Co, approached Sydney Barratt to say that A&W could not possibly want Boake Roberts' flavour and fragrance operations, only to find that Bush had become a target. Negotiations proceeded more speedily than with Boake Roberts. Indeed, when they were underway in February 1961, a report in the Daily Mail following a rise in the Bush share price suggested a leak ("nice for those who knew"), which led to an accelerated conclusion of negotiations on the following day after prolonged simultaneous Board meetings.[2] So in March 1961 Bush joined the Albright & Wilson Group, the consideration being the issue of A&W shares to a value of £8.5 million, more than twice the price paid for Boake Roberts.

A history of W.J. Bush & Co.

Bush originated in 1851, the year when Arthur Albright started making phosphorus at Oldbury. William John Bush, aged 22, started in business in Bishopsgate, in the City of London. As a pupil of a physician he became interested in chemicals and allied products. He produced essential oils, tinctures and extracts by steam distillation as well as ethers and esters in a small factory in Liverpool Street and later in Artillery Lane. In 1885, when the business had outgrown the Artillery Lane premises, the firm acquired a site at Ash Grove, Hackney (East London), which was to remain the Bush headquarters for the next 88 years. W.J. Bush has been described as the originator of the flavouring essence industry in Britain. He and his wife, Mary Ann Yarroll, had seven sons and three daughters. All but one of his sons went into the family business.

The eldest, William Ernest, was born in 1860 and as a young man travelled extensively in Europe. He was the British Juror for chemicals at the Antwerp Exhibition in 1885, President of the Chemical Section at the Brussels Exhibition in 1888, and in 1889 was created a Baron of the Duchy of Saxe-Coburg and Gotha in recognition of his services. Also in 1889, he married an American prima donna, Pauline Joran, and became Chairman of Bush on the death of his father at the age of 60. William Ernest's colourful leadership of the firm was cut short through a railway accident in 1903, when he was only 42.

The third son, James Mortimer, who succeeded William Ernest as Chairman and remained Chairman until his death in 1941, was born in 1863 at Ash Grove, Hackney. He studied chemistry in the laboratories of the Pharmaceutical Society in London and began working at Bishopsgate in 1880.

Following the move to Ash Grove, the firm expanded energetically in Britain and abroad. In 1886, Potter & Moore (established in 1749) was purchased, in order to acquire knowledge in the distillation of the essential oils of peppermint,

[2] Frank Schon, who was not present, complained of a lack of information and asked for a statement setting out the sequence of events from the outset and for an opportunity for the Albright & Wilson Directors to discuss policy on future diversification. He had also abstained from voting on the Boake Roberts acquisition because of a lack of information.

camomile and lavender. Potter & Moore had a high reputation for lavender; the product name "Mitcham Lavender Water" was derived from the location of the Potter & Moore factory at Mitcham in Surrey.[3]

Expansion of Bush outside Britain was a notable feature around the end of the 19th century. In 1890 a factory was set up at Mili, Messina (Sicily), close to the source of the famous Sicilian essential oils. A branch was opened in Melbourne in 1893. In 1899, W.J. Bush & Co Inc was established, with a factory at Linden, New Jersey, and a head office in New York. In the following year, James Mortimer Bush went to Moscow and set up a factory there, which prospered until the revolution of 1917 (many years later, Eric Bush visited the factory with Eric Bolton, the son of the original factory manager F.C. Bolton, and found it still in existence, but making pies). In 1906 premises were leased at Grasse, in the South of France, the home of floral essential oils. W.J. Bush & Co (Canada) Ltd was formed in 1912, with a head office and factory in Montreal, and in 1913 the US subsidiary acquired a factory at National City, California, for citrus products.

W.J. Bush & Co became a limited company in 1897 (5 years after Albright & Wilson took the same step), with William Ernest as Chairman and two of his brothers, James Mortimer and Alfred Walter, as joint Managing Directors. In 1901 they recruited Dr Percy Isherwood as Chief Chemist, a move even more significant for Bush than the recruitment of Richard Threlfall had been for Albright & Wilson a little earlier. Dr Isherwood was the son of a prominent chemical engineer who had erected a number of factories in the Widnes and Runcorn area. He went to the universities of Heidelburg and Wurzburg, where he obtained his PhD, and then took up a research fellowship at the Central Technical College in South Kensington (which became part of London University). Before joining Bush he was employed by United Alkali and Brunner Mond (later part of ICI). It was through his leadership that Bush's chemical interests were developed.

In 1904, Bush began making vanillin (synthetic vanilla) from ozone oxidation of isoeugenol and built what was then the largest ozone plant in the world. That was followed by aubepine and heliotropine. Other products introduced in the early years of the century were toluene derivatives: benzyl alcohol, benzyl acetate, benzyl benzoate and benzyl cyanide used in preservatives, paints, lubricants and insecticides, terpineol (an aromatic and antiseptic), citral and geraniol (synthetic aromatics), nicotine and chloroform.

The 1914–18 war led to a tenfold increase in the demand for Bush chemicals, partly because supplies from Germany ceased. To cope with the demand, Dr

---

[3] Because Potter & Moore was a competitor of some of Bush's customers, selling retail toiletries, Bush took pains to conceal their connection. During research preceding its bid for Bush, Albright & Wilson found that Bush owned Mortimer Investments Ltd, and that that company owned Potter & Moore; Eric Bush appeared to be somewhat surprised that the connection had been discovered.

Isherwood established a factory in Widnes on the West Bank of the river Mersey. Salicylic acid, an intermediate for aspirin, was made there from 1915. In 1916, Dr Isherwood erected a plant to make pure zinc; apart from the merits of the technology, it is hard to see the relevance to the company's business. His achievements in chemistry were recognised by the award of the OBE in 1916. He became a Director of Bush in 1915, joint Managing Director in 1935 and Chairman in 1941 until his death in 1954. He was a senior figure in the chemical industry, becoming Chairman of the Association of British Chemical Manufacturers in 1943 and President in 1945. He was also Chairman of the British Essence Manufacturers Association and a Fellow of the American Chemical Society.

A company was established in South Africa in 1928, initially in Cape Town and three years later with a second factory in Johannesburg.[4] A branch was formed in New Zealand in 1938 and an Indian company was set up in 1956. New factories were built in Canada in 1951 and in South Africa in 1956.

During the 1939–45 war, Bush greatly expanded its UK chemical manufacture; production of a toluene-based anti-gas chemical was increased 40-fold from its level in 1939 and new products included intermediates for penicillin and sulphonamides. Other important products were salicylic acid and DDT.

In 1946–7 there were notable developments in Bush's UK flavours business. In 1946 premises were bought at Witham, Essex, for soft fruit processing (transferred there from Ash Grove), producing mainly concentrated fruit juices. In 1952, a spray drier was installed and Bush's Tru-Sil fruit and flavoured powders marketed with great success. Powdered colours were added in 1961, also transferred from Ash Grove. In 1947, premises were leased at Tottenham, in North London, for the production and concentration of citrus juices (also hitherto at Ash Grove); the extensive cellars, used to store hundreds of barrels of juice, were originally built for the storage of lager said to have been for the Germans living in London. When the lease expired in 1965, the Tottenham operations were moved to Witham, where additional land was purchased. Laboratories for flavours and for chemical research were built at Ash Grove in the 1950s.

While Bush was the leading company in flavours in the UK, Australia and South Africa, and also strong in Canada, it was a minor player in fragrances. There was, however, one significant and profitable fragrance operation: selling to African markets, on a franchise basis. The business originated with Eric Burgess, who joined Bush in 1907 and served the company for 54 years, travelling extensively in Europe, India, South America and Africa. In 1920, at the request of several

[4] During the 1939–45 war Eric Bush received a letter from the Managing Director in South Africa, Peter White, telling him that the headquarters and manufacturing had been moved from Cape Town to Johannesburg and explaining that communications in wartime had made consultation about the move impracticable.

Sudanese merchants, he investigated the production of a special perfume for that market. The result was *Bint el Sudan* (Woman of Sudan), with a distinctive label based on a photograph of a bare-breasted girl taken by Eric Burgess. The perfume became widely sold in Sudan and other parts of Africa and sales grew to a quarter of a million bottles a month. The formula became Bush's most valuable secret, protected from copying by having 92 constituents and a two-stage production process in which one of the intermediate ingredients was the finished perfume. (See also p.229.)

Bush's other principal involvement with fragrances was through its ownership of Potter & Moore. In 1928, 42 years after acquisition, the company was reconstituted as a separate unit for the production of branded toiletries for retail sale. In 1937, a new factory at Leyton in East London was opened by Gracie Fields, one of the best-known entertainers of the day. The Mitcham factory then became a chemical works, with vanillin as the main product. Leyton's products included soaps, perfumes, bath salts, creams, talcum powders and other cosmetics. Much later, in 1958, deodorants became an important line, after the acquisition of the Delavelle & Freshness business and the launch of *Go* stick deodorant.

The purchase, and its consequences

The circumstances in which Bush proved to be open to an offer from Albright & Wilson were different from those that had prevailed with Boake Roberts a year earlier. Bush made a trading surplus of over £1 million in 1959 and had adequate cash resources. It was, however, very much a family-controlled company, run on what Keith Piercy described as "old fashioned lines".

The Chairman, Eric Lionel Bush, was the second son of James Mortimer Bush, born in 1900. At his father's request he studied chemistry at Oxford, although his ambition was to become an actor and he was a keen member of the Oxford University Dramatic Society. He joined the family company in 1922 and in 1926 formed a dramatic section in the Bush sports club. From then on, a play was put on annually (except from 1939 to 1945, when Eric was serving in the Royal Artillery) in London for four nights just before Christmas, for the benefit of employees and customers, with Eric playing the leading role and producing. The standard of the performances was high and the employees playing in them knew well that the play had priority in the weeks of rehearsal. It was traditional for Eric to present long-serving employees with their gold watches on stage at the conclusion of the performance and that was followed by a sumptuous supper. The fact that there was an annual dramatic performance, free to employees, was listed as one of the employees' amenities, in the "Welcome to Bush" booklet, which also assured newcomers that their "well-being and happiness whilst with this Company are of real consequence to the Directors and Management".

Bush was indeed a paternalistic company. The amenities for employees in 1952 also included a profit-sharing bonus linked to the Ordinary dividend, a pension scheme with life insurance, medical services, sickness and accident pay, pay during National Service and Territorial Army training, a minimum of 2 weeks' holiday, long service awards, a Sports & Social Club and an annual outing. There were many employees with long service, including several who had served for more than 50 years. Eric and his cousin Brinsley (Sales Director, who died in 1953) were responsible for introducing most of these benefits.

The other side of the coin was an "unbusinesslike" management of the Company. "To the outsider," remarked Keith Piercy, "there appeared to be no clearly discernible management structure...with Eric Bush as the genial father figure at the head, presiding over what to the newcomer seemed to be interminable meetings in the Board room at Ash Grove". His cousin, Cecil Ferdinand Bush, who had become a Director in 1942, was ill. The former Research Director, H.W. Vernon, had left and had not been replaced. The main driving force came from Arthur John McIntyre, who joined Bush in 1919 and became a Director in 1942. He was shrewd, able and commanded great authority but operated very much as a one-man band and was away from the UK for a significant amount of time, visiting the Bush empire overseas.

After A&W acquired the company, it was a long time before its results could be reported – Bush did not prepare its accounts on a monthly or even quarterly basis. The accounting system for West Bank (Widnes) was entirely separate; David Livingstone, when he attempted to discover its financial position, found "the West Bank accounts are written in a code that I have been unable to break".

Over the years, plants had been added at Ash Grove and West Bank without any rational plan and with standards of hygiene and safety that were a long way behind the acceptable practices of the day. Few people knew where everything was. At West Bank, where only 10 out of the 20 acres had been developed, some of the buildings were so close together that vehicular access was impossible. One description of the factory was "a Dr Isherwood catastrophe" – he was an inventive chemist but not good at planning plants. At Ash Grove the site was constricted and much of the office accommodation was in a number of small houses along the road giving access to the factory.

While the quality of the Bush products was high and its reputation excellent, the practice of accepting orders for non-standard products meant that the product list was unmanageably long: it included some 4,500 flavourings. By 1960 the impetus to expand, in the UK and beyond, had been lost. So the thoughts of the family turned to amalgamation. Eric is said to have had an opportunity to merge with Boake Roberts but did not take it; the Distillers Company was also considered as a partner. So A&W's bid was timely.

Stafford Allen

After the acquisition of Boake Roberts and Bush Keith Piercy remembers, "The next step was so logical that it was almost inevitable". Nevertheless, Albright & Wilson did not quickly and deliberately set out to acquire Stafford Allen. The A&W Board minutes of July 1963 record that an approach had been made by Roger Allen, Chairman of Stafford Allen & Sons Ltd, a family firm whose shares were not quoted on any stock exchange. Roger, who was the great-grandson of the founder of the firm, had married Barbara, daughter of Kenneth Wilson (then A&W Chairman). The Allens, like the Albrights and Wilsons, were Quakers. So there were connections. Moreover, Roger had concluded that Stafford Allen would be unlikely to survive and prosper on its own.

The A&W Board declined the initial offer and made a counter-offer (unusually, it was minuted that there was dissent from four Board members – Bill Albright, Wilson Carter, Frank Schon and Professor Newitt, a non-executive Director and former Courtauld Professor of Chemical Engineering at Imperial College). There followed discussions and an investigation conducted by Michael Peard (head of the Development Department of A&W since 1958), who had performed a similar role before the acquisitions of Boake Roberts and Bush. That led in October to a compromise offer midway between the Stafford Allen and A&W figures, which was accepted, valuing the company at just under £2.5 million, about 10 times the pretax profit of the previous year. The acquisition was announced in January 1964. Smaller than the other two acquisitions in the field of flavours and fragrances, Stafford Allen was complementary and added a valuable dimension.

A history of Stafford Allen

Stafford Allen & Sons was founded in 1833 by William Allen, senior partner in the pharmaceutical firm of Allen & Hanbury. He chose his nephew Stafford Allen to start a business that would produce natural drugs of a higher quality than were then available. Stafford took into partnership Charles May, who ran a business at Ampthill (Bedfordshire) cultivating medicinal plants and distilling essential oils; his brother Francis was one of the founders of the match firm Bryant & May. The Allen-May partnership broke up in 1843 when Stafford's brother George, who had been apprenticed to Charles May, became a partner in the firm, which was then renamed S & G Allen. George Allen in turn left the partnership in 1857 and returned to Ampthill to make extracts and other chemicals and run a herb farm.

Stafford Allen brought his sons Edward and William into the firm which then adopted its final name of Stafford Allen & Sons. Edward's sons joined the firm – Edward Watlock in 1887 and George Stafford in 1890. William's son Kenneth

Bush Boake Allen Board 1964: l. to r.: Denis Arnold (Secretary), Bertram White, Ray Gregory, Keith Piercy, Eric Bush, Ron Mason, Roger Allen, Timber Woods.

Harold Wilson, Prime Minister, with Frank Schon at the inauguration of 4th & 5th anhydrite kilns at Whitehaven.

Midland Silicones, Barry, distillation columns 1963.

Erco's Port Maitland (Ontario) plant for the production of sodium tripolyphosphate & other phosphates.

Clarkson joined in 1896; his sons Roger Kenneth and Anthony William were at the head of the company at the time it became a part of Albright & Wilson. Roger became Chairman in 1960 on the retirement of his father; he had joined the firm when he left school in 1932, aged 19. It was a tragedy for Stafford Allen and for Bush, Boake, Allen (into which his family company had by then merged) when he died in 1966 at the age of 53. His brother, Tony, four years his junior, was the last of the family in the business, until he retired in 1973.

The business was founded at Cowper Street, Finsbury (North London). It began by milling botanical materials and extracting drugs in stills; Stafford Allen became the largest producer of galenicals (the term for drugs of botanical origin, e.g. liquorice) in Europe. Early products also included silver nitrate, iodine and potassium iodide, and mercurial ointments and plasters. There was a natural progression to the grinding of spices, the extraction of essential oils and the manufacture of flavours and perfumery products. Products were packed and despatched at a site at Ardleigh Green, in Essex, and in 1898 the Cowper Street premises were extended to cope with the demand for white pepper, which was developed by decorticating and grinding black pepper.

The most important development in the expansion of the business came in 1899 when a 300 acre site was bought at Long Melford, in Suffolk, where crops grown included lavender, rosemary, peppermint, clary sage, camomile and dill and essential oils were distilled – they soon became famous for their superior quality. Long Melford used a 1000-strong herd of prize winning Pedigree Large White pigs in the process; they were fed on the spent plant matter and provided manure for the crops. The farms were greatly enlarged through the purchase of adjoining properties as they came onto the market.

The Cowper Street premises were outgrown between the wars, when larger offices and factory space were acquired in Wharf Road, off City Road in London, backing onto the Regent's Canal. That became the headquarters of Stafford Allen and continued to be occupied until 1972, by which time all the manufacturing operations had been transferred to Long Melford.

Stafford Allen's expertise in extraction led to a diversity of specialised products. One of the most successful lines was Saromex spices, produced by extracting the aromatics from spices and depositing the extracts on a base of salt, dextrose, flour or rusk, to give a reliable and bacteria-free product. Chlorophyll was extracted from grass and, later, hop extract from hops – the firm also introduced and marketed the insecticide pyrethrum. The person largely responsible for that addition was William Francis Merritt (described as an "outsider"), who became a Director in 1921 and was later Managing Director. His son, Reginald Peter, became a Director after the 1939–45 War and became the company's buyer.

In 1964, Stafford Allen had one joint venture: a US company, Saromex Inc., in partnership with Charles L. Huisking & Co Inc., making and marketing the Saromex range. They also had two subsidiaries: Warrick Bros made medicated pastilles and lozenges, the best known being Rinstead (for treating sore gums); Wyleys Ltd, founded in Coventry in 1750, was bought by Stafford Allen in 1952 – it started as a retail chemist and became a wholesale supplier, largely of galenicals to chemists' shops, and made daily deliveries of products such as Hills Bronchial Balsam which was made at Long Melford. At the time of the acquisition by A&W, thought was being given to buying further distributors.

Bush, Boake, Allen

Three weeks after the acquisition of Stafford Allen was made known (Jan 1964), it was announced that a company – Bush, Boake, Allen Ltd – had been formed to "coordinate" the activities of the three flavour and perfumery companies. It was said at the time that "by joining forces and planning as one unit it is hoped to achieve rapid expansion and secure the largest possible share of markets throughout the world". This followed a general trend of consolidation. Companies that led the way included Van Ameringen-Haebler(USA) and Polak & Schwarz (Netherlands), who merged in 1959 to form International Flavours & Fragrances (IFF). In the same year Bayer acquired full ownership of Haarman & Reimer, to which was added Schimmel. Other growing major players were Givaudan, Firmenich, Norda and Fritzsche. The combined sales of Boake, Bush and Stafford Allen at the beginning of the 1960s were about £12 million, similar to those of IFF.

In the years following acquisition, there were several important expansions in Boake Roberts and Bush. Of greatest long-term significance for Boake Roberts was the decision in January 1962 to establish a large synthetic aromatics plant, building on the success achieved with the Rainham plant. In March 1963 £1.7 million was authorised for a large plant, occupying 10 acres at Dan's Road, Widnes, with minor expenditure at Rainham. The first stage was completed in mid-1964 and the second stage in the following year. Problems with chemical efficiencies and the quality of some products, plus a slow build up of sales, led to losses in the 1960s. In contrast to the phthalates plant on the same site, however, the plant eventually became of outstanding value to BBA.

Also in 1962 Bush announced a project to build a large benzoic acid plant at its West Bank, Widnes works using technology licensed from the USA for the air oxidation of toluene – it was to be the most advanced plant in Europe. Benzoic acid was the key product, used directly and indirectly for pharmaceuticals, preservatives, paints, corrosion inhibitors, plasticisers and aromatic raw materials. The plant came on stream in 1964 but experienced severe problems, including the dissolving of parts of the plant, which required a further three years to solve.

Bush was more successful in its overseas activities. In 1962 it took over the Boake Roberts flavour and fragrance operations in Australia and South Africa and in March 1963 it established a substantial operation in Nigeria, through the acquisition of Geka Trading Company in Kano, Northern Nigeria, which sold fragrances and toiletries in the local marketplaces. Geka had been founded in 1962 by a Swiss entrepreneur, Jean-Louis Tremollieres, and was run by three European expatriates. Sir John Colville, formerly Private Secretary to Sir Winston Churchill and to the Queen and at the time on the staff of A&W's merchant banker, Hill Samuel, was well acquainted with Nigeria and strongly recommended the purchase, forecasting that the country would remain peaceful and prosperous. In the event, the Prime Minister was murdered and the Biafran War followed; even so, Bush Nigeria (as Geka was renamed) continued to trade and expand, and became an important contributor to BBA's profits. At the end of 1963 Ghana Chemical Industries was purchased; this smaller company never attained the importance of Bush Nigeria because of the political upheavals in Ghana, which from time to time caused operations to be suspended. The Nigerian operation was again expanded in 1965 through the acquisition of a small company, Turare N'Hausawa.

In October 1963, Bush announced plans to establish a company in Greece to process lemons and oranges to provide citrus oils and juices. Bush Hellas was formed with Greek partners who were engaged in packing and selling fruit and vegetables to the UK, Scandinavia and other destinations in Europe. It was believed that the two factories, at Aeghion and Sparta, were so located that the nearby fruit trees would not suffer from frosts. Unfortunately the winter of 1964 was the worst for 33 years. Further troubles and losses followed and at the beginning of 1968 A&W disposed of its interest.

Over the years, Bush's deliberate isolation of Potter & Moore (acquired in 1886) had limited its development and led to a loss of market position. Albright & Wilson, which had no experience of branded retail toiletries, was unable to reverse the trend. The brand became increasingly down-market: the largest-selling line was the coffrets produced for the Christmas trade and sold through Woolworths. There were quality problems with *Go* stick deodorant (which shrank) and *Le Rouge Baiser* lipstick (which melted). In 1963 a more aggressive marketing strategy was adopted but it was abandoned when the advertising expenditure in the UK over twelve months exceeded the value of sales. So in 1968 the Potter & Moore toiletries business was sold, to E.C. de Witt, for whom the main attraction was less the UK operations than the companies that had been established in Australia and South Africa.

The pharmaceutical side of Potter & Moore was strengthened by integrating it with the Stafford Allen subsidiary, Warrick Bros, and by the acquisition in July 1965 of Meggeson and Company, whose main product line was the Meggezone pastilles.

(It is interesting to note that all three of the companies were founded in the 18th Century.) The acquisition had the attraction that Meggeson could manufacture Warrick Bros products, hitherto made externally under contract. Nevertheless, within a year efforts were being made to dispose of the whole pharmaceutical business, with some interest being shown by Schering and Beechams. In March 1967 the whole was sold to Schering for £200,000, a staggering £123,000 less than the sum paid for Meggesons. As with the toiletries side of Potter & Moore, the first strategy was growth and the next disposal after disillusion.

One of the more exotic developments was the formation in 1965 of Stafford Allen (New Guinea), to manufacture pyrethrum extract for insecticides, capitalising on the favourable climate and altitude in the highlands. The factory was opened in May 1965 and initially operated successfully, but before long the local workforce lost their enthusiasm for harvesting flowers – by 1968 collections made up only half the quantity that was needed to make the plant profitable. The embarrassed Administration admitted that there was not much that they could do. They tried offering the growers the alternatives of growing pyrethrum or going to the "kalabus" (pidgin for prison), but there was no urge to get money. Those who had worked for a time would bury their wages in the ground and cease to grow pyrethrum. Logistics were also a problem, with roads almost impassable and flights to and from Mount Hagen hazardous – indeed, Nick Stravs, the manager of the factory (a guerrilla in Yugoslavia during the war) was killed in an aeroplane crash while visiting the site. In 1973, the company was taken over by the government and the production of pyrethrum extract ceased.

In North America, Bush had a flavours operation in Montreal and Stafford Allen a small US joint venture, Saromex Inc.. In 1965, the partner in the joint venture was bought out and Bush Boake Allen Inc. was set up with an office in Emerson, New Jersey. That was followed in mid-1966 by the acquisition of Seeley Inc., whose main products were the "WONFs" (with other natural flavours). Progress in the USA was, however, very slow and profits were not made until many years later.

In the years immediately following Albright & Wilson's acquisition of Boake Roberts, Bush and Stafford Allen there was a decline in their combined profits: Boake Roberts's trading profit fell from nearly £600,000 in 1960 to less than a quarter of that in 1965, Bush from £¾ million in 1961 to less than £½ million in 1965; Stafford Allen's profit in 1965, however, was more than 50% higher than in 1964 and nearly up to the level of Bush.

Although, as has already been quoted, a Press release in February 1964 announced the formation of Bush, Boake, Allen Ltd "to coordinate the activities" of the three companies, little was done then or during the next two years to bring them together. In part, inaction was due to the obligations encouraged by the statements made at the time of the acquisitions: Boake Roberts "will continue to function under its own name and management ... retaining its own traditions, initiative, and freedom of action within a framework of Group policy"; "It is the intention that W.J. Bush will, as part of the Albright & Wilson Group, continue to operate under its own name and management". In October 1963, Sir Sydney Barratt (who had been knighted in the Queen's birthday honours in 1961) spoke of "ever-increasing cooperation between Abrac and Bush" which he bizzarely likened to Romeo and Juliet. The treatment accorded to Stafford Allen was a little different, probably because it was not a public company: its Chairman (Roger Allen) was not appointed to the Board of Albright & Wilson Ltd. Also, it was announced that the aim was "full integration" of the three companies by 1st January 1965, with day-to-day running remaining with the three Boards in the mean time. The stated plan was for reorganisation into two divisions, flavouring materials and chemicals/perfumery products. Sydney Barratt, at the time that he spoke of Romeo and Juliet, said that he envisaged Stafford Allen being taken into Bush and chemicals/perfumery products being run by Boake Roberts.

In the event, it was not until July 1966 that BBA began to operate. The Press release in May declared: "The purpose of this merger is to forge a new international organisation backed by the strength of the Albright & Wilson Group," and stated that there were to be four "product divisions" – flavour, perfumery, pharmaceutical and industrial chemical. In fact there were to be only two operating divisions, flavour (including pharmaceuticals) and chemical (including perfumery). Under the Chief Executive, Bertram White, formerly the Chairman of Boake Roberts, the managing director of flavours was Dr Ray Gregory and of chemicals Ron Mason. Ray Gregory was a chemist who had joined the Albright & Wilson research department in 1937 and until 1955 worked on phosphorus and phosphates. In that year he joined Midland Silicones, becoming joint managing director. In 1961, he moved to head A&W's new Inter-Company Planning department, and then became a director of Bush in April 1963 and its managing director a year later. His background and experience were therefore in chemicals unrelated to the BBA business. Ron Mason was also a chemist, who joined Boake Roberts in 1938 and became a director in 1960.

The Chairman of BBA was Eric Bush. His message at the time BBA came into operation included the words: "Bush Boake Allen is...the result of careful study, having due regard for personnel factors, by a board composed of directors of each of the companies. By this means we have achieved our object with goodwill and understanding. To become one trading company we must learn to become one team. This we are resolved to do". Unfortunately, goodwill and understanding were by no means universal. From 1961 to 1966 Sir Sydney had held to the concept of a federal system, rather than a melting-pot, which had helped to perpetuate separateness instead of welding the companies together. Also, the backgrounds for the three companies were so different that staff continued to identify with their origin; there appeared to be a better chance of promotion if the boss came from the same stable.

The greatest difficulty in coming to terms with a unified company was experienced by the Stafford Allen employees. They had enjoyed the advantages of a small family company, prosperous and headed by an entrepreneur who managed to command intense loyalty from his staff by a combination of autocracy in decisions and delegation in operations. Roger Allen would read the incoming correspondence and see his senior managers daily. There were no management committees or systems and few figures to show where profits were being made but there were tangible rewards for success in sales or technical achievement. Roger Allen was persuaded that merger with Albright & Wilson was the right course and his staff believed and trusted him. It was not long before he began to have doubts: he met Eric Bush and his senior staff, who were referred to by the stage names they had in the latest Bush play. On a visit to Stratford, confronted by the chemical odours, he said, "that is not us". Roger was not offered a place on the Albright & Wilson Board. In the 1966 BBA organisation Stafford Allen's operations were placed under a Bush man (a chemist) with a Boake Roberts Chief Executive and a Bush Chairman.

In May 1966, three weeks after the announcement that BBA was to come into operation on July 1st, Roger held a dinner of his senior managers, at which he said how sorry he was that he had agreed to the sale of Stafford Allen; he left the table and in the adjoining room died of a heart attack, at the age of 53. Keith Piercy (the A&W Director on the BBA Board) wrote that he was flabbergasted when, at the Quaker funeral service for Roger Allen, a member of staff rose and spoke of the general feeling of discontent and unease in the company as a result of the take-over. Eric Bush then rose and said that what was being done was with Roger Allen's entire approval and would be to the benefit of all. The Stafford Allen business certainly survived, apart from the galenicals (which orthodox costing indicated to be unprofitable), as did the staff, but the loss of Roger Allen removed the man who might have made a great success of running the whole BBA operation.

In the following years BBA underwent several reorganisations. Eric Bush retired at the end of 1966 and died a year later. Ray Gregory departed at the beginning of 1968 when the two divisions of BBA were merged and a functional organisation created, reporting to Roger Allen's brother Tony as managing director. At the next turn of the wheel, after the departure of Tony Allen, there were three business units – flavours, fragrances and chemicals. It seemed that, whatever the organisation, the achievement of an integrated operation was a long and very difficult process. Perhaps the answer would have been to have had three units doing what they could do best – Boake Roberts running chemicals and compound perfumes, Bush flavours and Stafford Allen its extraction products. In Australia, a unified operation was achieved by the departure of all but Bush staff, who then handled the products of the three companies – a solution not feasible in the UK. BBA remained for Albright & Wilson an area of promise never properly understood or effectively exploited.

Associated Chemical Companies Ltd – ACC

The next important acquisition by Albright & Wilson was Associated Chemical Companies Ltd (ACC). The motive for this acquisition was not a business move, as was the case with the three BBA companies. While A&W had general ambitions to expand by acquisition, the first approach in this instance came from John Hutton-Wilson, Chairman of ACC, in September 1964. He had received an approach from Dow Chemical and had no wish to be taken over by an American company, having devoted years to bringing together a collection of small British chemical companies. As Chairman of the Association of British Chemical Manufacturers (which later merged with the Association of Chemical & Allied Employers to become the Chemical Industries Association) he wished to see a growing British chemical industry.

The Albright & Wilson Directors expressed no firm opinions for or against the acquisition. There were few points of contact between the two companies' businesses. ACC would, however, introduce a measure of diversification and some potential for development and would add about one fifth to the sales and balance sheet total (and about 15% to trading profit). An offer in February 1965 of A&W shares worth around £8 million was accepted.

A history of ACC

The ACC story began in 1833 when a fertiliser works was built at Eaglescliffe (Durham) by John Hutton-Wilson's great-grandfather, Robert Wilson. The works was alongside and linked with the Stockton & Darlington Railway (opened in 1826). For nearly 100 years the factory mainly produced single and triple superphosphate, with oil and cake mills as a minor addition. In the late 1920s there was diversification into chrome chemicals in competition with J. & J. White of Rutherglen (Glasgow) and E.P. Potter of Bolton (Lancashire). The main markets for the products were in tanning, pigments and chrome plating. After the second world war, it became clear that the three companies could not individually afford the capital investment required to install the large units needed to satisfy demand and compete internationally. So in 1951 and 1953 Potter and White were acquired and the merged company was given the name British Chrome & Chemicals Ltd. Production was then increased at Eaglescliffe; the Glasgow and Bolton works were closed in 1965.

The need to finance the £2.5 million modernisation and development plan that followed the creation of British Chrome & Chemicals led in 1957 to a merger with Brotherton and Company, which had funds of £1 million to invest and similarly wished to create larger groupings in the chemical industry. The two companies retained their own names and operated independently until 1962 when they began operating under the name of their parent company, Associated Chemical Companies.

Brotherton and Company was started at Wakefield in 1878 by Charles Brotherton, a young man who at the age of 21 hit on the idea of making aqueous ammonia and ammonium sulphate from purifying the gas liquors discharged to drain by gas works. He set up another works, at Nechells in Birmingham, to which gas liquors were conveyed by one of the first chemical pipelines and by rail wagons. Still in operation when ACC was acquired by A&W, the plant also made sulphuric acid from spent oxide by the old lead chamber process. One of the features of the Wakefield site when it became part of A&W was its collection of old Lancashire boilers, used to store liquors until they rusted away. Together with much of the production plant and ponds containing chemical residues these gave an impression of age and decay.

In 1917 Brotherton acquired the Bromborough Chemical Works (Merseyside) from the Board of Trade, which had confiscated it from the Berlin Aniline Company during the war. It is said that Brotherton outbid Lever by matching their bids in pounds with bids in guineas, and so in due course the factory became almost surrounded by the Port Sunlight works of Levers. Originally a small plant on the site made hydrosulphites, used as reducing agents by the textile industry and later in bleaching wood pulp, oils, fats and soaps. Later, liquid and gaseous sulphur dioxide were sold for food and drink preservation and in sugar and edible oil refining. Brotherton became a public company in 1949, when death duties forced the sale of some of the family's shares.

Meanwhile, the range of fertilisers at Eaglescliffe was extended by adding granulated superphosphates and high analysis compound fertilisers, and a programme of acquisitions began. In 1958, Robert Stephenson & Son of Beverley (Yorkshire) was acquired. Its business had begun with a linseed and cottonseed crushing mill, which eventually became part of William E. Marshall and Alliance Feeds, of Hull. Fertiliser merchanting was added in 1942, leading to the manufacture of granulated and compound fertilisers. A soil testing laboratory was established at Beverley to provide technical service to farmers. In 1947 Farm Protection Ltd was formed to engage in contract spraying and in 1956 the company began marketing MCPA (2-methyl-4-chlorophenoxyacetic acid, a selective herbicide) under the trade name Farmon, adding Residuren residual herbicide for the treatment of bulbs. In 1959, a significant step forward was taken when the agency for Du Pont agricultural chemicals in the UK and Ireland was obtained.

The next addition to the agricultural side of ACC took place in 1961, when The Farmers Company was acquired. Headquartered in Brigg (Lincolnshire), it had fertiliser manufacturing plants at Barton-on-Humber (Lincolnshire) and Misterton (Nottinghamshire), serving Lincolnshire, the Midlands and part of the South of England. It also operated a contract fertiliser spreading service, grew seeds under contract, dried grain and made animal feed compounds.

The increasing complexity of the ACC organisation led in 1962 to the formation of two divisions – ACC (Fertilisers) Ltd and ACC (Mfg) Ltd – and in the following year to the creation of a new headquarters at Harrogate in place of the head offices at Eaglescliffe and Leeds (Brothertons). Acquisitions continued. In 1964, the quaintly named Mays Chemical Manure Company, making fertilisers at Bourne (Lincolnshire), was acquired from the family, one of whom was Raymond Mays, the famous racing driver. Later in the same year, J.Jordan & Sons (Kendal) Ltd, an agricultural merchant selling animal feeds manufactured by Marshalls, and C. Hammond & Co Ltd, another agricultural merchant, were bought. In the next year, the industrial side added Detel Paints Ltd (of Ruislip, Middlesex), an outlet for chrome chemicals.

As well as these numerous companies and sites in the UK, there was one overseas subsidiary, ACC (Chrome & Chemicals) Ltd in Montreal. ACC had 2,300 employees in total, about one fifth the number employed by A&W worldwide. Total sales were about £15 million, equally divided between the agricultural and industrial sides. Pretax profit in 1964, the last year before being taken over, was a little over £1 million.[5] ACC's profits, despite the series of acquisitions, had remained on a plateau from 1958, when pretax profit was over £900,000.

The purchase, and its consequences

A&W had thus acquired a collection of small, long-established family companies, with many sites, elderly plants and only moderate profitability. John Hutton-Wilson had managed to bring the companies together to a degree not achieved with BBA. "Integration within the ACC Group," the Albright Magazine was able to say, "has been achieved with astonishing speed and success". Managers had been moved between the units, including between the industrial and agricultural sides, and there was a unified headquarters. Once again, however, A&W was reluctant to integrate ACC fully and announced, "Associated Chemicals will operate under its own name and management as part of the A&W group".

There were plans for rationalisation and modernisation, not only in chrome chemicals but also in fertilisers. The latter centred on the project at Barton-on-

---

[5] In that year, A&W's sales were £71 million and its pretax profit £7.5 million.

Humber to construct a plant to make high-analysis compound fertilisers by a new process and to make nitric acid from ammonia. (See p.226) The project, involving the expenditure of £2 million, was authorised by the A&W Board four months after the acquisition. The return forecast was 21%. ACC's share of the UK market was around 5%, with a more significant share in northern and eastern England. The Board agreed that the policy with regard to fertilisers in the UK "should be to retain ACC's present business and to support it to the extent of enabling it to maintain the present proportion of the market".

Despite a long-established policy to avoid fertilisers and its unsatisfactory experience in Canada, A&W had thus taken a definite step into fertilisers in the UK. In a highly competitive market, A&W would be a minor player, starting with a scattering of small units and with hopes founded on the future introduction of new technology and on the existing good relations with customers, arising from providing a range of services.

In the event, the Barton plant experienced severe problems and did not operate well until mid-1969. For the next five years after that, profits from the UK agricultural business grew, peaking at over £3 million in 1974. From then on, however, the UK fertiliser industry was increasingly under pressure from imports from continental Europe. While the pesticides business of Farm Protection prospered, the return from fertilisers was poor. A&W's disposal of its agricultural business in 1984 was followed by the exit from fertilisers of the main UK companies, ICI, Fisons and Shell, with the market eventually being taken over by continental European companies.

Mergers

As has already been noted, Sir Sydney Barratt had long held the view that there was a need for greater consolidation in the British chemical industry, where apart from ICI there were no large British companies.

The gap between ICI and the rest was huge[6]: in 1960, ICI's sales were £558 million, against £43 million for A&W, £46 million for Fisons and £15 million for Laporte. A table published for 1959 shows a similar disparity in profits. ICI's trading profit (before depreciation and tax) was £121 million. Excluding companies only partly in chemicals (the oil companies, Distillers, British Oxygen, Boots), the next largest was Albright & Wilson with £6.9 million. Behind A&W came Glaxo (£6.6m.), Borax (£5.6m.), Fisons (£5.3m.), Monsanto (£4.5m.) and Laporte (£2.9m.). The picture was changing slightly through the acquisitions by A&W and others (Laporte made five acquisitions in 1960–61) but the disparity

---

[6] For 1955 figures, see Ch2, page 66

was still marked. Ranked by net assets, ICI in 1960 was the largest British firm (excluding Shell, as a transnational company). A&W ranked 58, Beecham 65, Fisons 66, Glaxo 79 and Laporte 97.

Potential competition from continental Europe was also of increasing importance. In Germany, the three IG Farben successor companies had sales in 1960 in the range £220–280 million, while the three largest French companies had sales of £120–180 million and the figure for Montecatini in Italy was over £180 million.

In August 1962, A&W was approached by Borax with a view to a merger. A period of intensive discussion and exchange of information ensued. The two companies had some common ground; both were mainly in inorganic chemicals with some overlap in customer industries. Most of Borax's business, however, was in the USA and the Board of its subsidiary, US Borax, exercised a strong influence over the whole company's affairs, especially in capital expenditure decisions. When Sir Sydney Barratt learnt of that he called for talks to be discontinued: he had no wish for strong American influence. A statement was issued saying that there had been discussions between A&W and Borax which had been broken off by mutual and amicable agreement.

Of greater significance was the revival in 1964 of the possibility of a merger between A&W and Fisons, previously discussed in 1957. The approach came from Fisons, which was also considering establishing a second major chemical company in the UK. In August 1964, Sir John Carmichael (Chief Executive of Fisons) made contact with Sir Sydney Barratt, who reported to the A&W Board, "Such a move would not only provide strength through size, which is so important in the chemical industry, but would also improve the economics of the supply of P2O5, which would support the Group's phosphate business". Discussions continued until November but broke up because of disparity in the market valuations of the two companies, reflecting the difference in profits: Fisons' pretax profit for the twelve months to 30th June was under £4 million, whereas A&W's in the twelve months to 31st December was over £7.5 million. Sir Sydney reported, "Fisons are of the opinion that current market valuations of the two companies do not properly reflect their own growth prospects ... The disparity of size in market valuation is so great that it would have to be reflected in Board representation. No proposals acceptable to both sides have therefore been found".

In January 1965, however, the Chairman of Fisons (Lord Netherthorpe) approached Sir Sydney to say that Fisons would accept a minority position on a merged Board and that the first Chairman should come from Albright & Wilson; also that it would be a true merger, with the shareholders of neither company receiving an enhanced price for their shares. Negotiations were reopened and by April a draft scheme for the management of the merged companies was produced. The A&W Board expressed general but not unanimous agreement that a merger was desirable. At the time (June 1965), the market capitalisations of the two companies gave a ratio of 65:35 in A&W's favour, but the two companies' profit forecasts for 1967 gave a ratio closer to 55:45. Kenneth Keith (chief executive of Hill Samuel, which was advising A&W), said that in a merger there should be little deviation from current market values; he stressed that a pre-requisite should be a demonstration of expected commercial advantages.

Within a month, it became clear that the gap between the expectations of the two companies and their merchant banks was too large to be bridged, and discussions were terminated. Apart from financial considerations, there had always been difficulty over Board representation and the name to be given to the merged company. Reportedly, A&W was not keen on 'Alfison', as suggested by Fisons.

Fisons had also envisaged including both Laporte and Associated Chemical Companies in the merged company. Although A&W acquired ACC and there were discussions with Laporte, without agreement between A&W and Fisons it was considered that the strategy of forming a second major chemical grouping could not proceed. Later (in 1970) Laporte survived a takeover bid from Burmah Oil and then in 1971 began its partnership with the Belgian company Solvay. Solvay's shareholding in Laporte effectively blocked any acquisition or merger attempt by others.

In the meantime, A&W's position had changed drastically and the period of mergers and acquisitions for A&W had passed. So Sir Sydney was never able to figure as a latter-day Lord McGowan (who had been a leading force in the merger of four companies to form ICI in 1926). The concept of a large second force in the British chemical industry perhaps acted as a distraction, without much hope of achieving a grouping of significant size; in March 1965, the market capitalisation of ICI was over £950 million, while the combined capitalisation of A&W, Fisons, Laporte, Monsanto (UK), Borax and Glaxo was less than £220 million.

Developments

While the emphasis in this period was on acquisitions, there were expansions in all the countries in which A&W was engaged, several with positive long-term results but including some less well-conceived moves in Canada.

Canada

In April 1962 *Chemical Week* published an article entitled "Match King Makes Good in Chemicals". In it, A&W was praised for avoiding the sharp fall in profits experienced by other British chemical companies in 1961. A year later, however,

The Sunday Telegraph published an article[7] under the heading "Canadian Drain", which started with the question "What is wrong with Albright & Wilson?" and went on to point out that, excluding acquisitions, profit had fallen in 1962 for the third year in succession. "There can be no doubt that the culprit is the Electric Reduction Company of Canada," it continued, adding, "a major part of the group's available investment resources has been poured down the Canadian drain...This has been a sorry story of misdirected investment". Sir Sydney regarded the article as an attack on his leadership and drafted a reply for delivery at the Annual General Meeting if the subject arose. The reply was approved by the Board, with Frank Schon voting against – he had always considered the investment in Port Maitland (p.58) a mistake, with Canada at a constant disadvantage in competition with cheap phosphoric acid and phosphate fertilisers made in Florida.

The Port Maitland plant came on stream in July 1961, for the manufacture of phosphoric acid and superphosphates. Frank Schon continued to criticise the investment and suggested that alternative uses for the plant should be investigated. A year later, when sales were low and the plant was performing poorly, Frank asked for City advice on whether to give stockholders information about Port Maitland; the answer was that it was not necessary because Erco accounted for less than 10% of Group profit. In March 1963 he asked that it be minuted that he thought the references to Erco in the Chairman's Statement too optimistic.

There had been concern in Canada and in England that Erco had insufficient strength of management. A Canadian finance house, Woods Gordon, was engaged to look into the situation; it recommended the recruitment of additional senior executives. In August 1962, E.R. Kinsley was appointed Executive Vice-President of Erco.

Edward Rice Kinsley was born in 1927 in Toronto and spent part of his childhood in England, where his father worked as a commercial artist. He returned to Canada in 1938 and graduated in 1947 from the University of Toronto with a First in mathematics and physics. He joined Texas Instruments and for seven years worked in the provinces of Western Canada before being posted first to Calcutta and then to London. In 1958 he was awarded a Sloan Fellowship, which provided him with a year's study in industrial management at the Massachusetts Institute of Technology, leading to a Master's degree in industrial management. He then moved to the headquarters of Texas Instruments in Dallas, Texas, where he started a new

---

[7] Subsequently it was found that the article in The Sunday Telegraph had been the result of Frank Schon's acquaintance with the author (Nigel Lawson) – in an article of September 1962 Lawson had praised the growth of Marchon and suggested that it should be floated separately, with a minority of the shares being distributed to the shareholders of Albright & Wilson Ltd. Frank Schon also provided the information for an article in The Sunday Times in July 1963 in which Marchon – and particularly Marchon Italiana –was praised and criticism made of the poor profit performance of Boake Roberts and Erco.

activity, applying geophysics and geochemistry to US government programmes relating to the earth, oceans and outer space. He wished to return to Canada, however, and after meeting Sir Sydney in New York he accepted the offer of a senior position in Erco. His relatively brief time with Albright & Wilson was to prove of great significance in the history of the company.

Less than a year after Ed Kinsley joined Erco, Sir Sydney reported to the A&W Board that he was losing confidence in Dr D.E. Jones, President of Erco since 1953, and that Kinsley was not willing to continue to work with him. In September 1963, therefore, Kinsley was appointed chief executive of Erco, with Sir Sydney temporarily assuming the title of President until Kinsley became President in November 1964 (and a member of the Young Presidents' Club, being under 40 years old).

Early moves by Kinsley included the formation of a Chlorate Division, to exploit Erco's technology as well as sales of sodium chlorate, and of a Technical Division. To head the latter he recruited Ed Bissaillon, then Technical Manager of Hooker's Phosphorus Division, following service as Vice-President of Engineering with Shea Chemical Corporation, another of the US phosphorus producers. In November 1964, two more Divisions were formed – Industrial Phosphates, under Lloyd Lillico (later President of Erco), and Agricultural Chemicals, whose manager was Dr Roy Pennington. To complete the reorganisation, Kinsley obtained the A&W Board's agreement at the end of 1964 to set up a new headquarters and laboratory in Toronto, which was given the title 'Innovation Centre'.

Capital expenditure projects included plants for granular superphosphate and fluoride recovery at Port Maitland and a 50% expansion of the Vancouver chlorate plant. By the middle of 1964, Port Maitland was operating to capacity. There was a shortage of phosphoric acid and, with Varennes also operating to capacity, supplies of thermal acid were also limited.

Despite these signs of progress and Erco's moving into profit in 1963, the agricultural business continued to make losses because of high raw material costs and low selling prices. Yet Ed Kinsley continued to look to fertilisers for expansion. One proposal in 1965 was to acquire 15% of a new company to be formed near New Orleans and build a $25 million fertiliser plant with a guarantee for Erco to take a substantial part of the phosphoric acid produced. That did not materialise. As will be described in the next chapter, other schemes did materialise, with disastrous results.

The Sunday Telegraph article, though perceptive, did not lead to a widespread or lasting adverse view of Albright & Wilson's progress and potential. Thus, for example, the Stock Exchange Gazette in March 1965 wrote: "Last year the group kept its above-average trading record unsullied and ... the long-term prospects are good...the relatively high investment rating is justified".

United Kingdom

Between 1959 and 1965, the largest contribution to increased profit (other than acquisitions) came from **Midland Silicones** (MS). A reference to the origin of the joint venture between Albright & Wilson (60%) and Dow Corning Corporation, of Midland, Michigan (40%) has already been made (p.14). The venture moved into profit in 1957 and by 1959 was making a pretax profit of nearly £½ million. By 1965, that had grown to £1¼ million, giving a return of 30% on sales. In 1965, MS had over 900 employees (three times the number in 1958) at the factory at Barry (South Wales) and the sales office and headquarters, which in 1964 moved from London to Reading. The speciality and technological basis of MS was reflected in the fact that production workers were outnumbered by technical, sales and administrative staff by nearly 50%.

From 1959 to 1965, over £3 million was invested in new plants and expansions at Barry, including extension upstream towards raw materials and downstream towards end-products. A seven-year agreement was concluded with Dow Corning at the end of 1959, providing for payments from MS to Dow Corning for the supply of know-how. In 1963 a research department was established at Barry, and technical service facilities were expanded almost continuously. MS was in this period the largest maker of silicones in Europe; penetration into continental Europe was aided by the setting up of companies in Holland and Denmark for sales and technical service.

The attributes of silicones – thermal stability, water-repellancy, resistance to oxidation, non-stick property, suppression of foam, chemical inertness and non-toxicity – were a unique combination leading to many industrial and domestic uses. These included incorporation into polishes, lubricants, paints, sealants, mould-release compounds, cold-cure rubbers, water-repellent treatments for textiles and masonry, antifoam additives, hydraulic fluids and insulants – the list of applications grew with success in "double selling", i.e. arousing interest among users of products that potentially might contain silicones.

This success story fulfilled one of A&W's strategic aims: to increase involvement in speciality products with high technical and service elements, which would show strong growth, and withstand competition through innovation and service to customers. The one serious drawback was the dependence upon Dow Corning for most of the technology. That was to prove a crucial problem.

Investment by **Marchon** at Whitehaven was a significant feature of the period 1960–65. First in importance was the expansion and development of the wet phosphoric acid base established in the mid-1950s. In February 1960, a third anhydrite kiln was authorised (see p.41), doubling the capacity for sulphuric acid and cement; it was opened in May 1962 by Lord Fleck, former Chairman of ICI. Three years later, in May 1965, the Prime Minister, Harold Wilson, inaugurated the building of the fourth and fifth kilns, doubling capacity again, to 400,000 tpa of acid and the same quantity of cement. At a time when the UK was short of dollars and sulphur was at a high price, the saving of 140,000 tpa of sulphur imports was an attraction to the government.

A new phosphoric acid plant (F3) was built in 1961, a "wet salts" plant (for making orthophosphate liquor) in 1962 and a second STPP plant in 1966, bringing capacity up to 200,000 tpa to match the increased sulphuric acid capacity. The infrastructure for the Whitehaven phosphoric acid and phosphate operations was also strengthened. Two new ships, *Marchon Venturer* and *Marchon Enterprise*, joined *Marchon Trader* for the transportation of phosphate rock into Whitehaven harbour, where silos were built for temporary storage. From there, the phosphate rock was taken through the town and up the hill to the factory by an almost continuous shuttle of heavy lorries – a project to build a rail spur up to the factory was authorised in 1963 but then abandoned.

For A&W, economics were not the only aspect in favour of expansion of wet phosphoric acid capacity. Also significant was the poor performance of the Portishead phosphorus plant and the closure of the plant at Oldbury, announced at the end of 1963.

While sales of STPP continued to grow, however, prices were under pressure; profit margins were sharply reduced in 1960 when the main customers enforced prices based on US prices for STPP plus 10%. For the next three years Marchon's profits plateaued, before resuming their growth in 1964.

There were several other significant developments by Marchon in this period. A 20,000 tpa alcohol plant was built and a plant for continuous sulphonation (p.317) using sulphur trioxide, which represented vital steps forward in basic processes for the production of detergents and toiletries. Marchon provided know-how for two detergent plants built in the USSR by Constructors John Brown. Exports grew, leading to a Queen's Award; Her Majesty Queen Elizabeth the Queen Mother visited Whitehaven in October 1964 and in the 1966 Queen's Birthday honours Frank Schon received a knighthood. Sir Frank envisaged further substantial growth of Marchon and in June 1966 he proposed the expenditure of £20 million (minus a government grant of £7.5 million) to expand the production of sulphuric acid from anhydrite from 400,000 tpa to 1 million. He believed that he could sell the cement and the sulphuric acid from the additional kilns. It was not to be; no more kilns were built after the fifth, for reasons that will become apparent in the next chapter.

Australia

Reference has already been made (p.36) to the creation in 1935 of Gardinol Chemical Co in Australia for the manufacture of synthetic detergents. The company was liquidated in 1940 by order of the High Court of Australia and its assets put up for public tender. The successful tenderer, with a bid of £121 (the currency was not yet dollars), formed a new company, Gardinol Chemical Company (Australasia), initially to make chemicals for the textile and chemical industries. In 1945, the company commenced a research programme that over the next 15 years produced several important processes and products. They included an Italian-designed continuous sulphonation plant based on sulphur (one of the first installations in the world) and drum-dried powder detergents. Those developments put Gardinol in the forefront of the industry and in direct competition with the Marchon range of products being marketed by Albright & Wilson (Australia), which was also manufacturing materials for toiletries on a small scale.

Despite Gardinol's technical and financial success, its owners decided to sell out because of the capital required for new plants. An approach was made to ICIANZ, which had some interests in the field, but in support of ICIANZ's joint venture with A&W the bid was referred to A&W (Australia). The company was acquired on 1st January 1966, for AUD 293,000. The acquisition enabled A&W (Australia) to dominate the market and the purchase price was soon recouped out of profits.

With Gardinol came entry, albeit in a small way, into another range of products. In 1962, Gardinol had become a licensee of Union Chemique Belge to manufacture a range of acrylic resin solutions and emulsions for the paint, building, paper, adhesive and other industries from a plant (built in 1964) at the factory at Box Hill, Melbourne. Although A&W continued with acrylics, significant profit was not made from them for many years.

The entry of Marchon into the A&W group in 1955 had an important impact on the core phosphates business of A&W (Australia). Marchon had been selling into Australia, using another agent. As sales of domestically produced STPP in Australia grew, it became economic to move from thermal phosphoric acid to the wet route. In 1961 ICIANZ acquired Commonwealth Fertilizers & Chemicals and built a wet process phosphoric acid (WPA) plant on a site next to A&W (Australia). In November 1962 an agreement was concluded for the supply of WPA from ICIANZ to A&W (Australia) putting an end to the need for A&W (Australia) to import phosphorus to supplement the output of its furnaces.

In April 1964 A&W (Australia) approved an orthophosphate plant based on WPA which came on stream in September 1965. The WPA plant's location on deep water and adjacent to ICIANZ's sulphuric acid plant meant that the operation was highly competitive. A threat from Australian Fertilizers to enter the industrial phosphates field, based on a WPA plant, was averted when ICIANZ acquired a controlling interest in that company.

One of the two phosphorus furnaces at Yarraville was closed in 1966 as a consequence of the changeover to WPA for detergent phosphates. The second was closed in 1972 because of requirements of the Clean Air Division of the Commission of Public Health. Phosphorus vapour escaping from the furnace was highly visible, in an area not far from the centre of Melbourne, and the modifications needed to prevent it would have been prohibitively expensive.

The partnership with ICIANZ was invaluable in the formative years. Up to 1954, A&W (Australia) fell administratively under the Alkali Phosphate Group of ICIANZ, of which the Controller was Howard Strong, who had been with ICIANZ since 1933. In 1954, A&W (Australia) took over the responsibility for sales from ICIANZ and as compensation 2.5% of the shares were transferred to ICIANZ. Howard Strong then became Chairman and Managing Director of A&W (Australia). He remained Managing Director until 1960, when he was succeeded by R.C. (Dick) Edquist. Dick, who had joined A&W (Australia) in 1945, was to serve as Managing Director until 1974. Howard Strong continued as Chairman until 1963, when for the first time a Chairman unconnected with ICIANZ was appointed: Alan R. Lobban, a partner in the Melbourne legal firm of Blake & Riggall, held the position for the next 21 years. He was succeeded in 1984 by J.A. Hancock, an ICIANZ Director, who served until 1991 when the partnership with ICIANZ ended after more than 50 years – a marriage exceptionally long for the chemical industry.

To the favourable position in raw materials was added a technical strength, a one-shot process for making STPP from a solution of phosphate salts. The process was patented in the names of Mark Maunsell (the inventor of the 'Maunsell Burner' used to produce thermal phosphoric acid (p.6) and Dick Edquist, who had become the Technical Director when Maunsell moved to Erco in 1954. It was adopted in the Philippines by Polyphosphates Inc, in which A&W subsequently acquired a 40% shareholding. Elsewhere in A&W, however, it never replaced the traditional two-stage process of drying the phosphate solution first and then converting the orthophosphate into polyphosphate by heating in a kiln.

The prosperity of A&W (Australia) at that time, as was the case with most of Australian secondary industry, was heavily dependent on protection from imports. The small population, small plant sizes and high labour costs made production uncompetitive. To those disadvantages were added what has been described by the Australian historian, Professor George Blainey, as "the tyranny of distance" – the long haul from manufacturing points to customers, compounded by high local shipping costs; the distance from Sydney to Perth is one and a half times the distance from London to Moscow.

Until 1960, import licensing conferred a high degree of protection. In the late 1950s, the approaching end of licensing and the increased threat from imports led to the formation of the Australian Chemical Industry Council (ACIC) whose initial focus was a strategy to obtain tariff protection. The first industry selected for review by the Government was indeed the chemical industry. Each company had to present its case and then submit to a public hearing before the Tariff Board. A&W (Australia) and Gardinol were both very active in the process and George James, General Manager of Gardinol before its acquisition by A&W, was the second President of the ACIC. Both companies were successful in obtaining protection. From the 1970s onwards, however, there was increasing pressure for tariffs to be reduced; eventually their level for chemicals was reduced from the peak of up to 40% to a nominal 5%. As a consequence, some companies ceased to manufacture in Australia while others, including A&W (Australia) continued, but with product selection or capital investment to achieve competitive costs.

Other developments

Investments in this period included a 50% expansion in phosphate plasticisers at Rainham. In 1965 Albright, Morarji & Pandit was formed in India for the manufacture of STPP with a 45% holding for A&W, while in Ireland A&W's holding was increased from a minority to 80%. There were also some shrinkages: Lubrizol Corporation, A&W's majority partner in Lubrizol Great Britain Ltd, purchased A&W's share and the profitable manufacture of the oil additives at Oldbury ceased at the end of 1964. Of less significance, except historically, was the sale in 1962 of Bristol Mineral & Land Company, a subsidiary since 1941; its business in strontium salts, based on the mining of celestine near Bristol, had ceased to be competitive with overseas producers.

It was probably fortunate for A&W that a project for a joint venture with Petrofina (Great Britain) Ltd to build a refinery at Killingholme, Lincolnshire, did not materialise. The proposal was to invest £12 million for the production of 100,000 tpa of vinyl chloride, for conversion to PVC. But, as Keith Piercy (who was in charge of the project) records, A&W "began to have doubts about the wisdom of becoming the third producer of PVC in Britain," and within a few months the idea was abandoned. It is hard to see why consideration was ever given to entering into a field in which Albright & Wilson had no special knowledge or market position.

In the early 1960s **computers** and other new technology (for example, subscriber trunk dialling or STD) were starting to arouse interest. By the middle of 1965, there were just over 1,000 computers at work in Britain; David Fishlock, Technology Editor of the New Scientist, forecast in an article in the Albright Magazine that numbers would have grown to over 5,000 by 1974. In terms of usage of computers, Britain in 1965 was lagging behind every other industrial nation in Europe except Austria. The Ministry of Technology, set up by the Labour government elected in 1964, had an objective to promote the use of computers, but the example of Albright & Wilson indicates the magnitude of the task.

A&W was slow to accept computers. In March 1963, Neil Peech (an external Director of Albright & Wilson Ltd and Chairman of Steetley) was told that while the Group did not own a computer it did hire computer time, and there was soon to be a conference on data processing at which "brief consideration" would be given to computers. At the conference there was more emphasis on punched cards (which had been introduced in A&W in 1959); it was agreed that computers might be acquired at some future date. A year later, it was decided to rent two computers for commercial and scientific work at Oldbury and early in 1965 a computer was rented by BBA to process its punched cards. Later that year ACC acquired an electronic data processor, saying, "a complete computer unit was also considered by ACC but rejected on the grounds that it was more costly, required greater space and had a capacity well beyond the company's needs". Midland Silicones finally ordered a computer at the beginning of 1967. In a test in 1972 a computer carried out a depreciation programme which was done manually, at the same time, to give managers proof of the machine's reliability.

A&W's first process control computer was a Diogenes, installed in mid-1979 on the phosphate plasticiser plant at Rainham; computer control of plants, today commonplace in the chemical industry, was still not the rule in A&W at the end of the 1970s, when the £20 million F5 phosphoric plant was built at Whitehaven (p.213). Shortly after that, computer controls were introduced at Long Harbour (p.200); their success heralded the inclusion of computer controls in all new plants.

Organisation

In 1963 Christopher Wilson and Richie Threlfall retired and Bryan Topley, the Deputy Chairman, withdrew from executive duties because of ill-health. A.V. (Vic) Sherwood, Treasurer since 1957, was appointed Finance Director in April 1964. In November 1964 Sir Owen Wansbrough-Jones was appointed Executive Vice-Chairman, responsible for the day-to-day management of the parent company and the person to whom the chief executives of the UK operating companies reported. Sir Sydney, who at the age of 66 was contemplating retirement, was to continue to be responsible for "guiding Group policy on major matters" and for the Canadian and Australian subsidiaries.

Sir Owen Wansbrough-Jones joined Albright & Wilson in 1959 at the age of 54 as Technical Director, succeeding Bryan Topley in his executive role. Sir Owen ('Wansbrough' to his senior colleagues) studied physical chemistry and became a Fellow of Trinity Hall, Cambridge. He took a commission during the war, and held a number of technical positions, mainly connected with chemical warfare, becoming a Brigadier in 1945 and then in 1946 Director of Special Weapons and Vehicles in the War Office, from which he progressed to the position of Chief

Scientist in the Ministry of Supply in 1953, until he joined A&W. He was given the KBE in 1955.

On his appointment as Executive Vice-Chairman he indicated the changes that he would like to see: he wished to strengthen the personnel function, coordinate research and development (not sufficiently achieved during his 5 years as Technical Director), have a fuller discussion of investment opportunities at monthly meetings of senior executives and add an executive director to study production facilities so as to optimise the use of assets.

For some months two working parties had been reviewing the organisation and functioning of the Group; the senior comprised some of the Directors plus Dr Ray Gregory (manager of inter-company planning until April 1963, when he became a Director of Bush), and the junior, which was led by Ray Gregory, comprised a number of senior staff at the head office. The latter drafted a report recommending changes in organisation, a better definition of objectives and improved planning and reporting. The senior body broadly accepted the report but considered that an external review was necessary.

At its November 1964 meeting the Board decided that management consultants should be engaged to investigate the structure of the Group – McKinsey & Co were chosen. In the mid-1960s they reviewed a large part of the British chemical industry, including ICI, Shell, Geigy and Fisons (Group services). In December 1965, the Board agreed the terms for a major organisational study: to make a comprehensive review of the Company's present situation and future opportunities, to assist in the formulation of longer-term objectives and strategy, to identify opportunities for shorter-term profit improvement and to recommend changes in management organisation and processes. The results of that review are described in the next chapter.

*****

In this period seeds were sown in Canada and Britain that were to produce a crop of disasters in the following five years. They were to have a profound effect on the future of Albright & Wilson and force the company dangerously close to extinction.

Chapter 4

THE YEARS OF DISASTER

1965 - 1971

"We are confident that the steps we have taken in the last two years have given us the required foundation for profitable expansion, the results of which will become increasingly apparent in 1970 and subsequent years"
(Sir Owen Wansbrough-Jones, 1968 Annual Report, March 1969)

Overview

Keith Piercy, looking back on this period, likened it to the seven lean years suffered in Egypt, as described in the book of Genesis. It was, however, not external circumstances that afflicted Albright & Wilson but the results of the decisions made within the Company.

Economic and political background

The second half of the 1960s was a time of economic turbulence, particularly in Britain. The Labour government of Harold Wilson (1964-1970) and the subsequent Conservative government of Edward Heath battled with balance of payments and inflation problems. The Labour government created the Department of Economic Affairs, set up a National Board for Prices & Incomes and attempted to restrain the rise in prices & incomes by a compulsory early warning system, a standstill in wage increases, prices and dividends, increases in interest rates and in taxation, and measures to restrain imports and encourage exports.

The results were a recession in 1965-7 and severe balance of payments deficits, leading to devaluation of the £ in November 1967 (from 2.80 to 2.40 to the $) and emergency loans from the International Monetary Fund and central banks. The devaluation was followed by a 6% rise in industrial production in 1968 and by an improvement in the balance of payments, to a large surplus in 1971, but at the expense of sharply rising inflation, to nearly 6% per annum in 1968-69 and 9.5% in 1970-71; unemployment, which had been 1.4% in 1965, rose in 1971 to 3.8%. The Conservative government failed to solve the problems of inflation and the balance of payments worsened again after 1970.

Economic problems were not confined to Britain. From the end of 1967, the United States experienced a run on the dollar and a record deficit in its balance of payments in 1970. In August 1971, it suspended convertibility of the dollar into gold (at $35 per ounce). That was followed by revaluation of the West German mark, Japanese yen and other strong currencies and the setting of new parities for world currencies.

Other features of the period were:

- the UK was rebuffed in its attempts to join the European Common Market in 1967 and 1968 but was accepted in 1971, along with Ireland, Norway and Denmark, for entry from 1st January 1973
- tariffs within the EEC were abolished and common external tariffs were established in July 1968

- the UK converted to decimal currency in February 1971
- a Selective Employment Tax was introduced in February 1966, with the aim of increasing employment in manufacturing in the UK
- Rhodesia's unilateral declaration of independence led to sanctions
- the Israeli 6-day war in June 1967 succeeded in extending its frontiers
- disturbances in Northern Ireland, leading to direct rule and policing by the army, began in October 1968
- world-wide satellite communications were established, the Americans landed on the moon (1969), colour television started in Britain (1967), Concorde flew (1969), the Polaris submarines were commissioned (1967-8) and the Nuclear Non-proliferation Treaty came into force (1970)
- the USA began withdrawing troops from Vietnam in July 1969 and in 1971 lifted its 21-year embargo on trade with China
- Soviet troops ended the Dubcek government in Czechoslovakia (1968)

A&W's results

The results of Albright & Wilson in this period give some idea of the severity of the problems experienced:-

Progress 1965 - 1971

£ million	1965	1966	1967	1968	1969	1970	1971
Sales	**90.3**	**96.4**	**105.9**	**111.9**	**120.5**	**129.0**	**123.9**
Profit before interest & tax	8.0	6.7	6.8	7.3	5.3	5.9	6.7
Interest payable	-0.6	1.2	1.8	2.1	3.6	4.0	3.8
Pretax profit	**7.4**	**5.5**	**5.0**	**5.2**	**1.7**	**1.6**	**2.9**
Tax	1.8	2.2	2.0	2.0	0.7	0.5	0.9
Profit after tax	5.6	3.3	3.0	3.2	1.0	1.1	2.0
Adjustments	0.1		-0.2	1.3	-4.3	-1.3	-2.9
Profit after adjustments	**5.7**	**3.3**	**2.8**	**1.9**	**-3.3**	**-0.3**	**-0.9**
Ordinary dividend	21%	21%	15%	15%	7%	2%	4%
Capital expenditure	9.6	12.6	16.0	19.0	7.1	7.6	7.2
Investments	0.5	0.8	1.5	2.2	0.8	0.3	-
Net cap. emp. (end of year)	**70.0**	**83.5**	**98.9**	**110.5**	**106.3**	**107.9**	**115.5**

The figures, as published, show a sharp decline in profits after 1968. The position in fact was worse than that. From 1968 to 1971 there were substantial write-offs, the reasons for which will be explained, particularly in the account given below of the Belledune Fertilizer investment. At the time the accounts were produced, it was acceptable for items regarded as not part of ordinary trading to be excluded from the profit & loss account, a practice that would not have been acceptable in later years. In 1968, there was still a profit of nearly £2 million after the "below-line" write-off but in the next three years 1968-71, there were "below-line" write-offs of £8.9 million, against the total profit of £4.1 million shown for that period. So in 1969-71 Albright & Wilson was making serious losses. One of the contributory factors was the interest burden resulting from borrowing to finance the heavy programme of capital expenditure and investments. By the end of 1969 borrowings exceeded the total of Ordinary share capital and reserves. Only a nominal dividend was paid for 1970, which was not truly covered by the profit earned in that year.

The three main causes of the deterioration were Belledune Fertilizer, the Long Harbour project, and the headquarters organisation and people.

Belledune Fertilizer

While in the history of Albright & Wilson the Long Harbour project has the greatest prominence, it was preceded by a less well known project that proved to be an unqualified mistake and a significant drain on funds at a critical time.

Concept & financing

From start to finish, the Belledune Fertilizer project was a disaster. It took time, effort and money and after nearly 8 years left behind no benefits to A&W and a weakened financial position.

It is not clear just when Ed Kinsley first considered pursuing the project. It must have been about a year after joining Erco as Executive Vice-President in August 1962. He had shown himself keen to develop sales of phosphatic fertiliser materials from Port Maitland but Port Maitland's supply of sulphuric acid from Sherbrooke Metallurgical nearby was expensive and the tonnage was limited.

Another driving factor was the prospect of large shipments of fertilisers to developing countries. The US programme of Aid for International Development (AID) was supporting a rapidly growing tonnage of fertiliser exports; from 1961 to 1966, the proportion of world trade in fertiliser nitrogen based on tied aid rose from nil to over 60%. According to the Organisation for Economic Cooperation & Development (OECD), in 1964-5 $800 million of assistance was directed to agriculture by OECD countries and the major multilateral agencies.

In 1963-4, there was a developing boom in base metal industries in Eastern Canada, exploiting deposits of zinc, lead and iron pyrites. A by-product of the smelting was sulphuric acid at low cost, leading to phosphoric acid for fertilisers. There were three developments: at Timmins in Northern Ontario, by Texas Gulf, at Valleyfield in Quebec, by Noranda, and at Bathurst in New Brunswick, by Brunswick Mining & Smelting Corporation (BMS). There was also a plant at Copper Cliff, Ontario, operated by Canadian Industries (CIL) and International Nickel, which was capable of producing an extra 200,000 tons pa of sulphuric acid.

BMS had the advantage of large deposits and a year-round port, at Belledune Point, for raw materials and products. There were plans for expenditure, estimated at £40 million, for chemical, metallurgical and port facilities and possibly a steel mill. BMS was headed by K.C. Irving, who also headed companies in New Brunswick operating in petroleum, paper and caustic/chlorine, with assets estimated to total over £200 million. W.M. Mitchell, an external Director of Erco, was personally well known to Irving (who was guardian to Mitchell's wife). During 1964 he and Ed Kinsley had several meetings in New Brunswick and Toronto with Irving and Jim Boylen, a mining entrepreneur who had discovered the Brunswick deposits in 1953. Ed Kinsley's objective was to make Erco Irving's choice as BMS's partner in a company to make phosphoric acid and fertilisers. Other possible partners included CIL, Cyanamid, Dow Chemical, Allied Chemical, Sogemines, Shell and Esso. Dr Forrest Musgrave, overseas liaison assistant to Sir Sydney at Knightsbridge, wrote a report for the Albright & Wilson Board in December 1964 in which he stated "there are undoubtedly a number of Companies interested, although Mr Irving has the reputation of being a very difficult partner". Later that month Ed Kinsley met Irving and was told that BMS did not need a financial contribution to the cost of the fertiliser plant and "would only tolerate a partnership if they considered this would benefit the operation significantly". They claimed that they had had discussions with Fisons and with Albatros but said that they were willing to consider Erco as a partner. Ed wrote: "it is up to us...to sell ourselves to the Brunswick organization in every possible way" and suggested that Erco could buy its fuel oil for Buckingham and Varennes from Irving Oil and engage in joint ventures in transportation.

The initial response from Knightsbridge was cautious: there was concern at the vulnerability of a one-product plant and it was foreseen that marketing the diammonium phosphate (DAP) produced would be a great problem. There was also concern at the possible impact on sales from Port Maitland. It was suggested that Arthur D. Little, a leading American firm of market and business consultants, should be retained to report on market prospects.

The terms proposed by BMS a few days later, in a letter from John D. Park, the Chairman of Engineering Consultants (an Irving company), were based on the assumption that 800,000 tons pa of sulphuric acid would be supplied by BMS to make 640,000 tons pa of DAP. "The fertiliser company", he wrote, "could depend on getting sulphuric acid at the lowest possible cost...We would expect both partners to contribute in every way possible to promote the growth of the company and ensure its success". The nominal equity would be held equally by the two partners; one-third of the capital would be provided by redeemable preference shares held by the partners and the rest borrowed. The division of profits would be for 15% return on the shareholders' investment (after interest but before depreciation) to go to the fertiliser company, with the excess being divided 20% to the fertiliser company and 80% to BMS. With no tax expected to be payable for the first 7 years of operation (provided that the plant was operating up to 60% of capacity by 1st March 1967), the shareholders' investment would be repaid (by redemption of the preference shares) by the end of that period.

The terms appeared attractive to Ed Kinsley and in January 1965 he raised with BMS the possibility of moving some of Erco's industrial phosphates operations to Belledune, taking 20% of the phosphoric acid produced. BMS, however, while conceding that Erco could have a plant alongside, refused to allow the joint company to be restricted from itself producing industrial phosphates. For his part, Irving would not say anything about his plans for making steel.

A few days later, at a meeting in London, doubts were voiced about the supply of sulphuric acid and its suitability for making phosphoric acid of the required quality. It was ascertained that only 176,000 tons pa of sulphuric acid would be produced from the smelting of base metal ores, leaving some 600,000 tons to be produced from pyrites. There was some concern at arsenic and selenium impurities in the acid. Doubts were also cast on the viability of the possible steelmaking operation at Belledune. Sir Charles Goodye, President of the British Iron & Steel Research Association (and well-known to Bryan Topley), said that he doubted the ability of the proposed Stelco/Lurgi plant (unproven on a commercial scale) to compete with blast furnaces; the likely scale (250,000 tons pa) was too small and the probable impurities in the iron would be a problem. Plenty of iron ore was available for competitors in the Atlantic area and existing steel-making capacity was said to be adequate. Sir Sydney asked for more information about Irving and Boylen; there is no record that it was provided.

Ed Kinsley presented a paper on the BFL project to the Albright & Wilson Board on 15th January 1965. In it he reported that DAP facilities recently announced in Louisiana and Florida would add 900,000 tons pa to the North American supply. He therefore forecast that only 200,000 tons pa of the Belledune output of DAP would be sold within North America and the balance overseas. He proposed that the phosphoric acid capacity at Belledune should be equivalent to 800,000 tpa of DAP, enabling Erco to sell phosphoric acid and triple superphosphate and also to make cheap sodium tripolyphosphate, using salt instead of soda ash. As for finance, he believed "The dollars required (a capital cost of $21 million plus $9 million for working capital) could almost certainly be found in Canada, certainly requiring A&W guarantee, but not requiring the transmission of sterling funds into Canada". He asked for a decision by the end of February, in order to be able to obtain tax concessions. His proposals were well received. The Albright & Wilson Board minutes record: "It was agreed that Erco was presented with an outstanding opportunity and that negotiations with BM & S for a joint company... should proceed".

Within days, however, variations in the proposed terms began to appear. Irving said that because BMS would be committed to heavy expenditure A&W might like to put up more than 50% of the share capital, but without having a majority of the equity. In fact, it appeared that Irving wanted A&W to have only 49% of the equity but to underwrite part or all of the borrowing. Kinsley suggested to the A&W Executive that Erco should invest more funds, but not as equity, but the Executive rejected the suggestion. The Executive wanted a closer definition of the cost of sulphuric acid and did not accept Kinsley's statement that it would average about $6 per ton. It also rejected Kinsley's suggestion that A&W should be prepared to own phosphate rock deposits. It was accepted that the Irving Construction Company should be responsible for the engineering and construction of the fertiliser plant.

Soon after it emerged that cheap ammonia was not available and so BMS proposed that the fertiliser company should invest in an ammonia plant at a cost of $10 million, a move supported by Kinsley. Irving continued to play hard to get and refused to confirm Erco as a partner, indicating that he preferred Socal (Standard Oil of California). He then produced revised financial proposals, which were put to the A&W Board in March. They were for $14 million to be borrowed and guaranteed by the partners equally, $7 million to be lent by A&W in the form of redeemable preferred shares, guaranteed to be redeemed by BMS at the end of 5 years if not repaid before, and only nominal equity. The fertiliser company was to be called The Brunswick Fertilizer Company (BFC) and a second joint company, the Brunswick Chemical Company (BCC), would be formed to make ammonia and be the vehicle for future developments. Sales would be by Erco, charging for its services at cost; Kinsley stated that he was confident of being able to sell the whole output. The basic price for sulphuric acid from BMS was to be $8 per ton.

The A&W Board approved the terms. Frank Schon, however, asked that the obligation of BMS to supply sulphuric acid be made clear and that the price of the acid should be reconsidered if the profitability of the company was affected by competition. When the resulting draft agreement was drawn up, however, it included the statement that BMS was not required to process "more lead or zinc concentrates than were required for its normal operation". There was no obligation on BMS to supply sulphuric acid if it was not available from its smelter. The A&W Board considered it was not advisable to press for a clause that the acid price should be reconsidered if the minimum profitability was not attainable. The BMS backing for the preferred stock was reduced to an undertaking to take up 50% of the stock if not redeemed within 5 years. The proposal to build an ammonia plant was dropped.

The agreement was eventually signed on 11th May 1965. It made clear that BMS was not required to deliver sulphuric acid if "sulphur bearing gases are not available for the manufacture of sulphuric acid due to the reduction in operations or shutting down of the Outokumpu Sulphur Smelter and/or the Imperial Smelting Furnace"; in the event of any failure of design, engineering or operation BMS would be able to claim force majeure and avoid liability. The document even included the sentence "BMS will welcome any suggestions A&W may wish to make with respect to the manufacture of sulphuric acid"! The A&W Directors of BFC were to be Ed Kinsley, Forrest Musgrave and Vic Sherwood.

A Press release was issued on 24th May 1965, announcing a joint venture to construct a "$23 million chemical/fertilizer complex", to make phosphatic fertiliser material equivalent to 680,000 tons per annum, to come into full production early in 1967. The Chairman of Brunswick Fertilizer Corporation Ltd was to be M.J. Boylen (also Chairman of BMS) and the President Ed Kinsley, with K.C. Irving a Vice-President and Director. From the $140 million mining and refining development of BMS about 850,000 tons per annum of "effluent sulphuric acid" would be made available. It was claimed that "the new company will be one of the lowest cost producers in the world". In the concluding paragraph of the release it was stated: "The financing of the project will be from Canadian sources principally by long term borrowing. No finance from the UK will be called for, and there will be, therefore, no capital outflow from this country".

The first meeting of the designated BFC Board took place in June 1965. The account of that meeting states that Irving made it clear that Erco and A&W were only his second choice and that "the Agreement would be difficult to operate to the satisfaction of both partners without full cooperation and sound ethics, particularly from A&W/Erco". Erco was no longer to be responsible for sales but would recruit staff for BFC to perform that task. BMS would build an ammonia plant without participation by A&W.

The potential problems that had been only just below the surface started to emerge in August 1965. BMS wrote to A&W to ask for an extension to the deadline for conditions precedent in the Agreement, notably a provincial guarantee for the financing of Bay Steel (the main Irving company involved). A 3-month extension was agreed. Two weeks later Boylen proposed that the scope of the project should be halved - BMS had been worried for some time about the size of their whole undertaking. Kinsley told Boylen that he favoured phasing the operation because of the "immense job represented by selling product". Irving was said by Boylen to be "as opposed as ever to the partnership" and was believed to want simply to sell the sulphuric acid produced by BMS, but Boylen was prepared to continue with a DAP operation. (He also suggested to Kinsley that they should work on a similar project in Newfoundland, where Boylen had a mining operation; A&W's response was "There is no interest at present" and fortunately it did not pursue the offer.)

Sir Sydney at that time (August 1965) wrote to authorise the ordering of equipment from the BMS company Engineering Consultants Ltd, adding: "However, you will presumably modify the actual order placed, in line with any reduction in the scale of the operation...We have considered here the proposal to halve the scale of operations. In general, A&W is willing to consider favourably any proposal that BMS make...we should like an explanation for the new scale". Calculations were made in London, based on halving the size of the phosphoric acid plant and reducing the DAP plant by one-third, which indicated that the capital cost would still be $20 million. Next month a meeting chaired by Sir Owen Wansbrough-Jones decided that "M.J. Boylen will be invited to dinner in London as a social gesture. ERK (Kinsley) will be asked whether business should be discussed. If so, an office meeting at 1, Knightsbridge Green will be arranged instead of a dinner". The visit did not take place because two days later BMS terminated the Agreement of May 1965 on the grounds that they had been unable to obtain a provincial guarantee of $35 million of Bay Steel bonds.

The next step was a proposal by BMS for the DAP operation to be scaled down to one-quarter of the original, i.e. 160,000 tons (instead of 640,000), requiring 215,000 tons of sulphuric acid. Capital cost of a quarter-size fertiliser plant was estimated at $12 million, plus $2.5 million working capital. BMS proposed that A&W would be wholly responsible for financing, with no guarantees by BMS, and would be entitled to 30% of any equity profit. Sulphuric acid would be supplied at 50% of posted price, i.e. $13 per ton. With sales averaging 80% of the posted price for DAP (at that time $87 per ton), cash flow at full output would be only $1 million, before depreciation and loan repayments. In the light of the news that a DAP plant was to be built at New Orleans, to sell DAP at $67 per ton, the proposals cannot have held much attraction. Not surprisingly, Forrest Musgrave reported "It is ERK's opinion..that we do not have stable, efficient partners in BMS and he does not feel confident about permanent good relations with them for the future".

A counter-proposal was made to BMS a month later, for a lower price for sulphuric acid, equal sharing of profits, selling by Erco for a 2% commission, one-third of capital provided by A&W as redeemable preferred stock and the balance in loans, guaranteed as a last resort by A&W. It was rejected by BMS as not in the interest of its shareholders. Sir Owen Wansbrough-Jones persisted, writing to

Boylen: "We do not believe that any new situation has arisen which warrants our abandonment of the project and we are anxious to proceed with the original intention of jointly building and operating the fertiliser plant".

In response, in a meeting between Kinsley, Irving and Boylen in January 1966, agreement in principle was reached on terms for a new partnership, in a company to be called Belledune Fertilizer Ltd (BFL). BMS agreed to supply to BFL all its output of sulphuric acid, up to 425,000 tons pa (giving 180,000 tons of DAP), at 35% of list price for the first 250,000 tons pa and 45% for the rest, minimum $8. Profit on the DAP from the first 250,000 tons was to be shared equally, with the BMS share rising to 60% at the full tonnage. $5 million of the capital of $19 million was to be supplied by A&W as 7% preferred shares, up to $13.5 million by loans, guaranteed by A&W, and $500,000 by equity by the partners equally. The $3 million working capital would be borrowed from the bank. It was hoped to get a grant of $3.2 million but the tax concessions were no longer available.

There remained two fundamental problems. First, BMS was short of money and the federal government was no longer willing to provide dock facilities; Kinsley suggested that A&W should contribute a further $3.5 million for dock and storage facilities, but received no support. Second, BMS would not be able to make more than 240,000 tons pa of acid and was not obliged to deliver if sulphur-bearing gases were not available. (BMS did agree that BFL could purchase acid from third parties if BMS could not supply.) Frank Schon asked Ed Lopker, his consultant on phosphoric acid plants, to advise on the feasibility of BMS's plans. He reported that not only did BMS have to build a 30-mile railroad to transport the ores but also that the ores were very refractory and not yielding high-grade concentrates by normal processes. Production from iron pyrites would also be a problem because of the presence of copper, making the iron pellets unsuitable for feed to steel plants. Finally, BMS refused to agree not to sell ores (rather than processing them) because of a long-term agreement to supply concentrates to Sogemines, which limited the tonnage that could be processed to the equivalent of 215,000 tons pa of sulphuric acid.

The new proposals were due to be considered at an A&W Board meeting in April 1966. Prior to the meeting, Sir Owen Wansbrough-Jones wrote to Kinsley to ask about the marketing of DAP, since other Directors had said they wanted that information. He wrote: "I have debated with myself as to whether I should ask you for this information, recognising that we had some when the higher scale of output was being considered...Still, things change and my colleagues are certainly entitled to ask questions, and...I concluded that at risk of giving you even more work I ought to write...and this I hope you will endorse yourself. The information we have here must by now be about eighteen months out of date...I hope you can help me".

At the Board meeting in April, Kinsley said that he was expecting BFL's output of DAP to be initially 160,000 tons pa, rising later to 320,000. He was confident of

Edward Rice Kinsley, President of Erco, Chief Executive of Albright & Wilson 1967.

Sir Owen Wansbrough-Jones, KBE, CB, Technical Director 1959, Chairman 1967.

Belledune Fertiliser plant 1967.
[photo: Bathurst Photo Service]

Long Harbour phosphorus plant January 1969, with phosphorus carrier loading at jetty.

Phosphorus carriers alongside Portishead factory March 1969, with first shipment from Long Harbour being unloaded.

A section of Long Harbour electrodes.

Long Harbour nipples for linking electrode sections.

Sketch of the Albright Pioneer showing the 4 'bottles', each containing 1,250 tons of phosphorus; the two unique ships were built on Tyneside in 1968.

selling 250,000 tons in Canada and the northern USA, with the balance farther afield. Sherwood said that the cash contribution by Erco/A&W would be limited to $5,250,000 and that the whole outlay would be recouped within 5 years, operating at the lower level, and three years at the higher level. The project was agreed, with three abstentions. One of them was John Hutton-Wilson, concerning whom it was minuted: "Mr Hutton-Wilson was concerned at the (A&W) Group's forecast cash shortage and thought that priority should be given to expenditure to restore profitability of the basic products, including phosphorus. He believed the risks involved in New Brunswick were considerable and the stability of our partners was open to question. He felt that more information should have been given about the areas into which the product was to be sold and the realisation obtainable. For these reasons he suggested the project should not be given priority in capital expenditure". It was an accurate and perceptive view, characteristic of John Hutton-Wilson, but he did not carry the majority of Directors with him.

The new Agreement was executed in May 1966, without any undertaking from BMS to expand the acid plant; Kinsley "felt that BMS already had sufficient incentive to supply as much acid as BFL wanted and, furthermore, would be unlikely to agree". Capital expenditure of $13 million was authorised, although loan finance had not been arranged. It was decided that there would be a public issue of First Mortgage Bonds, guaranteed by A&W and with the backing of a report from Arthur D. Little (ADL).

When the draft report was produced in November 1966, Kinsley wrote to General Gavin (of ADL) criticising it strongly: "an entirely inadequate and biased report...the opinion of the project leader with respect to the over supply of P_2O_5 from North American sources over the next few years has biased his opinion about the project, while completely omitting reference or mention of the true strengths". He went on to list points of difference (e.g. he claimed that BFL would be the largest unit of its kind in the world and therefore cost competitive and mentioned possible exports to China) but acknowledged: "we are indeed grateful for the warning given on the over supply position for the next few years and the difficulties we will face in marketing this product".

The revised report issued in December contained some modifications but nevertheless pointed out that there were 29 other DAP plants in North America, that BFL would have a cost disadvantage of about $5 per ton against Florida producers and that for the next 4 years the industry would be operating at below 70% of capacity, with sales not reaching capacity until about 1975. Selling prices would therefore be depressed. The report stated "We do not believe that sulfuric acid supply will be a limiting factor to BFL's production capability". The evaluation by Arthur D. Little was nevertheless based on a netback to BFL of over $72 (Canadian) - which Kinsley said he was confident of achieving - and showed a return of 14-15%

for a 15-year life. That projection was to prove very over-optimistic but it did give the support sought for the prospectus for the Bonds.

The prospectus for $12 million of 7.25% First Mortgage Sinking Fund Bonds was drawn up in April 1967. A&W was required to guarantee the Bonds and BFL's performance of its obligations, to enter into a deficiency Agreement for the construction costs (i.e. to make up for any shortfall in funds during the construction period) and to guarantee the $3.5 million bank borrowing to finance working capital. The rate of dividend on A&W's Preferred stock was reduced from 7% to 6% but Erco was entitled to a 3% commission on BFL's sales. The start of production was postponed from September to November because of delays in the construction of the dock, which the government had agreed to build and lease to BFL.

Issue of the prospectus was, however, delayed. BMS's had run into difficulties: there were severe problems because of lead, zinc and copper in its iron pyrites and several companies were suing Irving for payment of their accounts. In June 1967 control of the company was acquired by Noranda, one of the leading Canadian mining companies, which injected $50 million.

Further delays occurred while the terms proposed for the Bonds were being negotiated with the leading institution that had been approached to subscribe. The rate of interest was raised to 8% and further restrictions and obligations were placed on A&W, including the requirement to take up $4 million of the Bonds (temporarily taken up by the bank) if not in institutional hands by the end of June 1969. A revised version of the Arthur D. Little report was issued in August 1967; it reduced the forecast of profitability slightly, to 13% for a 15-year life and (incorrectly) referred to a "firm commitment" by BMS to supply a minimum of 240,000 tons pa of acid, but it also estimated that the capacity utilisation in 1969-70 in North America would be only 56% and cast doubts on export prospects.

The Ontario Securities Commission at last approved the issue in November 1967, when a Press release stated that the $19 million plant was nearing completion and was designed to produce 350,000 tons pa of DAP. It also said that BFL expected to be eligible for a grant of $3.5 million, would qualify for accelerated depreciation allowances and would receive Provincial guarantees for bridging loans until the full proceeds of the Bond issue had been received. The issue was for $8 million out of the $12 million required, because one institutional investor was not prepared to subscribe before 1969. The Press release included the statement that Albright & Wilson had guaranteed the whole $12 million but there was no other reference to possible obligations on A&W; they included the guarantee of bank loans and a Deficiency Agreement, providing that if BFL was unable to get any more funds needed to bring the plant into production on terms more favourable than on the Bonds A&W would subscribe for more Preferred shares as necessary. There were also limits on short-term borrowing.

Operation and closure

The BFL plant was commissioned in November 1967. The Annual Report of A&W, issued in March 1968, reported that the plant was in commercial production and that BMS was "making available sulphuric acid, an important raw material, at an advantageous price". A slow start-up, however, meant that the spring 1968 selling season was missed and sales for the whole year were less than 47,000 tons. With an average netback of below $58 per ton, a loss of $2.4 million before depreciation ($3.7 million after depreciation) was sustained. The lenders had asked, early in 1968, for an updated report from Arthur D. Little. Issued in June 1968, it reported a heavy overcapacity in phosphate fertilisers. Prices for exports were so low that BFL could not compete. BFL was especially vulnerable because it was a one-product company. BMS was unable to supply even the 210,000 tons of acid previously forecast. Noranda offered to buy a pyrites plant to produce 300,000 tons pa of sulphuric acid but required a take or pay contract for 15 years at a price of $15.75 per ton, which was clearly unrealistic. A D Little forecast losses for 1968-1970 but still calculated the 15-year profit to be 10.7%, adding that "10% is generally considered to be acceptable by the chemical industry in North America".

Because BFL was unable to meet the financial criteria prescribed in the terms for the Bonds, A&W was forced to remit $3 million in October 1968 and to increase its guarantees of bank borrowing by $2.5 million. Noranda offered to reduce the price of acid by $2 per ton, but the value of the reduction was to be treated as a loan, whose repayment would slow down the repayment of the money invested by A&W. A further $500,000 was remitted in March 1969, as losses continued.

Sir Owen Wansbrough-Jones had requested a report on BFL from an internal group, the "Short Range Planning Group" (comprising the Development Director, Michael Peard; the Treasurer, Tony Ward; the Assistant Treasurer, Wilf Shillaker; and the Planning Manager, Hugh Podger), which was presented in March 1969. It reported that BMS had had severe technical problems with its smelter because of impurities in the ores and deficiencies in the plant design and equipment, so limiting the supply of acid to 110,000 tons in 1969 and a likely maximum of 190,000 tons eventually. BFL had long-term commitments relating to the transportation of phosphate rock and the Belledune dock and cessation of production might lead to repayment of the grant of $3.5 million. Sale of the company might, however, raise not much more than $1 million net towards repayment of the Bonds. On the basis of the report it was decided to continue operations.

A further $3 million was remitted by A&W in July. Although sales in 1969 reached 100,000 tons of DAP and the average selling price rose slightly, to $61, there was a loss before depreciation of nearly $2 million ($3.3 million after depreciation). Sale of the company was again considered by the A&W Board but rejected because of the requirement then to repay the Bonds and because Noranda offered to reduce the price of sulphuric acid from $11.60 to $4 per ton until the benefit amounted to 50% of the Preferred stock (subscribed by A&W) plus accrued interest. The lenders also agreed to defer the start of repayment of the Bonds from 1970 to 1975 and to relax the stipulations regarding working-capital. As stated in the 1969 A&W Annual Report, those actions "should avoid the need for any further remittances for the foreseeable future. There is, however, little prospect of the company becoming profitable for several years, and it has therefore been thought prudent to write $8,250,000 off the total investment of Can.$11,112,000".

The continuing losses in 1970, however, required the remittance of a further $0.9 million in the early part of the year. The terms of the Bonds were further amended in May, including an increase in the rate of interest to 9%. The loss in 1970 was $1.6 million before depreciation (nearly $3 million after); although there was some improvement in selling prices, to over $63, the tonnage sold fell to 86,000 because of a continued shortage of sulphuric acid. The A&W Board therefore decided to write off its remaining investment, by a provision of £1.1 million against reserves.

During 1971 further studies were made of the alternatives available. Finally in August the decision was taken to exit from BFL, as long as that could be done at no greater cost than the redemption of the Bonds. The Erco management was in favour of staying in BFL in the expectation that the cash flow would be neutral, a view supported by David Livingstone. The Chairman (then Sir Richard Powell - see page 157) was adamant, however, saying "I don't care - just get rid of it". Negotiations with Noranda eventually led to the sale of A&W's interest in April 1972 for just under $4 million, but with A&W providing the cash to repay the Bonds. The net cost, of £3,250,000, was provided in the 1971 accounts.

So, over a period of nearly 8 years, the senior management in Canada and the UK had expended much time and effort and cash of more than £7.5 million had been lost (excluding interest lost on the amounts invested and investment dollar premiums sacrificed[1]). There had been a defensive element in the original concept, a fear that another company might have intruded on Erco's position in industrial phosphates - just as had been argued when the investment was made at Port Maitland. When the BFL project was discussed with Fisons in March 1965, they said that they were aiming to reduce their fertiliser interests overseas but could understand that A&W might want to go ahead for defensive reasons.

Yet it is difficult not to conclude that the real driving force behind the project, which persisted despite the many setbacks and increasingly obvious problems, was

---

[1] At that time, under UK exchange controls, investment dollars (arising from investments or available for investment outside the UK) were at a premium; a condition for remittances by A&W to Canada was that A&W would lose any premium on realisation of its holding of Hooker Shares.

an ambition to expand Erco to become a major player in the North American, or at least the Canadian, industrial scene.

In addition to the Belledune project, that ambition manifested itself in the investments at Port Maitland and in Kinsley's proposal in December 1965 for a 15% investment in a $25 million venture by Quintana Petroleum in New Orleans to make phosphoric acid, triple superphosphate and DAP, which was not approved by the A&W Board. He also considered in 1965 collaboration with Shell in fertilisers in Western Canada and, in 1966, setting up a plant for roasting pyrites.

Those projects and ideas, however, and even the Belledune venture, were not of the same order of magnitude as the Long Harbour project, which became the major preoccupation of Albright & Wilson in this period.

Long Harbour

In the history of Albright & Wilson in the twentieth century, it is no exaggeration to say that the Long Harbour project was the key happening that determined the course of the Company's remaining existence.

Conception, design and construction

Towards the end of May 1965 Erco held its first Long Range Planning Conference, chaired by Ed Kinsley. Included in the plans was an ambition to make a public issue of 25% of the stock in Erco towards the end of 1967. The growth projected for the whole company was massive (as seems to be characteristic of long-range plans), with sales in 1975 more than five times those forecast for 1965. The growth in industrial phosphates, however, was expected to be much less rapid. The strategies included: "Halt further major expansion in phosphate through thermal process...Develop new phosphate chemicals and replace phosphate imports to offset thermal transfer to wet process".

Within days, the outlook changed fundamentally. The Newfoundland provincial government placed an advertisement in newspapers, including the British press, offering a large amount of power on long-term contract at a low price. The advertisement was seen by many in Albright & Wilson, including the members of a team that had been searching for a way to become more competitive in the production of phosphorus. The team, consisting of David Livingstone (Sales Director of Albright & Wilson (Mfg), the UK subsidiary then making phosphorus at Oldbury and Portishead), Basil Robbins (a senior engineer) and Peter Salmon (a senior accountant, later Finance Director, of that subsidiary) had looked at Pointe Noire, where a huge power scheme using the River Congo was being considered (but had not been implemented), and at Balangen in Norway, where a development with Norsk Hydro on a site north of the Arctic Circle was under serious consideration. The Newfoundland opportunity was attractive not only because of the power cost but also because there was the prospect of a location suitable for shipment in of phosphate rock and shipment out of phosphorus to America, the UK and the rest of the world.

David Livingstone wrote without delay to the Premier of Newfoundland, the Hon. Joseph Smallwood. An official brochure was sent promptly and on June 10th David wrote again, saying that A&W was interested in purchasing substantial quantities of power and giving an indication of requirements. A month later, the Premier telephoned (not a common occurrence in those days) to indicate the inducements on offer in addition to cheap power and urged that a representative should visit him personally.

A team from England comprising Alf Loveless (Chief Engineer of Albright & Wilson (Mfg)), Basil Robbins and Mark Maunsell went early in July to Toronto for discussions with the Erco team. Mark Maunsell, an industrial chemist, had joined Albright & Wilson in England in 1935 at the age of 22 and had gained experience of the phosphorus plants at Widnes and - briefly - at Oldbury, before moving to Australia in 1941. In Australia he built up a collection of articles on phosphorus production from American, French and German technical journals, the most important being a remarkable series of reports from the Tennessee Valley Authority, published in the journal "Chemical Engineering" in 1938. (As mentioned earlier, the Varennes furnaces were a TVA design, publicly available at negligible cost.) He was chiefly responsible for the design of the furnace built at Yarraville, Melbourne, in 1943. He became Technical Director of Albright & Wilson (Australia) and Works Manager at Yarraville in 1944. A second furnace was commissioned in 1954. During his time at Yarraville he succeeded in inventing a process for converting phosphorus to phosphoric acid (the "Maunsell burner") which was adopted at Port Maitland and at Kirkby. In 1954, he was transferred from Australia to Canada, as a Vice President and Technical Director, returning some years later to England.

At the meeting in Toronto, the Erco team was led by Ed Kinsley, Lloyd Lillico, Ed Bissaillon and Claude Hollands. Lloyd George Lillico, whose parents had emigrated to Canada from Britain, joined Erco in 1939 at the age of 20 as a laboratory technician. After moving into production, he had experience of the Buckingham furnaces before being transferred to Varennes as works manager (1957-1959). From there he moved to Toronto as General Manager - Production and then General Manager - Industrial Phosphates at the beginning of 1965, becoming a vice-president later in the year. Ed Bissaillon had joined Erco in December 1963 as Manager of the Technical Division (see p.96). Claude Hollands came to A&W in 1949, aged 23, as assistant cost accountant and became Group

Cost Accountant; he moved to Erco as Treasurer in 1959 and was appointed Vice-President - Administration in 1965. The joint team thus included experience in phosphorus production and accounting expertise.

The team looked at five possible courses of action:

• to continue to run the phosphorus plants at Varennes and Portishead without further modification
• to uprate Portishead and run Varennes at a reduced rate
• to build in Newfoundland and continue with Varennes but shut Portishead
• to concentrate all production in Newfoundland
• to concentrate all production at Varennes.

Preliminary conclusions, based on an estimated power cost at both Newfoundland and Varennes of 3 mills (i.e. 0.3 cents per kwh), were that the cheapest course would be to concentrate in Newfoundland, with Varennes slightly more expensive because of the assumed absence of grants there.

The matters to be considered were set out in a report from Basil Robbins early in September: site, raw materials (choice of materials and feed preparation), furnace design (scale-up of Portishead or a Tennessee Valley Authority design), electrode suspension (rope and winch or hydraulic), electrodes (premachined graphite or Soderberg paste), precipitators (single or dual, mechanical or electrical, plate or tube), mud treatment (refurnace or neutralise), effluent (treatment to meet local standards for gaseous and liquid effluent), slag (dig out and dump or granulate and pump), design responsibility (Erco or A&W (Mfg) or both or external). These were the vital elements that were to have an immense importance for the Company in the years ahead.

Later in September the A&W Board authorised the expenditure of £10,000 for studies of the possibility of making phosphorus in Newfoundland. Soon afterwards Kinsley, Lillico and Bissaillon visited Newfoundland. They were shown possible sites in Placentia Bay, on the south-east of the island, about 70 miles from the capital, St John's. The location was well placed for shipping and was stated to be ice-free at all times; it was also close to a deposit of silica, one of the three raw materials required. A power cost of 2.5 mills was mentioned (which compared favourably with a cost of 4.45 mills quoted by Quebec Hydro for expansion at Varennes).

The estimated capital cost for a plant to produce 115 million lbs per annum was just under 30 million Canadian dollars (£10 million), including £1.5 million for a phosphorus carrier and $0.45 million for an effluent plant. The estimates had been pared down through savings on the pelletising plant and the elimination of a phosphate rock store, a process control computer and fume stacks. Consequently the saving in capital cost by instead raising Varennes capacity to 115 million lbs was estimated to be only $4 million, which would be paid back by cost savings in Newfoundland in 4 years. There was some concern that the surrounding hills would cause atmospheric pollution but it was reported that "No present regulations exist for either air or water pollution and discussions with authorities would suggest that our operations would be well below tolerable limits for some time to come". Even for the perhaps less environmentally-conscious 1970s, that statement appears at best blinkered optimism.

The party came away keen to proceed: "extremely favourably impressed... waxing very enthusiastic". It was found that there had been visits by Grace and by Kaiser Aluminum; the first posed a threat of the manufacture of phosphorus and phosphates, while the second would have a power requirement of the same order as that required for phosphorus furnaces. "We should complete our assessment with the minimum of delay" it was said. Kinsley wanted to take an option on the favoured site in Placentia Bay and to back it with a stake in a phosphate mine in the Carolinas and the building of a 30,000 ton carrier for the phosphate rock. He envisaged the manufacture in Newfoundland of industrial phosphates and sodium chlorate.

The Company was sufficiently convinced of the possibility of building a new phosphorus plant to issue a Press notice at the beginning of November 1965, saying: "Albright & Wilson Ltd announces that its subsidiary, Electric Reduction Company of Canada Ltd, plans to build large new electric furnace capacity for the production of elemental phosphorus in Eastern Canada. The selection of a suitable site is now under active consideration".

The first known mention of the name Long Harbour was in a note by Wilson Carter (Chairman of Albright & Wilson Mfg) in November concerning the source of power. A hydro plant was to be built at Baie d'Espoir, on the southern coast of Newfoundland; the first stage would deliver power in March 1967, with a second stage in 1969. There was also an expectation that huge quantities of power would be available from the Churchill Falls in 1971; the price of 2.5 mills was based on averaging the forecast costs of power from Baie d'Espoir and Churchill Falls.

Towards the end of November, the Premier of Newfoundland (usually referred to as Joey Smallwood) visited London and met Sir Sydney, Sir Owen, Wilson Carter, Vic Sherwood and Forrest Musgrave. The upshot of the meeting was an option, until 30.5.66, for power at 2.5 mills for 25 years, on a take-or-pay basis for the first 80 MW, and a grant of 200 acres of land.

In a report in January 1966 Kinsley raised his sights to propose initial output of 145 million lbs per annum, rising to 200 million over 10 years, and even suggested that the initial output might be 200 million lbs, with surplus being sold for fertilisers. He firmly believed that the price of sulphur would rise significantly, putting wet phosphoric acid at a disadvantage against acid from phosphorus. For a capacity of 145 million lbs, he proposed two 60 MW furnaces; the cost for the larger plant was estimated at $33 million, not including a ship. (Three such furnaces would be required for 200 million lbs per annum.)

The capital cost was based on some significant assumptions concerning effluents from the plant. Fluorine emitted from the pelletising plant, amounting to 15,000 tons per annum, would be discharged via wet scrubbers to the sea. Although phosphorus lost in dust would amount to 2% of the phosphorus present in the raw material, it was "not considered economic to design for negligible dust losses in the initial installation". And although the capital cost estimate included provision for recovering phosphorus from mud, there was an option to save $1 million by discharging phosphorus to the sea, amounting to 0.2-0.5% of the input phosphorus (i.e. 30,000-70,000 lbs per annum).

Regarding the chosen location, Kinsley wrote: "For persons accustomed to living in small towns, the Long Harbour site seems to be ideally situated...The temperature...would not appear to be a disadvantage as far as hiring Easterners is concerned...for those people who like out-of-door sports such as fishing and sailing, facilities would be excellent...people can travel from St John's to Long Harbour...on as good a road as is likely to be found anywhere in Canada". The adverse climate and isolation experienced by those who were subsequently at Long Harbour gave the lie to that description.

The conclusion of the report was that "a large phosphorus plant in Newfoundland is not only feasible, but would also return to the investment profits at least above "standard", with the probability of reaching a very attractive level". The return then quoted, assuming government grants and based on a 15 year life, was 13-16%.

There was some disagreement on the management of the planning of the Long Harbour project. Wilson Carter wanted Mark Maunsell, as the person with the most extensive knowledge of phosphorus, to head the planning team but Ed Kinsley wanted the direction to be based in Canada. In the event, Ernest Brazier, from the A&W (Mfg) engineering department, was appointed project manager, reporting to Ed Bissaillon. Mark Maunsell's role was to be in design. Lloyd Lillico was to plan and organise the operational and commercial aspects and Wilson Carter would deal with the ships. There would be a review group representing both sides and Wilson Carter would make reports to the Albright & Wilson Board.

One of the major issues raised at that stage was whether to go outside the A&W group for the design and construction of the plant. Wilson Carter at an early stage suggested that the contract be placed with Uhde, a subsidiary of Hoechst. Keith Piercy and John Christopherson supported that view. In February 1966, Carter and Sir Owen visited Knapsack Griesheim, the phosphorus producer within the

Hoechst group, for which Uhde had built a 50 MW furnace. Uhde had also recently built a phosphorus complex for the Russians at Chemkent. Knapsack at that time was considering building furnaces in Holland using power from offshore natural gas. It was thought possible that they would want their own furnace at Long Harbour, and would invest in a joint company, but because of the project in Holland that proved to be of no interest to them. In any event, however, they were interested in providing technical assistance through Uhde.

The Uhde technology used Soderberg electrodes, formed by feeding carbon paste, about 2 metres at a time, into steel tubes on the top of the furnace, while the furnace was running. The furnace was a relatively small rounded triangle accommodating three electrodes, with continuous tapping and granulation of the slag, two large precipitators per furnace and a pelletised feed - all features very different from the Albright & Wilson experience. There was a clean, fume-free, atmosphere on top of the furnace, in contrast to the typical A&W furnace top, with flaming gas, smoke, dust and heat. Removal of the slag, granulated through discharge into water, was simple and with little or no fume, whereas the A&W practice was to tap into pits, with much fume, and then to dig out the pits with large excavators.

Uhde was therefore asked to quote for a plant to make 145 million lbs per annum with ancillaries to cope with a possible later expansion to 200 million lbs. Uhde's quotation, based on two standard 50 MW furnaces, was $51.84 million, including a fee of $2 million, taxes and duty of $4.9 million and a contingency of $1.3 million. Bissaillon then looked for a North American quotation to compare with Uhde - there had earlier been an approach from the contractor that had recently built a 45 MW plant for Virginia Carolina - but there is no evidence of a quotation from any other contractor. In the end, therefore, the comparison was between Uhde and in-house design and project management.

The estimated cost quoted by Erco for the plant, including a $2 million contingency but excluding the ships and Portishead and Port Maitland terminal costs, and before taking into account government grants, was $36 million. The difference from the Uhde quotation of nearly $52 million was such that Erco was able to conclude: "This large difference in capital cost precludes further consideration of the Uhde proposal since the extra capital expenditure would result in a maximum reduction of $750,000 per year in operating expenses". The conclusion was accepted by the A&W Board, to whom the claimed capital cost savings outweighed the risk of a design with no supporting track record.

The principal responsibility for the in-house design of the furnaces was put into the hands of Mark Maunsell. Although Mark Maunsell was one of the most experienced people in A&W in phosphorus furnace design and operation, he had been involved only with small and simple furnaces. Both the furnaces at Yarraville were small (2 MW) and uncomplicated. There were no electrostatic precipitators to remove the dust from the furnace gases because Mark Maunsell calculated that the power requirements would make them uneconomic. Nor was there equipment for preparation of the furnace feed, or pumps for furnace gas control. Experiments for the granulation of slag were abandoned and effluent controls were slight. Good operation of the Australian furnaces depended very much on the experience of the operators and consultation with Maunsell.

Drawing on his experience he designed two circular furnaces, each of 60 MW capacity. The 'White Book' produced by Erco in April 1966, which constituted the request for approval by the A&W Board, said that his design "represents a modest and carefully calculated extension of modern design criteria used in two recent U.S. furnaces...Compares closely to the rounded triangle design of the latest German furnaces". In fact, the "modest extension" meant that the furnaces would be the largest phosphorus furnaces in the world and very much larger than any furnaces previously built by A&W. The largest for A&W hitherto were the three uprated Portishead furnaces, which had a rated capacity of 14-15 MW, the other Portishead furnaces having a rating of 10 MW. While the 10 MW furnaces ran quite well, the uprated ones never operated at full load (see page 27), only occasionally achieving 10-12 MW. Thus, for A&W, the Long Harbour furnaces represented a tremendous leap forward.

The furnaces for Long Harbour were designed with an external diameter of 43 feet and an internal diameter of 35'6" and a height above the carbon blocks of the hearth of nearly 21'. Initially there were to be three electrodes with a diameter of 60 inches. Later, towards the end of 1967, it was decided that the diameter of the electrodes should be reduced to 55 inches; the decision seems to have been taken because of the experience of Monsanto, which had found that 60" preformed carbon electrodes were unmanageable and had reduced them similarly. The problem for Long Harbour then was that the furnaces were even more oversized than in the original design; the feed to the furnaces was not fully melted throughout and that contributed to difficulties with the electrodes, offtake gas temperatures and slag tapping. A later rebuild of the furnaces, bringing the electrodes closer together, improved conditions in the centre of the furnaces but did not deal with incomplete melting at the walls.

The Uhde furnaces built at Vlissingen in Holland in 1968-70, although rated at 60 MW and having Soderberg electrodes with a diameter of 1.5 metres (59") were much smaller and rounded triangles rather then circular and did not have a problem of melting the furnace burden. The Varennes TVA-design furnaces were not circular and much shallower and also did not suffer from the blockages experienced at Portishead and Long Harbour.

The aspect of the design that was later to receive the greatest attention and criticism was the method of suspending the electrodes. Ernest Brazier, the Project

Manager, recommended hydraulic suspension, made by Lectromelt. Many other furnaces used rigid suspension by Lectromelt but this was the first instance of its use for a phosphorus furnace. The expected advantage of hydraulic suspension over the usual rope suspension was that it would enable the electrodes to be raised and lowered more simply without lateral movement and would reduce downtime. In order to accommodate the mechanism for the movement of the electrodes, free of the clutter of feed chutes, etc. on the furnace top, there was a stack of 7 electrode pieces, which was 58 feet high and weighed 58 tons (against 22 feet and 9 tons at Varennes). For the suspension system to succeed, the hydraulic mechanism and clamps had to work well, conditions within the furnace had to be such as not to cause lateral movement in the electrode stack and the electrodes themselves had to be well cast and machined so as to fit together perfectly - tolerances were much lower than with rope suspension. Although Soderberg electrodes were also held rigidly, their formation in situ, their short length and stable furnace conditions avoided the sort of problems encountered at Long Harbour.

The third major feature in the design was the feed preparation and delivery to the furnaces. The initial design for preparation of the phosphate rock input was a compacting plant (a concept similar to that tried at Portishead). The idea eventually adopted was a pelletising plant, made by Allis-Chalmers, of a type not previously used by A&W. The pellets were to be made by feeding a mixture of ground phosphate rock and water to pans of 18 ft diameter. The plant was to require considerable modification before eventually satisfactory pellets were consistently produced. Tens of thousands of tons of reject material were produced, which took nine years to rework. The design for feeding the phosphate pellets, silica and coke to the furnaces was a sophisticated arrangement of pneumatically operated slide valves, also new to A&W. One of the valves jammed on the first day of operation because of a shortage of compressed air; the whole system was then by-passed and never used again.

Another innovation for A&W was the design of the electrostatic precipitators, which were intended to remove dust entrained in the gas from the furnaces and so to minimise the creation of phosphorus-containing mud. The Varennes precipitators were sturdy simple plates, whereas the (purchased) Long Harbour design was for theoretically more efficient jacketed tubes, whose effective operation depended on avoiding excessive gas temperatures and preventing the ingress of air leading to corrosion by phosphoric acid. Once again, the attempt to make improvements through adopting technology untried by A&W was to prove unwise. The risk of failure was increased by the flimsiness of the mild steel tubes; testing before the plant was commissioned revealed leaks hat several crews of welders working round the clock for weeks were unable to cure entirely.

As work on the design proceeded, strenuous efforts were made to keep the estimated cost within the figure originally quoted. Economies were made, including reducing the size of both the pelletising and furnace buildings and changing to mild instead of stainless steel in gas lines and other parts of the plant. The effluent treatment plant was eliminated, allowing untreated discharge into the sea.

The White Book of April 1966 (see page 125) did not conceal that there would be discharges to sea and atmosphere of phosphorus, fluorine, dust losses in handling raw materials (estimated at 2%) and gases from furnace tapping. While it was planned to dump slag on land and in the surrounding coves for some years, it was envisaged that it would later be dumped in Placentia Bay. "Mud production", the report stated, "will be minimized and, it is hoped, all mud will be returned to the furnaces". (In practice, the failure of the precipitators and the unwillingness to risk refurnacing mud after an explosion at Varennes meant that there was a great deal of mud to dispose of.) It was assumed that the dilution of effluents in the sea and atmosphere would be enough to avoid problems. The assumption regarding dilution in the sea was unfortunately not based on any scientific evaluation: three years later, there was a meeting with Dr Leslie Cooper, consultant oceanographer to ICI, who stated that the choice of Long Harbour for the plant was unfortunate because there was poor flushing in the bay and little water flow into it from brooks; moreover, fine particulate phosphorus would not settle out and so there would be an accumulation in the local fishing grounds.

The profitability calculated for the project, as reported in the White Book, was a somewhat complex calculation, taking credit for capital saved through not expanding at Varennes and Portishead, allowing for Federal and Provincial Government financial assistance and assuming that 7.5% of the output would be sold for fertilisers in the UK. It was claimed that the calculation understated the return because of a "conservative approach to opportunities for savings and growth in business". The calculated rate of return (internal rate of return, by a discounted cash flow evaluation) was 12%, over 15 years, with a pay-back of investment in 4 years from start-up.

A week after the issue of the White Book a large meeting was convened at short notice at Fleatham House, Marchon's guest house near the Whitehaven factory, to consider the Long Harbour project, particularly in comparison with expanding in wet acid. The meeting was attended by about 60 representatives from Marchon, Albright & Wilson (Mfg), Erco and ACC, including Frank Schon and the other senior executives of Marchon, Mark Maunsell and Ernest Brazier of the design team, and David Anthony (Managing Director of A&W Mfg) and his senior phosphorus technical staff.

An appendix to the White Book (written by Bob Dickie of Marchon) described progress on obtaining an exclusive licence for the UK, Canada and Australia for the process for purifying wet phosphoric acid developed by Dr Baniel of IMI (Israel

Mining Industries), for which patents were pending. Frank Schon and others had recently visited Israel, where a programme had been agreed for constructing a bench unit followed by a pilot plant at Whitehaven. At the conference it was argued that the wet route should be pursued in preference to making a major investment in a phosphorus plant. It was agreed that 7 million lbs of the 64 million lbs UK requirement for phosphorus could be replaced by wet acid without difficulty; to replace a further 30 million lbs would require further development work.

Nevertheless, as reported to the Board of Albright & Wilson Ltd, "the consensus of those present was in favour of the Newfoundland project proceeding". One of those present, Alan Williams (whose work on the purification of wet phosphoric acid for most of the next 30 years was recognised by the award of the MBE in 1997 see page 209), has described how he had the impression that the result of the meeting had been pre-determined. The main arguments put forward for proceeding with the Newfoundland project were:

- it would be unwise to miss the opportunity of obtaining exceptionally cheap power (which might be taken up by a competitor)
- the forecast 4-year payback on the project meant that even if wet acid displaced a significant part of the phosphorus requirement it would not happen until the investment had been recouped
- surplus phosphorus could always be sold for fertiliser use
- (to quote the White Book) "Failure to build additional capacity because present locations are uneconomical would only result in a steady erosion of our present business"
- the project was profitable and the return had been conservatively estimated.

It is interesting to note that the White Book included a table showing that the estimated cost of phosphorus delivered to the UK from Newfoundland (including duty under the Common Market external tariff) would be a little higher than was estimated from the planned Uhde plant in Holland. It was, however argued that "Newfoundland costs are conservative" - which perhaps is why the summary of the report on its first page claimed "this investment will provide the lowest cost source of phosphorus in the world".

The report went on to say "If we are to continue as a major world supplier of phosphorus compounds we can tolerate the purchase of elemental phosphorus only as an intermediate measure until additional capacity can be justified". Certainly at that time the trend in the chemical industry was to become more basic in raw materials, i.e. to manufacture or own the source of the materials rather than rely on purchasing them. There were some voices opposing that view - as featured in the defence mounted by Courtaulds against the bid by ICI - but the move to concentrating on downstream development (i.e. purchasing basic materials and making speciality products) did not become general for another two decades.

In the two weeks following the conference at Whitehaven, there were several meetings in London, including two meetings of the A&W Board. Among points discussed at some length was whether it would be possible to obtain power in the UK at a low enough price to make continued production of phosphorus economical. John Hutton-Wilson (who was not present but gave his views in writing) and Frank Schon urged that attempts should be made to persuade the Government that concessions should be made in order not to lose an important domestic manufacture. Sir Owen Wansbrough-Jones had spoken to the Department of Economic Affairs, the Gas Council, the Atomic Energy Authority and the Central Electricity Generating Board but had been unable to secure any offer of power at a competitive price for at least the next 6 years, by which time A&W believed the Long Harbour project would have paid for itself.

The sources of funds for the project were also considered. Apart from paying for the two phosphorus carriers, it was expected that no finance would be required from the UK, since the whole of the Long Harbour cost would be met by borrowing in North America and by government grants. Some of the borrowing would be guaranteed by the Province and some probably by Albright & Wilson Ltd.

In 1966 UK exchange controls were still in force. It was therefore necessary to get the consent of the Bank of England and the Treasury to allow the investment in Canada and a guarantee by Albright & Wilson Ltd of part of the borrowing. That involved convincing them that continued manufacture of phosphorus in the UK was not economic, that there would not be a substantial adverse effect on the balance of payments and that the Long Harbour project was sound. The necessary consents were given. The Company demonstrated that although the importation of phosphorus would involve a greater expenditure of foreign exchange than importing phosphate rock, imports of products from competitors would be prevented and exports would be increased. There would also be an inflow of dividends from Erco based on the profits from Long Harbour.

Before the A&W Board met to take a final decision on the Long Harbour project, one other crucial aspect was discussed at a meeting of the Chairman with Wilson Carter, Ed Kinsley and Vic Sherwood plus Mark Maunsell and Ed Bissaillon. Sir Sydney Barratt asked whether they were convinced that there was sufficient know-how in A&W/Erco to build such large furnaces. Mark Maunsell assured him that the design was "on the conservative side" and the furnaces might be operated at 25% above the designed load. Wilson Carter said that the necessary know-how for the electrode suspension system was being bought and Mark Maunsell said that it had been proved by the suppliers. Ed Bissaillon claimed that there should be no difficulties with the pelletising system.

Another question asked at that meeting was whether the economics of the project would be affected by a devaluation of sterling. The answer given was that no allowance for such a contingency should be made since if there were a devaluation against the dollar it would be only temporary, as the dollar would itself be devalued almost immediately in line with sterling. Eighteen months later sterling was devalued from 2.80 to 2.40 dollars, with no subsequent recovery.

When the Board met on 25th May 1966 to take a decision on the Long Harbour project, Frank Schon attempted to block the proposal. He acknowledged the advantages of cheap power and governmental incentives but was not convinced that the possibilities for cheaper power in the UK had been fully explored and in any case believed that the major part of the UK's phosphorus requirements could be met by upgraded wet acid. He did not agree that sulphur prices were as high as generally quoted and would rise and suggested that while further development work was being done on upgrading wet acid there could be a short-term arrangement with Knapsack. Since, however, he was the only Director present who doubted the wisdom of the scheme he was prepared to accept the otherwise unanimous decision. (John Hutton-Wilson, who also was not in favour of the project, was not present.) So it was resolved to proceed with the building of the plant, to guarantee loans up to $15 million and to allow Erco to enter into a take-or-pay contract for electric power for 25 years from start-up.

Two days later, a Press release announced that a $40 million plant was to be built at Long Harbour and that agreement had been reached on a 25-year contract for the supply of power. Production was planned to begin in 1968. The lack of unanimity at Board level, however, persisted. At the June Board meeting, John Hutton-Wilson said that if he had been present at the previous meeting he would have voted against the Long Harbour project. Frank Schon put forward a proposal for spending £20 million at Whitehaven to expand the capacity for sulphuric acid and cement instead of building at Long Harbour.

Early in July Schon wrote to Sir Owen Wansbrough-Jones to say that at a meeting of Marchon and ACC there was a unanimous conclusion that the Newfoundland project should be re-examined; he proposed that there should be a moratorium on any further commitments associated with the project. A day later, John Hutton-Wilson also wrote to Sir Owen, saying: "Inconvenient though it may be I find it impossible not to reopen with you the question of the desirability or otherwise of proceeding with the Newfoundland project...I am convinced that there may be a practical alternative to the Newfoundland phosphorus scheme that might, for considerably less investment, give better financial returns whilst at the same time setting the scene for a better balanced and more advanced future operating pattern, both technologically and economically in the context of the overall phosphate interests of the Group, i.e. Baniel" (the wet acid process referred to on p.127).

He suggested that the use of wet acid in Canada would mean that the UK could have its residual phosphorus requirements supplied from Varennes. With the appropriate amount of technical effort and determination, he thought that the necessary upgrading process could be achieved before the Newfoundland plant could be commissioned. "The Baniel process is far more advanced than I had previously been led to believe", he wrote, "and in all the circumstances I consider that we should be guilty of burying our heads in the sand if we were to go headlong into Newfoundland without first conducting a thorough, unbiased and single-minded appraisal of the Baniel process and its potential as a practical alternative to the Newfoundland project". He added that this was "a matter that, rightly or wrongly, I believe to be of the utmost significance to the future of the A&W Group". He asked that his and Schon's letters should be circulated to the other Directors.

As a result of the stand taken by Schon and Hutton-Wilson, a meeting was held a few days later, attended by all of the executive Directors except Keith Piercy and by staff from the UK. At the meeting, Ed Lopker (Marchon's technical consultant on phosphoric acid and the designer of its most recent phosphoric acid plant) spoke in detail on his criticisms of the Long Harbour project:

- the costs of manufacture at Long Harbour were inaccurate and the estimated costs of competitors were overstated
- experience (by Monsanto and the Farmers' Cooperative) had shown the difficulty of a major scale-up of phosphorus furnaces and to move from 18 MW to 60 MW was impracticable, with the prospect of having to pay for power while the furnaces were not operating
- he did not believe that the rail link to Long Harbour would ever be built
- he doubted that the case for the full expected grants would be accepted
- the assumptions regarding the use of phosphorus for fertiliser acid were unsound and a large excess of phosphoric acid in the USA was impending
- Port Maitland's location made it vulnerable to competition from Florida producers in fertilisers
- the assumed future price for sulphur was too high
- he expected that wet acid upgrading processes would be developed in the USA and elsewhere.

It was decided to refer some of the questions to Arthur D. Little, which had been commissioned to produce a feasibility study for potential lenders, and to cost an alternative based on centralising phosphorus production at Varennes and maximising the use of wet acid in industrial phosphates. Regarding the technology, Sir Owen reported to the Board "We see no way of getting further outside information on technology and are content to rely on the joint recommendations of WC (Carter), AHL (Loveless), EJB (Bissaillon) and RMOM (Maunsell)".

A further meeting was held a month later, over a period of three days, attended by all the executive Directors and staff from Canada and the UK. Consideration was given to the prospects for general adoption of the wet acid route to phosphates and the impact on markets for phosphorus if that were to happen. Such a possibility was, however, thought to be several years away. The soundness of the Long Harbour project was again questioned but the minutes of the meeting record that "The meeting was assured that we have the design information and know-how to build the furnaces, and that doubts which have been expressed on that score are unfounded. Thus there is no necessity to take the more expensive design quoted by Uhde". The meeting ended with a statement by Sir Sydney that his survey showed that 70% of those present at the meeting (16 out of 23) were in favour of proceeding with the Newfoundland scheme (given the composition of the attendance, that was not surprising) and that he would recommend to the Board that it should proceed. He added that "he personally agreed it was essential if A&W were to hold their international position in the phosphorus and P2O5 world". A supplementary conclusion was that further development work on acid cleaning processes should continue and be encouraged. (What actually happened was that the work was run down until it was reactivated five years later.)

Argument rumbled on. At the Board meeting after the 3-day meeting, Schon and Hutton-Wilson said that the review had not caused them to change their minds. The power agreement was, however, signed without conditions except that Erco could cancel it prior to 1st December 1966 and the Premier of Newfoundland, Joey Smallwood, turned the first sod at the end of August. It was confirmed that Albright & Wilson Ltd would be required to guarantee $25 million of the borrowing by Erco.

The Arthur D. Little report was issued in October. Among its conclusions were: "plans are sound...in general agreement with both the capital requirements and the operating costs...The design for the two 60,000 megawatt (sic) furnaces is adequate and no unusual startup problems should be anticipated...(the plant should be) capable of producing at least the 145 million pounds of elemental phosphorus projected...In looking at design questions, we emphasized the critical areas of the furnace electrodes and feed preparation...While the two furnaces are large in comparison to most operating elsewhere today, there are other large furnaces in existence and we anticipate no difficulty with the design and size as proposed by Erco".

The report went on to refer to the threat that phosphates in detergents would be replaced because of concern that they could contribute to problems arising from the discharge of sewage into lakes, giving rise to eutrophication (the growth of algae and resulting oxygen starvation in the water). The report stated: "Substitution for phosphate builders is unlikely soon...In the unlikely event that there is a partial reduction in the use of phosphorus detergent builders, Erco has the ability to move the quantity of phosphorus in the form of phosphoric acid to other markets under its control such as animal feed supplements and fertilisers". (As will be described later, the reduction did occur and was severe.) The report also claimed that the phosphorus producers in Idaho and Tennessee (which also benefited from cheap power) would be at a competitive disadvantage against Long Harbour in supplying Eastern Canada and that there would be a cost advantage over Holland in phosphorus delivered to the UK (which was contrary to A&W's own earlier estimates).

During the A.D. Little investigation, David Livingstone wrote to Ed Kinsley to report on the information given to the investigators concerning the forecast growth in UK demand for phosphorus (assuming that wet acid would be used only for sodium tripolyphosphate and fertilisers). He said: "I was glad...that I was able to unleash a series of enthusiastic export and home salesmen on to them, all convinced that the figures were conservative...various new doubts and speculations have been raised at the Parent Company Board concerning the validity of the Newfoundland calculations. I would like you to know that the whole of Mfg is solidly behind the proposition, that our estimates and calculations are soundly based and have not been upset, and that we are eager to go with the minimum delay". He said that there was no cost advantage in purified wet acid and that the purest grades so far produced would not replace more than 20% of the consumption of phosphorus. He added "we shall produce the cheapest phosphorus in the world".

A summary of the Arthur D. Little report was distributed to the A&W Board but was not discussed.

The A&W Board also commissioned a risk analysis from McKinsey & Co. in June 1966. The procedure was to list all the factors expected to influence the profitability of the project and then to ask all those deemed to have knowledge of the factors to assign probabilities to the range of possible outcomes. The factors included capital costs, raw material costs, operating savings, transport costs, demand for the product, exchange rates, tariffs and process efficiency (i.e. recovery of phosphorus from the phosphate rock input). Surprisingly, the analysis did not cover aspects of technology, i.e. the probability of the plant working as designed.

When the decision to go ahead with a risk analysis was taken, Sir Owen wrote to Kinsley to reassure him, saying: "McKinsey & Co. know that our commitment in this project is such that we go forward, provided the conditions precedent that we have set are fulfilled, and that it would be very difficult to give effect to any adverse findings this technique produced. I am being perhaps a bit provocative but if adverse finds did emerge I would personally suspect either the technique or, more probably, the input...I repeat that McKinsey & Co. know that the Board decision has been taken, that commitments have been entered, and that withdrawal from these is not at our option". In the light of Sir Owen's remarks it is difficult to understand why the work was commissioned.

The McKinsey report in October 1966 concluded that going ahead with Long Harbour or maximising purified wet acid or buying from Hoechst or buying from Hoechst until 1972 (when cheaper power might be available in the UK and wet acid purification should have been developed) were all courses better than staying at Portishead and expanding Varennes, since that course implied "acceptance of a gradually deteriorating position in the world phosphorus industry". Devaluation of sterling by 15% was almost certain and would seriously depress the return from the Long Harbour project but there were possible offsets - an early start-up, a higher capacity than allowed for, a higher price for sales of phosphorus for fertilisers in the USA. Even without devaluation, McKinsey rated purchasing phosphorus from Hoechst ahead of Long Harbour. Going ahead with Long Harbour would impose considerable capital stringency on the whole A&W Group but Sir Owen had indicated that strategic considerations outweighed the financial ones and on that basis McKinsey concluded that the Long Harbour project should proceed. The risk analysis showed that the most likely return from the project, assuming no devaluation, was 12% (internal rate of return, by discounted cash flow) with a payback period of 4 years after start-up - which endorsed the estimate in the White Book.

McLeod, Young, Weir and White, Weld (the Canadian and US finance houses advising on the financing of the Long Harbour project) also produced a report in October 1966, which concluded that the plans were sound and included the statements: "No air or water pollution problems with regulatory groups are likely...no unusual startup problems should be anticipated. We further believe that two furnaces will be capable of producing at least the 145 million pounds of elemental phosphorus projected by the company...In looking at design questions, we emphasized the critical areas of the furnace electrodes and feed preparation...we anticipate no difficulty with the design and size as proposed by Erco. We...concluded the proposed equipment to be adequate...In our opinion the design and engineering work done to date by the company has been conservative...the Newfoundland operation would have a cost advantage over that produced on the Continent and delivered to the United Kingdom".

Despite this succession of favourable reports, Schon and Hutton-Wilson tried again, at the November Board meeting, to have the Long Harbour project deferred for 12 months while there was further investigation of the possibility of building a plant in a UK Development Area with power at a lower price. The Board of Trade had indicated that power might be available in 1972 at 0.4d per kwh, although no-one was prepared to give a firm undertaking. All the other Directors, however, thought that "Newfoundland presented a unique opportunity". So it was confirmed that the project should go ahead, subject to finance being arranged. Finding lenders was proving difficult and so an attempt would be made to extend the deadline for confirming acceptance of the power contract by two months. The Erco Board favoured accepting the power contract even if all the financing had not been arranged but Sir Sydney decided that it should be cancelled if the acceptance period could not be extended, since the contract would involve a minimum payment of £500,000 per annum from 1st January 1969. The extension was forthcoming.

Disagreement at Board level continued. In February 1967, Sir Frank again stated that he was not in favour of the project because of the commercial and technical risks. At the next Board meeting it was reported that the Highlands & Islands Development Board (Scotland) was offering power in 1971 at 0.34d. per kwh, with an interim price of 0.55d; that would result in phosphorus cheaper than Long Harbour phosphorus landed in the UK after a 9% duty. Kinsley said that if phosphorus were produced in the UK the Long Harbour output could be sold for fertilisers. It was agreed to place major contracts for Long Harbour and for the phosphorus carriers and Portishead terminal. Sir Frank again disagreed with the decisions. When at the meeting in April it was decided, on the advice of Hill Samuel (the merchant bank advising A&W), to confirm the power agreement, Sir Frank abstained from voting (Hutton-Wilson was not present).

Matters came to a head in May 1967, when Sir Frank resigned from the Board and from the Company. The disagreement on the Long Harbour project was, however, not the only reason for his resignation; the background to his departure is described in a later section of this chapter ("The departure of Frank Schon").

At the Board meeting in May 1967, the project was approved unconditionally, although there had been some unfavourable changes from the White Book details. The change in the rock preparation plant, from compaction to pelletising, added $1 million to the cost and a separate grant for the plant was refused. The government would also no longer provide the dock free but made a loan, repayable over 25 years. The ships were to cost more and the cost of moving phosphorus to Port Maitland would be higher. Site work had been delayed by severe weather. The cost of the Long Harbour plant was nevertheless held, despite the increase in the cost of the rock preparation plant, through economies in other items. The estimated return for the project was reduced from 12% to 11.5%. That depended on a start-up before the end of 1968, with production of 23 million lbs in 1968, 117 million in 1969 and 140 million (63,500 tonnes) per annum thereafter. At that level, half the output would be used in fertilisers and in spot sales.

While design and construction proceeded, there were further unfavourable developments. The devaluation of sterling was not followed by a restoration of the rate against the dollar. Some sales prospects cooled because of low-priced wet acid. Serious production difficulties at Portishead led to the decision to continue production at Oldbury, whose furnaces had been due to close at the end of 1967.

There were numerous failures in commissioning the industrial phosphates plant at Port Maitland, one of the main future users of Erco's phosphorus, because of economies in design and construction costs, and a 15% cost overrun was authorised to remedy the problems, which included corrosion and poor quality product.

Ed Kinsley's confidence was nevertheless sufficient for him to propose a 10-year take-or-pay contract for the shipment of phosphate rock for both Long Harbour and Belledune (which had not yet been commissioned). Although the A&W Board wanted to delay any contract until the Long Harbour plant was in operation, a contract was authorised in March 1968 by Sir Owen (who was by then Chairman) with Kinsley, Carter and Sherwood. It was to prove impossible to fulfil and expensive to abrogate.

The two phosphorus carriers were launched in 1968, the Albright Pioneer with a capacity for 5,000 tons of phosphorus and the Albright Explorer with half that capacity but designed for the full 5,000 tons if required. The ships were unique, a vital element in the whole Long Harbour strategy and performed well. Another positive step was the completion of financing, in August 1967, through borrowing in Canada and the USA a total of $40 million, $15 million guaranteed by the Province and $25 million by A&W, including its subsidiaries.

In an article in the Albright Magazine in August 1967, Mike Hyde, the Editor of Chemical Age, commented on the experience of ICI and others in bringing large chemical plants on stream and wrote: "The benefits to a company that can bring a big single-stream plant on stream without too much delay and get it operating at near to maximum capacity as quickly as possible are enormous. A&W's new phosphorus capacity in Newfoundland comes into this category - the potential benefits outweigh the disadvantages in scale-up. As ICI have found the snags of 'putting all your eggs in one basket' can be critical...Clearly, any chemical company building big needs iron nerves and a willingness to take the calculated risk. But to paraphrase Phelps 'the man who doesn't make mistakes, doesn't make anything'". Nearly two years later, in June 1969, he wrote: "There are not many companies in the medium-sized range that can afford to make a mistake on a £20 million project...That doubtless explains the cautious, conservative approach of the smaller producers to very large projects. It also explains why they tend to do their homework so much better than the big boys".

The Review by the Chairman in the Annual Report of Albright & Wilson Ltd for 1967, written in March 1968, contained the sentence "The full impact on profits of the Newfoundland project will not be felt until 1969". At the time that appeared to be a statement of the obvious but it later acquired a wholly negative meaning not envisaged then. The Report also stated that construction was on schedule, for one furnace to be completed in September 1968 and the second two months later.

The design work for Long Harbour was carried out in Florida. In September 1966 a majority share in Gulf Design Corporation, of Lakeland, Florida, was acquired by Erco; Kinsley became Chairman, while the founders of the company, Gene Sikora and Ed Taylor, continued as President and Executive Vice-President. Gulf Design had experience in designing and constructing industrial plants and had just completed one of the world's largest "grass roots" plants for making wet process phosphoric acid and phosphate fertilisers. The acquisition was primarily to provide resources for the design of the Long Harbour plant, but there were also thoughts of marketing proprietary processes to chemical companies world-wide. In the event, the latter did not happen and within two years, after the design work on Long Harbour was complete, Erco's interest was sold to the Badger Company. Initially, it was planned to include the know-how on phosphorus and thermal phosphoric acid for a royalty but that idea was subsequently rejected on strategic grounds (it is interesting to speculate on what use would have been made of the know-how if it had been passed over to the purchaser).

The team in Florida was headed by the Project Engineer, Ernest Brazier, and at its peak numbered 140. While the design work proceeded on schedule, there were a number of problems. The remoteness from Erco and A&W UK made it difficult to make use of operating experience at Varennes; Lloyd Lillico, Jim Medves (later Plant Manager for Long Harbour) and other operating staff tried to bring their experience with the Varennes plant to bear in the design of the precipitators, pumps, driers for coke and silica and electrode suspension and in the use of stainless steel, but to no avail. At a meeting in 1967 between the operating staff and the Corporate Engineering Department, ostensibly to provide an opportunity for the former to contribute to the design, it became clear that it was too late to modify the designs.

There was disagreement between Ernest Brazier and Mark Maunsell over the dimensions of the furnaces; Brazier managed to have the diameter reduced, but only by 1 foot. The concern of Ed Bissaillon (the project director) in Toronto was to keep the total cost down to the figure promised to Ed Kinsley through reducing the size of buildings and eliminating effluent treatment, etc.. Bissaillon had his representative present, to report what was going on, which led to meetings held at times when the "spy in the camp" was not present. Eventually, at the time of start-up of the plant, there was an overrun of $1 million on the capital cost, despite Bissaillon's efforts. Bissaillon left Erco shortly after the Long Harbour plant started up; it is not clear why he left but it may have been due to shortcomings in the plant or the death of Ed Kinsley in December 1968 (p.158).

The plant site, excluding the dock and the electricity substation, was not large - about 1/4 mile square - but needed much preparatory work. Apart from roadbuilding and laying power lines, it was necessary to provide a foundation for the plant by digging out 120,000 cubic yards of peat moss and filling the hole by flattening a

30-foot high hill. It was soon discovered how cold the site could be: although the winter temperature seldom fell below 20 F., strong winds from the South blew for eight or nine months of the year, with 40 mph common and gusts of 80-90 mph not unusual. Summers were short. After the plant had started up, the inclement weather was a severe disincentive to working there and it was necessary to undertake a "winterization" programme, involving substantial capital expenditure.

Over 90% of the employees at the plant were Newfoundlanders. Few had any experience of industry and none of phosphorus production. With adequate training and experience they were (as stated by Bob Chalmers, also later in charge of Long Harbour) good operators, but in the early days there were few who were given training in depth. Long Harbour was not a popular location for staff from elsewhere in Canada or from England because of bad working conditions, long hours and numerous problems, and the remoteness for the staff and their families, 70 miles from St John's. The first Plant Manager (Ken Bradley) and technical superintendent (Lynn Price) both came from Buckingham, Ted Hipkin (assistant to the plant manager) from Portishead, Alec Hunter (production superintendent) from Varennes and John Futers (maintenance superintendent) from Port Maitland, while George Irving, the Plant Engineer, had been at Long Harbour since June 1966, working on the design and on the construction with the main contractor, Kaiser Engineering.

Operation 1968-71

Commissioning of the pellet plant started in late summer of 1968. Serious problems were encountered in controlling the feed of rock and water to the balling pans. The output of satisfactory pellets was intermittent and would have been inadequate for the furnaces if they had been operating at their rated capacity. The problem of repairing leaks in the precipitators has already been described. The next problem was with the electrode suspension system. When the first electrode stick was being assembled (by screwing lengths together and slipping them down through the clamps holding them), a design fault caused the stick to crash down into the furnace when the fourth piece was added and the stick was still well above the furnace. That was remedied but other problems with the clamps holding the electrodes caused difficulties in later months and years.

The first furnace was started up on 8th December 1968, about three months after the planned date of September. (It was ironical that Hoechst's Flushing plant was officially opened in September, with capacity initially of 30,000 tpa of phosphorus, to be doubled within three years, the location being determined by cheap power from natural gas and proximity to the port of Rotterdam.) The start-up went smoothly with a load build-up to 50 MW and the first slag tap achieved within five hours. In the words of Ernest Brazier, "It worked like a dream bird".

There were, however, some early problems. One of the slide valves on the very sophisticated raw material feed system jammed on the first day. After several hours of trying to free the valve and nearing the time when a furnace shutdown would become mandatory, the system was by-passed, as had been rehearsed in contingency planning, and was never used again. The next problem was in tapping for ferrophosphorus, a potential by-product that was run off first when the furnace was tapped; it proved impossible to recover the ferrophosphorus as designed. And slag tapping was always a problem because the slag runners from the furnace to the slag pit were very long and tended to become clogged. On the ninth day the first electrode break occurred.

The most common electrode break was a nipple failure occurring at or very close to the point of entry into the furnace where two electrode pieces were screwed together via a smaller joining piece. When the break happened, the bottom 20 feet fell into the furnace causing arcing between it and the upper portion of the electrode stack. That could cause damage to the water seal around the electrode and if the water then entered the furnace it could cause an explosion or localised cooling. After a break, the broken portion had to be extracted within 24 hours so that it did not freeze within the furnace; if that happened it would be necessary either to drill out the electrode, leaving bits that would cause problems for weeks, or to shut down the furnace for a month. The procedure for extraction (which had been rehearsed before start-up) was to raise and remove all the upper electrode portions and then to lift out the red-hot broken portion by crane. In the case of the first break, the broken portion was raised only just in time; as time went on, however, the operators became expert in removing broken electrodes. Breaks continued, the third being on Christmas Day in 1968, within three weeks of start-up. The second furnace started up towards the end of January 1969; once again the start-up went reasonably well but troubles arose soon after the commissioning team had returned to their home locations.

The Statement by the Chairman in the 1968 Annual Report of Albright & Wilson, written at the end of March 1969, said: "Teething troubles have not been unduly severe for a project of this size and are being overcome as they arise...There are, however, good indications that the furnaces may well be capable of exceeding their rated capacity by a useful, and profitable, margin".

In the three months from February to April 1969, production averaged just over 400 tons per week, improving from 320 tons per week in February to nearly 500 tons per week in April. That was, however, well short of one of the conditions of the Bonds through which money was raised for Long Harbour, which required an average of 1,250 tons per week over a four-week period. The most obvious problem was the breakages of electrodes. Several theories to explain the breakages were put forward at the time and subsequently. The principal reason, according to Ernest

Brazier, who was responsible for the adoption of the Lectromelt system of suspension, was the poor machining of the Union Carbide electrodes, which meant that contact between the pieces and the nipples was not close enough, with the result that the joints tended to open and to overheat, so leading to breaks. The same electrodes were used by Monsanto but the rope suspension system was more tolerant than the rigid Lectromelt system and the column length was smaller. Moreover, Monsanto's stricter inspection of the electrodes led to rejection of less well machined pieces. Alf Loveless (Chief Engineer of Albright & Wilson Mfg) reported in September 1969 that the machining was poor and recommended that Italian electrodes should be tried, but they failed at the first attempt. Much later, In 1980, Ernest re-machined 200 of the Union Carbide electrodes, none of which overheated or broke; Union Carbide then installed a new machine and thereafter breakages were rare.

There were, however, other causes of difficulty with the electrodes. First, there were deficiencies with the suspension system. Very early on, it was found that raising the electrodes with a full column was a problem - the top nipple broke and the whole stick dropped. Torquing of the electrode pieces (i.e. tightening of the joints) was another problem; typically, a joint would take six weeks from first torquing to consumption in the furnace and during that time the joints tended to open. A second torquing was introduced, just before the joint entered the furnace, but was not regarded as reliable and could itself lead to breakages of nipples. There was also a design fault, creating a side thrust during the lowering of the electrodes, which was soon corrected by the manufacturer. Another design fault caused the holding clamps to open sometimes and drop the column into the furnace; that was not corrected but a procedure was adopted to overcome the problem. In 1970, when Clifford Vessey was transferred from the UK to manage Long Harbour, he introduced springs to compensate for the different expansion rates on the electrodes and the supporting rods; the majority view is that that change made no appreciable difference and certainly the breaks continued as before.

The conditions within the furnaces were of fundamental importance. The failure of the feed system led to an inconsistent mixture. The dimensions of the furnaces caused zones of heating, unmelted burden and sintering. The wish to minimise the loss of phosphorus in slag meant that there was a high silica content in the feed to the furnaces, which caused difficulties in tapping the furnaces and a build-up of dense material. The position of the three electrodes within the furnaces was inconsistent: too high, and there were excessive gas offtake temperatures destroying the fragile precipitators and leading to more phosphorus-containing mud; too low, and there were electrode breakages. The situation was aggravated by breakages causing discontinuous operation.

The first shipment of phosphorus to Portishead (a part-shipload) was made in

March and by April no. 1 furnace had been brought up to 75% of capacity; no. 2 furnace, however, was experiencing severe commissioning problems and was closed for repairs. It was therefore decided that Varennes should be kept open and not to seek sales of phosphorus to third parties for the time being. Mark Maunsell, however, wrote to Bill Albright early in April saying "I am beginning to feel that I really know how to operate a furnace!...the absolute value obtained on a 24" electrode can be factored to allow for a 55". These words perhaps point to the fundamental problem: the leap forward represented by a more than fivefold scale-up of equipment whose performance was complex and unpredictable.

Within weeks, at the beginning of May, the next blow fell. The plant was closed, because of the death of fish in the adjoining waters. As reported in the statement issued by the Company afterwards, the waste disposal system had been approved by the provincial and federal fisheries authorities (in the third Quarter of 1968) - "Both the Fisheries authorities and the company were confident that the proposed waste disposal system would be effective". The Evening Telegram in October 1968 reported: "Company officials told the press ...that pollution in the area of the plant would be "minimal" and that special precautions have been made and studies undertaken to prevent any contamination...Fluid wastes will be diluted with sea-water and pumped out to depths where the ocean currents can carry it away". At the time of start-up of the plant there was an accidental spill of 'phossy' water into the harbour and shortly thereafter dead fish were observed. In March there was a further fish-kill some distance from the plant and then dead fish were found in various parts of Placentia Bay, up to 40 miles from the plant. A biological survey commissioned by the Company blamed the practice of discharging water containing phosphorus into the Bay: up to 400 gallons per minute of phosphorus-containing water was being discharged during operation. The "hot spot" below the discharge pipe was calculated to contain 6 tons of phosphorus, and the seabed on the opposite side of the harbour contained 50 parts per million of phosphorus. The "hot spot" could be dealt with by dredging and dumping in ponds on shore, or concreting over. Future effluent would have to be treated on site, by filtration and ponding.

In order to avoid an injunction from the authorities, the plant was closed pending the installation of adequate effluent treatment. The capital cost of the treatment measures was estimated to be $400,000 immediately and $2.8 million in total, based on the system that had been used at Oldbury and the addition of large ponds. In an interview with the Financial Post, David Livingstone said: "It is now clear that when we built the Newfoundland plant we should have made the same arrangements for the treatment of effluent that we had already at Oldbury". Hoechst was consulted and expressed concern at possible seepage from the ponds, but the system adopted succeeded in containing liquid effluents. The Ministry of Fisheries & Forestry said in the Canadian Federal Parliament: "In future we must insist that phosphorus plants treat all their effluent on their own property, and that nothing leaves the plant that would in any way be deleterious to marine life". Advertisements on the West coast of the USA in June made a point of saying that no Newfoundland fish were sold there. Chemical Age reported the fishermen as saying "We want that plant closed, and closed for good". A settlement was eventually reached with the local fishermen, involving the payment of $750,000, including legal costs.

The furnaces were restarted in July. During the 8 weeks' shutdown, Erco had been losing $50,000 per day in wages and other running costs. Moreover, when the shutdown occurred, the Portishead furnaces were restarted and the Oldbury furnaces, which had been due to close at the end of April 1969, were kept open.There were also purchases of phosphorus from other producers. A&W was nevertheless short of phosphorus, leading to a cutback in sales of products made in the UK. The forecast impact of the increased costs and foregone sales was a loss in the second half of 1969 and an adverse effect on profit in the year 1969 of over $10 million.

At the same time John Hughes, the Technical Director, presented to the Board a revised capital expenditure statement for the Long Harbour. Expenditure to date in Canada, excluding the expenditure on effluent containment, pre-operating expenses of $1.4 million and financing costs of $1.8 million, was $48.3 million, against $37 million originally quoted for expenditure in Canada (but never actually formally authorised). The additional costs included $3.5 million for the dock and $2.1 million of capitalised interest, excess costs of site preparation and inflation ($4 million) and $1 million engineering costs above the $1.7 million originally quoted. In a further report, a month later, John Hughes estimated that the capital cost to the end of 1970, including the cost of dealing with effluents, would be $52 million. It had taken under two years for the capital cost to approach the quotation from Hoechst.

Yet it appeared that there was still optimism in A&W at senior levels. The statement published for the first six months of 1969 included the words "we confidently expect 1970 to show a sharp recovery in profit". Tony Ward, the Finance Director, said in June 1969 "We'll get Newfoundland right soon and I think we'll be back on plan by 1970". David Livingstone reported to the Board in November 1969 that the estimate of production in 1970 - 47,500 tons - was conservative and that it might reach 60,000 tons. Lloyd Lillico (President of Erco) told the Toronto Dominion Bank in January 1970 that the problem of electrode breakages appeared to have been solved. Maurice Laperriere (head of the Newfoundland Division of Erco) said in December 1969: "everything is more encouraging, particularly with the end of the electrode breakage problem...we could reach design capacity on a fairly sustained basis during the first quarter of 1970". The Statement by the Chairman in the 1969 Annual Report included in the first paragraph the sentence: "We believe that we are now through the worst of the trouble though there is still some way to go before the plant is in full routine production". The Statement went on to say: "Provided performance in Newfoundland improves in line with expectations, they (the Directors) foresee a substantial improvement in the 1970 results with steady progress thereafter to restore the Company's fortunes".

The road to recovery was to prove much longer and harder. As will be seen in the graph over the page, production never reached 60,000 tons (120 million lbs, assuming that short tons of 2,000 lbs were meant) in a year. The peak was in 1983, when 52,200 tonnes (115 million lbs) were produced. The original rated capacity was 145 million lbs.; output did not reach even half that level until 1977.

Following restart, furnace conditions were very variable. Electrode breaks continued and gas offtake temperatures varied from very high, which were severely destructive of the precipitators, to very low, which resulted in excessive phosphorus condensation in the precipitators. This in turn led to "phosphorus spills, fires, flooding of the floor to control fires and in general some of the worst working conditions imaginable" (Jim Medves, then working on special assignments reporting to Maurice Laperriere, later in charge of Long Harbour from mid-1979).

In September 1969, a number of A&W engineers met under Mike Cussons (Engineering Director of Marchon, seconded to Long Harbour in 1970 and later Manager of the Central Engineering Department of A&W) to consider the electrode breakages. They concluded that the Long Harbour electrode system was "fundamentally different from standard practice in the phosphorus industry". They discovered that because of the size of the furnaces and the separation of the three electrodes there were effectively three operations within each furnace. They suggested that the furnaces should be dug out to remove the accumulated burden and provide a fresh start. Mark Maunsell had been working for some time on what he called "OFO" (Optimised Furnace Operation) and published a document in October 1969 stating that the key to successful operation of the furnaces was correct sizing of the coke in the feed. His calculations, however, did not allow for the independent operation of the three electrodes. Several years were to pass before there was a comprehensive, integrated approach to solving the problems.

In 1970 there was an ice-storm at Long Harbour that brought down the power lines to the plant, forcing it to be out of operation for nearly three weeks. The speech by the Chairman at the AGM of the Company in May referred to that event as a freak of nature that should not recur. He said that both furnaces had operated at over 90% of their rated capacity but there had been mechanical problems: "phosphorus furnaces are temperamental creatures, and it takes time for the operators to master their tricks ... The problem now is to achieve consistent high performance over sustained periods ... There is therefore still a large element of uncertainty in relation to the current year. We shall, however, be disappointed if by its end the plant is not in full and steady production".

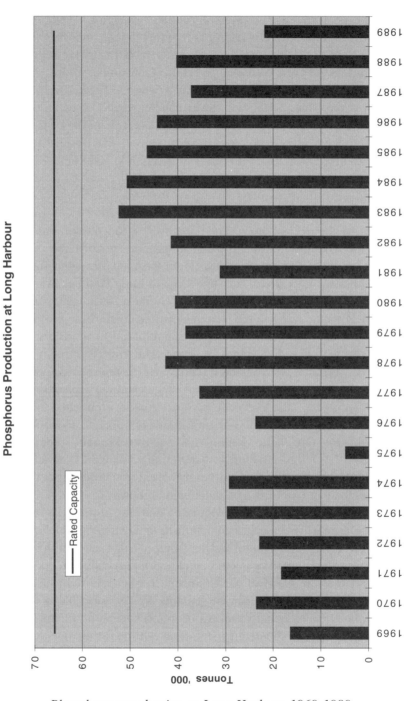

Phosphorus production at Long Harbour 1969-1989

As the year went on, however, problems continued, particularly broken electrodes. An Erco report in June said: "no-one is certain how the occurrence can be prevented. Since the Long Harbour design is unique, there is not much assistance we can get from anyone else...the whole system is only marginally operable". Three firms were asked to report on the electrodes problem. They recommended a tighter specification for the machining of electrodes, a reduced length of stack, more uniform furnace conditions, adjustments to the clamping springs, etc., but nothing appears to have resulted from the reports.

In July 1970, David Livingstone became the Director responsible for Erco, as well as for the UK phosphate and ACC operations. At that time, downtime was averaging over 50%. He analysed the reasons for the difficulties as being 35% basic design faults, 25% minor design faults, 25% construction faults, 15% management and labour faults. "Many of the basic design faults were a function of absurd parsimony in the original authorisation...We had underestimated the industrial innocence of local labour". The labour force at that time numbered 400, against the original estimate of 250, and it was to rise to over 500. There were still effluent problems, with some discharge of water to the sea, and fluorine damage up to 2 miles from the plant.

A visit by David Livingstone resulted in management changes. A phosphorus division, headed by Clifford Vessey (seconded from the position of Technical Development Manager of ACC), was set up, separate from the rest of Erco but also under Lloyd Lillico, the President of Erco. David Livingstone went to Newfoundland for three months. Soon after his arrival, he wrote to John Hutton-Wilson (then Managing Director of A&W) to tell of reactions to his presence; he wrote: "Lloyd looks like a man in the electric chair who has just had news of a power cut and hopes the lines are down". Referring to Omond Solandt (an external director of Erco), he wrote "Omond's feelings towards me are as warm as boarding house soup". He continued: "I am quite confident that Clifford and I can pull this situation round in a period of something like six months".

In November, a letter was sent from the Chairman of Albright & Wilson (Sir Richard Powell) to all stockholders, to inform them of problems that had arisen since the half-yearly statement issued in August. He wrote: "after a substantial period of improving operation, the phosphorus plant at Long Harbour in Newfoundland has experienced further technical problems which have severely curtailed production...problems remain relating to the operation of the electrode system for the furnaces and to the design of the precipitators and condensers. Modifications to design are in hand which are expected to ensure smooth operation... it has been necessary to buy some phosphorus from other producers".

Sir Richard's statement prompted a major article in The Sunday Times of 29th November 1970, which showed a chart of the fall in the share price from 24s. (£1.20) in mid-1968 to 4s. (20p.) after the announcement and included the following words:

"it is clear that either policy or management - the fourth in as many years - must once again be drastically changed. The problem that dwarfs all others for management is to get the Newfoundland phosphorus plant it set up to supply all the group's needs, to operate properly. Scheduled to cost £15 million this has already taken £25 million and money is still being spent at a rate of £1million a year. But it is not even covering operating costs although Sir Richard still claims there is nothing fundamentally wrong with it. Now the money is running out as the heavy debts start having to be repaid. This gave rise to wild City rumours last week that Albright is going bust....Already the profitable parts of the business in the UK....are feeling the strain of capital starvation and neglect from the overtaxed management. Profits have edged downwards. If this is to be stopped, Sir Richard and his team must either show rapidly that they are on top of the Newfoundland problem or make way for others who can do better....There are still two alternatives: the arrival of a bidder or, as we have for so long urged, a voluntary break-up of at least parts of Albright...Burmah Oil, which was poised to bid for the group in May, failed to get the overseas backing it was looking for and has cooled off. But the US Tenneco, overtly unmoved, must be wondering what to do with the 10% stake it bought at 13s. a time....A 60% share in Midland Silicones will probably be sold to US partner Dow Corning...If and when Newfoundland ever does work, the capital cost will have escalated so much that the cost advantages that originally swayed the fateful decision to build will have been dissipated. It can no longer be expected to bring profits back to the £7.5 million mid-sixties peak nor the shares remotely near their former glories".

Following Sir Richard's statement, for a while there was some improvement. Both furnaces were dug out to remove the carbon pieces that had accumulated from broken electrodes. When no.1 furnace was restarted it ran well, averaging 80 tons per day for a while, although David described conditions as "pretty foul". Further trials of Italian electrodes started. It was learnt that FMC had decided to reduce the size of its electrodes from 55" to 50", because of the amount of downtime caused by pieces of carbon in its furnaces. There were suggestions that A&W would have to do likewise but David was firm in his belief that problems could be overcome without that.

In the Annual Report for 1970 there were three pages on "The technical problems at Long Harbour", including the statement: "The design of the furnaces themselves has been fully vindicated, but we have been plagued by breaks in the electrodes and failures in their control mechanism which have drastically reduced the output of the plant...The effect of broken electrodes on furnace operation is severe and cumulative...Only three other phosphorus producers in the world operate furnaces of this size, and of the two using comparable electrodes, both, as we subsequently learned, had experienced similar difficulties. In its important elements, moreover, our control system was unique, so that other producers' experience, even if it had been readily available to us, would have been of only limited value...We are now convinced, however, that the solution to this problem has been found, and that we can look forward to operating the furnaces at high loads for indefinite periods of time". The other main problem mentioned was the precipitators, which were being rebuilt to a more rugged design, for completion during 1971. Minor modifications to the condensers would also be completed in the near future.

That optimism was based on Clifford Vessey's introduction of upsprings on the electrode suspension; they were intended to reduce the problems created by the weight of the electrodes, particularly in their movement up and down in the furnaces. Clifford wrote to David in January 1971 saying "No one doubts that we have found the solution to this problem". Before receiving that assurance, David's draft report had included the words: "It would have been safe for a Company say four times as large to make a technical leap of this magnitude...with hindsight it is arguable that the Company should have purchased a proven plant rather than set out to develop its own". In July, Clifford was still very optimistic. "I am convinced that the plant technical problems can be successfully solved and that a major change will be seen in the last four months of this year. The production level in 1972 will, in my opinion,be a minimum of 50,000 tons and probably be in excess of 55,000 tons".

In 1971 the precipitators were rebuilt and the mild steel gas lines were replaced by stainless. Production, however, remained low, mainly because of continued electrode breaks, which were not prevented by the upsprings - there were more breaks in 1971 than in 1970. Production in 1971 was well down on 1970 and costs were higher. There was still a long road to travel to achieve sustained improvement. That road is described in the next chapter.

The critical period

Compounding the very severe problems in Canada were changes in organization and management in the UK that were to create an almost insuperable crisis, whose resolution was to require undoing (as far as possible) some of the main changes made in 1965-70.

McKinsey

By 1965 Sir Sydney Barratt had signalled his 1967 retirement and Sir Owen Wansbrough-Jones had been designated his successor. The Board at that time was weighted towards the original Oldbury-centred Albright & Wilson, with four other long-serving Oldbury executives (Wilson Carter, John Christopherson, Keith Piercy and Vic Sherwood) and two former executives (Bill Albright and Bryan Topley). The remaining executive members had been added through the acquisitions - Frank Schon, Eric Bush, John Hutton-Wilson (ACC) and Bertram White (Boake Roberts) - and there were two non-executive Directors (Neil Peech, Chairman of Steetley, and Edward Reeve-Angel, who had a small business in paper trading).

The need for a review of the organisation and direction of the Company following the acquisitions in the previous five years had been recognised for some time. The appointment of McKinsey at the end of 1965 was unsurprising, particularly in the context of reviews prevalent in the UK at the time, especially in the chemical industry. It has been suggested, however, that Sir Sydney was looking for a way to reduce the power and influence of Frank Schon. When the Board agreed on the appointment, it was minuted that "there was no point in embarking on the study unless there was a determination to carry out the recommendations when the time came". That reads like giving McKinsey a blank cheque.

In October 1965 Sir Sydney and Sir Owen met Hugh Parker, the head of McKinsey in the UK, and arranged for a Memorandum of Proposal to be produced, and put to the Board in December. The Memorandum included some critical observations, such as: "While there have been efforts to rationalize and integrate the various subsidiary companies of the Group into a more rational whole, progress in this direction has been slow. The Group therefore remains a comparatively loose federation of subsidiary companies, each largely autonomous and independent of the others and of the Group, rather than the more integrated corporation that foreseeable conditions in the world chemical industry may require". There was, the Memorandum stated, "an almost unanimous view that such a re-examination is now not only timely but urgent". There was a need for greater integration, realignment of the operating units, better strategic planning, greater profit consciousness and profit orientation, more professional management, better management development, a more disciplined approach to management and more formal control processes. Finally, and most significantly, the McKinsey Memorandum stated that there should be a clearer distinction between the long-term strategic planning and policy-making role of the Board and the executive responsibility of the line organisation headed by the chief executive; the executive directors were severely overloaded and their immediate subordinates were badly frustrated through not being given enough responsibility.

The review was launched in April 1966 and included a major information-gathering operation going a long way beyond anything previously assembled within A&W, especially relating to markets (for example, a requirement to state trends in the number of salesmen, the sales per salesman and the number of customers per salesman). McKinsey's proposals were presented to the Board by Hugh Parker in November- December 1966. There was to be a Chief Executive and a "Managing Group" comprising the Chairman, Deputy Chairman, Chief Executive and three other Directors - Wilson Carter, Frank Schon and Vic Sherwood, all based at the London Office. The background to these proposals is described in a diary kept by Wilson Carter for the period October-December 1966.

Sir Sydney told Wilson Carter at the beginning of October that Hugh Parker had suggested that he should resign the Chairmanship. Sir Sydney was prepared to step down in favour of Sir Owen and to assist him if required; if, however, Frank Schon were to become Chairman, Sir Sydney would sever his connection with Albright & Wilson at once and completely. Assuming that Sir Owen became Chairman, the question was then who should be the Chief Executive. McKinsey had put forward three names - Frank Schon, Arthur Henderson (Managing Director of ACC) and Ed Kinsley. Sir Sydney and Sir Owen were firmly opposed to Frank's taking the position and thought Arthur Henderson could not do the job. Ed Kinsley had already indicated his willingness to move from Toronto to London. Sir Sydney thought that McKinsey would recommend relieving the other Board members of all executive responsibilities for the operating companies. A few days later, Sherwood told Carter that he strongly supported Kinsley but would resign as soon as he could if Schon became Chief Executive.

Carter thought that it was not a good plan for the existing executive directors to be "kicked upstairs"; Sir Sydney envisaged that Carter would have some sort of overseeing role for production and Sherwood for finance, but no similar role was foreseen for Schon, Bertram White and John Hutton-Wilson, and the relationship with the Chief Executive was very unclear. Similar thoughts were voiced to Carter by Sherwood next day. Later the same day, surprisingly, Sir Owen told Carter that he also thought that removing executive responsibilities from the Directors would not work and that the idea had been put by Sir Sydney to Hugh Parker. Hugh Parker next went to Toronto to see Kinsley and tell him of the proposed organisation. After that, Sherwood reported to Carter that Kinsley had hinted that Schon might be offered the position of Deputy Chairman, presumably to keep him quiet. Hugh Parker's view was that Schon's link with Whitehaven should only be temporary and non-executive.

Despite the misgivings expressed by at least three of the Directors, the scheme was put by McKinsey to the Board at the end of November. There appears to have been little comment at the time but soon after, at a meeting of Sir Owen with Topley, Carter, Schon and Sherwood, Schon stated his objections to the proposals: if the Directors were removed from their executive responsibilities they would soon lose their effectiveness, and he did not consider Kinsley to be suitable for the job of Chief Executive. Schon urged that organisational changes should be brought in slowly. At the December 1966 Board meeting, Sir Owen put forward the idea of a 'Managing Group' consisting of the Chairman-elect, the Deputy Chairman and the Chief Executive, plus Schon, Carter and Sherwood, but the idea did not appear to add anything of significance. Sir Frank asked for time for discussions with the Whitehaven management; Sir Sydney said that the proposals were confidential to the Board but Schon revealed that he had already discussed them with his management.

When the Board met in January 1967, Schon made it clear that he was continuing to discuss the proposals with his senior management and that they did not think that Kinsley had yet proved himself suitable for the position of Chief Executive. Schon also wished the Board, before deciding on the organisation, to decide its policy regarding Newfoundland and whether to concentrate on Europe or North America. There were problems that should receive attention before removing from decision-making those who had knowledge of the operations and market-place - apart from Newfoundland, there were problems at Belledune and the low profitability of Erco and BBA - and the move to the proposed organisation should be spread over two to three years.

Others expressed concern at taking Kinsley from Canada when there were such problems there. It was, however, claimed that senior staff in the UK were looking for change and indeed at that time there was a feeling that the long-established senior management were drifting rather than driving. Sir Sydney wanted to move as quickly as possible but Sir Frank said that if there were not a holding operation he would have to consider his position. Sir Frank wrote a series of memoranda to the members of the Board setting out his views, including that the choice of Chief Executive should remain open until the end of the year.

Sir Sydney's wishes prevailed, however, and the majority of the Board supported him. So at the beginning of March 1967 organisational changes were announced. Sir Sydney was to retire and hand over to Sir Owen at the end of June. The memorandum from Sir Sydney (written by McKinsey) went on to describe how the executive Directors were to lose their executive responsibilities: "involvement with day-to-day operating problems has made it increasingly difficult for individual directors, of for the Board as a whole, to do the longer range strategic planning that the Group will require...They will no longer have direct line responsibility for operating companies and head office departments, but each main Board director will in future be assigned several areas of special interest". Kinsley was to take up the position of Chief Executive as soon as he could hand over his responsibilities in Canada. All the heads of the operating divisions and central departments were to report directly to Kinsley. The memorandum concluded by saying: "The main purpose of the new organisation is to unify the Group into a stronger whole. But another important aim is to provide new challenge and new opportunity for the younger members of management".

The departure of Frank Schon

By the middle of April, the situation with Sir Frank had become critical. On 20th April he had a 7-hour meeting with Bryan Topley (the Deputy Chairman) during which he claimed that the scheme of reorganisation was designed to let the Board wither away - the areas of special interest were meaningless. He claimed that Hugh Parker (of McKinsey) had told him that he was the only man to run the company. He was prepared to accept Kinsley as Chief Executive if controlled by a group comprising the Chairman, Deputy Chairman, Chief Executive and Sir Frank as Vice-Chairman. He then gave an ultimatum, that he would resign if there was no positive move within the next four days.

On 24th April, Sir Sydney wrote to Sir Frank with a draft of an announcement, saying that when Sir Sydney was succeeded as Chairman by Sir Owen, Sir Frank would become one of two Vice-Chairmen (Wilson Carter being the other) and would be a member of a Central Standing Committee of the Board, which would "interpret existing Board policies and consider major variations or additions to them before presentation to the Board...also advise and help the Chief Executive, who will have line authority over operating divisions and central departments". Sir Frank, however, was not satisfied with those terms and handed in his resignation later the same day. The letter of resignation opened with the following words:

"There has been a history of disagreements on my part with Board policy. In the past I have recorded my differing views and left it at that. However, the decision to remove phosphorus manufacture from this country to Newfoundland, the general shift of emphasis in our operations from Europe to the North American Continent, and the risks which are incumbent in these moves have further increased my concern as to the way in which we are proceeding.

I have in the past expressed views on Board reorganisation and specifically laid emphasis on the need to rejuvenate the Board. I was willing to go along with the McKinsey Reorganisation Scheme, but disagree with the way in which it is being put into effect and which in my opinion will have many consequences highly unfavourable to the Company".

He went on to recall his years with Marchon and then with Albright & Wilson and to express his regret at resigning, which he wished to take effect from the earliest possible date.

On the following morning the resignations of the senior management of Marchon were received. Discussions with Sir Frank were then resumed. He demanded that he would be Vice-Chairman, that Kinsley be told that he was junior to him and that Sir Frank would be involved in commercial policies and would conduct any major commercial negotiations. Later he added that the Marchon group should not be included in the general reorganisation for some years, during which Otto Secher (Sir Frank's brother-in-law) would be Chairman of Marchon.

There followed some days of consultation among the Directors, ending with the decision to accept Sir Frank's resignation; if the senior management of Marchon held to their resignations, John Hutton-Wilson would take over as its chairman and managing director. On May 1st, after consultation with Hill Samuel, Sir Sydney wrote accepting Sir Frank's resignation, ending with the words "I cannot end without saying how sorrowful I am personally to accept this decision of yours after sincere and protracted efforts to meet your point of view". On May 5th 1967, his resignation was made public; in the Press release, Sir Sydney commented: "Sir Frank Schon's decision to withdraw from Albright & Wilson is a matter of deep personal regret to me. There have been differences about company policy which we have not been able to bridge".

The reasons for Sir Frank's resignation, as stated in his letter, were questioned, at the time and later, by what might be termed the "Oldbury" Directors[1]. Ostensibly, the main reason was disagreement on policy, particularly relating to Newfoundland, and with the way the McKinsey proposals on organisation were being implemented.

The evidence in Board minutes of Schon's consistent opposition to the Newfoundland project and other developments in Canada supports that it would have provided a reason for resignation. But it is also true that Schon's style of management and philosophy were so different from the "Oldbury" tradition that there was (as later described by David Livingstone) "a deteriorating relationship between Frank Schon and Sydney Barratt". Schon also saw the developments in Canada as a threat to Marchon, because of the choice of phosphorus rather than wet phosphoric acid as the route for expansion and because of the drain of funds to Canada. The deciding issue was the reorganisation in 1967, removing Schon from his power-base and concentrating power in the hands of Kinsley, who had been

---

[2] More than ten years later, when there was a tribute to Sir Frank on his retirement from the Chairmanship of the National Research & Development Corporation in a Bulletin of the NRDC, Bertram White (one of the Directors at the time) sent to David Livingstone a copy of a letter written by Sir Frank to Sir Owen in May 1966, relating to the Board meeting in that month, when the decision to proceed with the Long Harbour project was taken. Sir Frank wrote: "No formal vote was taken, as it was obvious that I was the only one out of step. I believe in democracy and though I have not changed my views I will row along with you". David Livingstone then wrote to the NRDC to say: "I must point out that Frank did not resign from the A&W Board as a consequence of the Newfoundland decision. It is true that he opposed this, but he is on record in the Board minutes as having agreed to go along with his other colleagues on the Board in supporting it. That was in May 1966. He resigned, in fact, a year later, for reasons connected I believe with the duties and locations of executive directors of the Board".

responsible for the major investments made and planned in Canada, which had a poor profit record, while Marchon had become the largest source of profit in Albright & Wilson.

It seems probable that Schon would have liked to have been the chief executive of Albright & Wilson (though probably not with the McKinsey organisation) and resigned when it became plain that he could not achieve that. He had been in the A&W group for some eleven years without becoming a member of the inner circle of Directors and Whitehaven continued to be remote, geographically and otherwise, from Knightsbridge and Oldbury. When Schon left A&W, he was 55 and still in full health, although no longer the hungry entrepreneur who, with Fred Marzillier, had built Marchon. Schon never again ran a commercial concern and, as far as is known, did not attempt to maintain connexions with Marchon or A&W. Many years later, when he had become Lord Schon, he was pleased to be invited by David Livingstone to visit Whitehaven works and the Knightsbridge office.

With the resignation of Schon and the Whitehaven directors on the Marchon Board there was a prospect of severe hiatus. The Times of May 10 carried a major article on its leader page, describing the Marchon resignations as "quite unprecedented in British industrial history" and referring to "The dispute which has raged for months in the boardroom of A&W". Schon's opposition to the Newfoundland project, as stated in his letter of resignation, was quoted and the article ended with the words "The only thing that could harm Whitehaven would be the failure of the Newfoundland project to live up to its promise. Whitehaven would then be hurt if the A&W group got into financial difficulties".

Following the resignations on 24th April of the Marchon Board members - Baines, Dickie, Fagandini, Halfpenny, Koebner and Secher - and Sir Frank's confirmation of his immediate resignation, Wilson Carter and John Hutton-Wilson were despatched to Whitehaven. Their initial impression was that all concerned were resolved to leave but very soon the situation began to change. Identical letters were sent to Sir Sydney confirming immediate resignation from the Marchon Board but stating a willingness to continue to serve "in a managerial capacity", to protect the "prosperity of the Whitehaven operation", until replacements could be found. Koebner and Halfpenny did not confirm their resignations and reserved their positions. Peter Baines made it clear that he was not prepared to join Schon in any other venture, saying that Schon was too hard a taskmaster (he had had only two weeks' holiday in five years). There was pressure on the former Directors of Marchon from the the next layer of management for them to stay.

Eventually, only two of the former Board members, apart from Schon, left the Company: Bob Dickie had wanted for some time to move to the South and Danny Fagandini had also signalled his wish to develop his career outside Marchon. Danny was later to return and to become Managing Director of the Marchon division. Otto

Secher, after a short period as Managing Director at Whitehaven, became Chairman of Marchon, until his retirement. Peter Baines was Managing Director from July 1967 for two years, until he became a Director of Albright & Wilson Ltd. Halfpenny and Koebner stayed as members of the divisional executive, in senior technical positions. The crisis passed and in the following year the Marchon division made a record profit.

What then were the consequences of Schon's departure? The general impression seems to be that there was some loss of impetus in commercial development but that that may have started before 1967, perhaps as early as the severance of his partnership with Marzillier, whose attention to detail complemented Schon's vision and initiative. Schon's dream of a major expansion of the anhydrite-based sulphuric acid capacity at Whitehaven was no longer realistic, as costs had moved in favour of the usual sulphur-burning route. Although his belief in the economic superiority of the wet process route to phosphoric acid was to prove correct in due course, in the immediate future the die had been cast in favour of phosphorus. The initiative for expansion into continental Europe through the establishment of Marchon Italiana was maintained with investments in France and then Spain, while the emphasis on exports that had in 1966 brought to Marchon one of the first Queen's Awards for Exports was sustained. The separateness of Marchon was not ended by Schon's departure (that continued for another twenty years, until the changes in organisation under Robin Paul). Certainly the impact of the events of April-May 1967 was less than had been expected at the time. In part, that was due to their being overshadowed by the greater crisis that followed.

Operations under Ed Kinsley

The organisation established following the McKinsey recommendations placed an extraordinary burden of responsibility on one man, Ed Kinsley, the Chief Executive. Reporting to him were the Division Managing Directors of the seven operating Divisions (Albright & Wilson (Mfg), Associated Chemical Companies, Marchon, Bush Boake Allen, Midland Silicones, Erco, Albright & Wilson (Australia)) and Albright & Wilson Ireland, and the heads of eleven central departments (Treasurer's, Personnel, Publicity, Planning, Development, Overseas, Secretary's, Phosphate Coordination, Commercial, Research, and Profit Improvement). The formerly executive Directors were given "Areas of Special Interest" in which they were expected to advise on policy and strategic planning and Wilson Carter and John Hutton-Wilson were appointed Vice-Chairmen. Without departments or staff and executive duties, their activities were very circumscribed. Ed Kinsley, in contrast, was so busy as to be virtually inaccessible to the other Directors; Keith Piercy (special interests - planning and Western Europe) recalled how he had to aim to see Kinsley before 8 am or after 7 pm.

The issues facing Kinsley or looming were substantial. The first task was to make the new organisation work. Several of the operating Divisions had new managing directors and there was a greatly increased central organisation; the Head Office staff grew from just over 100 to 140 and additional offices were rented in Bowater House, near 1 Knightsbridge Green, for the Directors and some of the central departments. Kinsley brought a new style of management, with the American concept of "completed staff work" and a greater measure of delegation than before. There were McKinsey schemes of "profit improvement programmes", "management action programmes", tactical and strategic planning and a continuing emphasis on measurement and the collection of marketing and other information.

There was a growing commitment to Belledune Fertilizer and to Long Harbour and major developments were under way in the UK. Capital expenditure in 1967 was higher than in any previous year. Kilns 4 and 5 at Whitehaven were commissioned during 1967, doubling the capacity for sulphuric acid and cement to 400,000 tons per annum. Commissioning began on the plants at Barton-on-Humber for the production of ammonium nitrate and high-analysis compound fertilisers. The expansion of chrome chemicals production at Eaglescliffe, making possible the closure of the Glasgow factory, was due to be commissioned in 1968. During 1967, an ammonium phosphates plant was completed at Kirkby and a continuous process plant for benzyl and benzal chloride at West Bank, Widnes. A pilot plant for the production of phosphine by a patented process was brought on stream at Oldbury; it was to prove one of A&W's most important innovations. The F4 phosphoric acid plant, using the Lopker technology, was authorised for Whitehaven, enabling two older plants to be closed. The formation of Marchon France was approved at the turn of the year. An expansion of sulphur dioxide capacity at Bromborough was authorised. And sales in 1967 exceeded £100 million for the first time.

There were, however, problems that were to grow into situations of critical difficulty in 1968 onwards. The almost overwhelming difficulties that developed at Belledune and Long Harbour have already been described. There was also the profoundly unsatisfactory position in Canadian fertilisers, based on Port Maitland, where sales were falling and losses increasing; in February 1968 the A&W Board expressed the hope that Kinsley would bring forward plans for dealing with the situation. Output from the Portishead phosphorus plant was low and the closure of the Oldbury plant had to be deferred. The plant at West Bank for the production of benzoic acid by air oxidation of toluene was overspent and repeatedly failed to work because of chemical attack on the materials of construction - a problem that was to persist until the end of 1968. The Barton prilling plant for high-analysis fertilisers suffered from caking difficulties until the latter part of 1969 and there was a succession of problems with the chrome chemicals plants at Eaglescliffe, leading to expenditure over the next three years that doubled the originally authorised cost of £2 million.

Midland Silicones in 1967 was highly profitable, achieving a trading profit of £1.2 million, equivalent to 25% on sales. Profits had been running at about that level since 1964, having grown rapidly since achieving the first profit in 1957. It was the largest manufacturer of silicones in Europe and since 1957 had spent over £4 million on plants and research and development facilities. A programme for a further £2 million expenditure in 1965-7 had been announced. The problem with Midland Silicones arose from its prosperity and from the fact that it was a company jointly owned by A&W (60%) and Dow Corning (of Midland, Michigan)(40%). Dow Corning was the source of most of the know-how employed in the company but as owner of only 40% of the share capital it did not have managerial control. In November 1966, Dow Corning proposed to set up its own sales company in the UK to sell against MS. A new 5-year agreement for the exchange of technology was signed in January 1967, which allowed Dow Corning to exploit silicones technology outside MS. By the middle of that year Dow Corning had confirmed its decision to sell against MS in the UK and the A&W Board decided to review its basic policy towards its partner. In January 1968 Dow Corning made an approach to buy A&W's holding in MS; the A&W Board was reluctant to sell. Two months later, Dow Corning offered its shareholding to A&W but the offer was rejected for fear that that would enable Dow Corning to enter fully into competition.

Pressure to end the partnership continued and in August A&W rejected an offer of £10 million for its holding and, reversing its earlier decision, indicated that it was willing to buy out its partner. For the time being, there was stalemate. Sales by MS continued to increase and Hans Limperg, a German electrical insulation company, was acquired. Profits, however, began to decline under the pressure of competition and the change in the partners' relationship. At the beginning of 1969, A&W agreed to set up a subsidiary of MS in the USA to sell in competition with Dow Corning, in retaliation for Dow Corning's action in the UK - which showed exasperation rather than an expectation of expanding profits.

Once again, the vulnerability of a joint venture position with a US company that was the source of the technology was demonstrated. In 1963, the partnership with Lubrizol had been terminated, with A&W's interest being bought for no more than a fraction of the profits that had been made in the heyday of the partnership. A&W's position in MS was stronger than in the Lubrizol venture because A&W had been in silicones almost from their beginning, MS was itself marketing to the end-customer and the joint company had quite extensive technical facilities at Barry. Nevertheless (as will be described later in this chapter) the partnership did not endure. To some extent, that was due to the parlous state of A&W at the end of the 1960s but it is hard to see how it could have continued without full cooperation between the partners.

Ed Kinsley was therefore faced with substantial problems in almost every part of the A&W Group. Profits had declined since the peak in 1965 and the Ordinary dividend was cut in 1967 to 15% from 21% in the previous two years. With accelerating capital expenditure and the investment in Belledune Fertilizer, borrowing was increasing rapidly from 15% of total capital employed at the start of 1965 to nearly 40% at the end of 1967.

The organisation and management of A&W were heavily dependent upon Kinsley. After the departure of Sir Sydney and the appointment of Sir Owen as Chairman, the resignation of Sir Frank and the changes in organisation, some concern was voiced in the Press about the management, including speculation in February 1968 that Dr Beeching (a former Director of ICI and best known for his pruning of the UK rail network) might be brought in as Chairman. Hill Samuel, A&W's merchant bank, was also concerned and in March 1968 persuaded A&W to appoint Sir Richard Powell, a Director of Hill Samuel, to the Board as a non-executive Director working one and a half days per week. Hill Samuel believed that it was not getting enough information, while being asked to assist particularly in financing for Canada.

Sir Richard had been Permanent Secretary of the Board of Trade (the Civil Servant at the head of the main Government department dealing with trade and industry) from 1960 until March 1968. Aged 58, he had had experience in several Civil Service departments, including periods in the United States and Australia. He joined Hill Samuel on retiring from the Civil Service. While, like Sir Owen, he had no direct experience in industry, he had had a great deal of contact with industrial companies.

Very soon after Sir Richard's appointment Ed Kinsley was taken ill with a malignant brain tumour. There is no indication that he had shown signs of his illness before March 1968, although there are some who think that it was having some effect before he left Canada. By June he was back, after surgery. At the Board meeting in June, Neil Peech (non-executive Director and Chairman of Steetley) said that he felt strongly that 19 people were too many to be reporting to Kinsley; in response, Sir Owen said that he would discuss with Kinsley ways of reducing the number. In the event, there was no change. It is not known what prognosis was made after Kinsley's operation. He himself, in a conversation at home with Wilf Shillaker, said how awful it was that after rising all the way up the scale he was going to lose everything because of his illness. Because of the possibility of recurrence of the tumour, it seems surprising that no steps were taken to reduce the load on the Chief Executive.

In the next four months, the cash position continued to cause concern, related to the requirements for Belledune and Long Harbour, both through remittances and potentially because of the guarantees that had been given by Albright & Wilson Ltd. Some relief was obtained through £2 million realised for part of the holding in

Hooker Chemical Company, when it was acquired by Occidental Petroleum, the balance being retained temporarily as Preference shares in Occidental. Hill Samuel demanded cash forecasts. It was reported that there were no capital expenditure plans for the Divisions, but it was estimated that about $20 million would be required to meet Canadian needs in the next two years. The auditors, Peat Marwick Mitchell, were called in to produce forecasts for 1968-71.

When Kinsley paid a visit to Canada in October there were reports of unusual and unacceptable behaviour by him. Then, at a meeting of the Chairman's Committee in London just after his return, on 17th October, he showed loss of speech and loss of continuity of thought that caused the Directors to call in the Company Medical Officer, Dr John Hughes, and a Consultant. Within a week Kinsley's condition had badly deteriorated. He died on 22nd December.

The crisis post-Kinsley

Wilson Carter kept a daily record of events from October 1968 to February 1969, which provides a detailed account of this critical period. He deals particularly with the financial position and the problems of organisation and direction. An important part was played by Hill Samuel, led by Kenneth Keith. KK complained that he was getting insufficient information and cooperation from A&W's Treasurer's Department and threatened to cease dealing with A&W. He also said that the organisation, especially the financial function, should be changed and strengthened.

A temporary reallocation of Kinsley's duties was arranged and Sir Owen was pressed by the other Directors to initiate a full reorganisation. Sir Owen then told Carter that he was coming to the view that A&W should be sold and aired the names of ICI, RTZ and BP. He thought ICI was unlikely because Sir Sydney had approached Holroyd of ICI in June 1967 and was told that ICI would not be interested. Alternatively, he thought that a Deputy Chairman should be appointed and the Board should then be reconstituted; names suggested were Beeching, or Iliffe or Aitken of Shell Chemical, but he doubted whether they would be interested. (Later, Sir Owen told Carter that he believed that what was required was a financial Deputy Chairman, rather than a technical man or one from the chemical industry.) Carter said to Hill Samuel that the interest in BFL should be sold as soon as possible and suggested Noranda (the eventual buyer - see page 118) or Canadian Industries (an ICI subsidiary). When Bob (later Sir Robert) Clark, Deputy Chairman of Hill Samuel, learnt of Sir Owen's view that A&W should be sold, he said "I hope you are not going to hawk yourself around. This could have disastrous effects". KK continued to press for a new Financial Director to replace Sherwood. Sir Owen, who was at that time acting as Chief Executive, indicated that he was looking to become a non-executive Chairman.

The immediate crisis at the beginning of November was the need for more cash for Erco, which had reached the limit of its borrowing facilities and was looking for a further $8 million. Hill Samuel was willing to lend $4.5 million against the security of the shares in Occidental; it was possible that they could find the balance through a European loan. The Directors' thoughts began to turn to the sale of parts of A&W, in particular parts of Erco and the holding in MS. Hill Samuel next reported that they could not raise a deutschemark loan and advised sale of the MS holding. Carter, however, was not prepared to sell MS and "pour the money down the Canadian drain" without tackling the cause of the problem and preferred to sell the whole of A&W. A team of 4 - Michael Peard (Development), Hugh Podger (Planning), Wilf Shillaker (Assistant Treasurer) and Tony Ward (Treasurer) - given the title of "Short Range Planning Group", was set up to look at various contingencies and solutions to problems.

In mid-November, Sir Owen visited ICI and asked Jack Callard (Deputy Chairman) if there were any likely candidates in ICI for the post of Managing Director of A&W; the response was that he would look into it but that ICI was short of good people. KK raised the same question with Sir Paul Chambers (former Chairman of ICI), who suggested Rowland Wright (the Personnel Director of ICI), but he eventually turned down the offer. KK on his own initiative also explored the possibility of a new Chairman for A&W; when told of that, Sir Owen indicated that he would have no objection to going.

The Peat Marwick report indicated that the financial situation could not be resolved through a loan because the possible maximum would not give any leeway for misfortunes. Hill Samuel again advocated selling MS, rather than the whole of A&W, since there was a possible quick buyer for MS and it was a bad time to try to sell A&W. The loan from Hill Samuel of Can.$5 million to meet Erco's outstanding bills was eventually approved by the Bank of England but $3 million more was forecast to be needed before the end of the year. KK also approached Warburgs to see if they might sound out FMC (a leading US producer of phosphorus and other chemicals) about putting capital and management into Erco. Early in December Sir Owen and Sherwood with the senior Erco management met FMC in New York. While FMC were interested in A&W's Canadian operations, they made it clear that what they really wanted was some arrangement involving A&W as a whole. Within two weeks of his return to London, Sir Owen decided to have no further discussions with FMC.

In London, meanwhile, the financial crisis was resolved for the time being through an agreement by Lloyds Bank (A&W's original and continuing bankers) to lend $7.5 million until March 1969, with an option to June 1969, provided that Hill Samuel continued its $5 million loan over the same period, which was agreed.

The crisis of management continued. John Hutton-Wilson (Joint Deputy

Chairman) told Carter that he was considering resigning in protest against the delays in tackling the crisis and ineffective management; the situation appeared to be out of Sir Owen's control. Carter interpreted that as an attempt to ask him to conduct a palace revolution, which he did not wish to do. Sir Owen attempted to persuade Carter to act as Managing Director for 3 or 4 months but Carter refused on grounds of age (he was due to retire at the end of the year). Sir Richard Powell believed that Hill Samuel would force a reorganisation of the Board and asked Carter to stay until the end of March 1969. He said that there was progress towards recruiting a chief executive: ICI was to be asked again if someone could come from there.

While the search for a chief executive was being pursued, it was decided that the organisation would revert to having executive directors reporting to a chief executive. If no external person could be found, a Managing Director would have to be found from existing resources. Sir Owen saw a number of leaders of major UK companies - Val Duncan of RTZ, Lord Netherthorpe of Fisons, David Barron of Shell, George Ashford of BP Chemicals, Peter Allen of ICI, Denning Pearson of Rolls-Royce and George Cole of Unilever - and it was agreed to employ headhunters as well. Increasingly, opinions were being expressed that Sir Owen should resign, not only by several of his fellow Directors but also by senior staff in the operating Divisions and by Kenneth Keith and Bob Clark of Hill Samuel (communicating to Sir Richard Powell, who was seen as a possible part-time Chairman). John Hutton-Wilson suggested David Livingstone for the job of Managing Director; Peter Baines told Sir Owen that he would be prepared to take the job.

In the event, nothing came of the search outside the company for a chief executive. Increasing pressure was brought to bear by Hill Samuel, who had had conversations with the Prudential Assurance Company which (untypically) authorised Hill Samuel to say that they were unhappy, in their position as Debenture holder and the largest institutional shareholder. In June 1969, Sir Owen resigned from the Board and Sir Richard became Chairman, on a part-time basis. John Hutton-Wilson was appointed Deputy Chairman and Managing Director. Sherwood resigned and Carter, Piercy and John Christopherson agreed to stay only until the end of September. Five new executive Directors, all in their forties, were appointed: Peter Baines (Commercial), John Hughes (Technical), David Livingstone (Operations), Michael Peard (Planning) and Tony Ward (Finance); Bertram White remained on the Board, with responsibility for the Personnel function. Responsibility for the operating Divisions was divided between Baines, Livingstone and White. The McKinsey pattern of organisation was thus abandoned, except for the general concept of operating through Divisions rather than subsidiary companies.

The Press release announcing the Board changes included a statement by Sir Owen: "It has been clear to us for some time that younger blood is needed in our top management. The death of Mr Kinsley caused us to revise our plans which now come to be announced at a time when we are faced with special difficulties in Canada".

The difficulties in Canada, at Long Harbour, Belledune and Port Maitland, have already been described. The Short Range Planning Group had produced forecasts for BFL, with the most optimistic showing further substantial loans every year from 1969 to 1972. Several companies, including Occidental, Texas Gulf, CIL (ICI in Canada), American Cyanamid, FMC and Burmah Oil, were showing interest in acquiring parts or the whole of A&W. The situation was precarious.

One helpful easing of the situation was that, as a result of a report by the Short Range Planning Group on the financial situation, Hill Samuel agreed early in January 1969 that the sale of MS was no longer needed for cash reasons. The A&W Board then decided that it did not wish to sell its holding and would not reconsider its decision for any offer below £12.5 million; it was also not interested in buying Dow Corning's 40%. When Dow Corning offered £10 million a month later, the A&W Board therefore rejected the offer and decided to set up a subsidiary in the USA in competition. As the year went on, however, and the problems in Canada grew more serious and persistent, Hill Samuel renewed pressure, through requesting further cash forecasts and raising the rate of interest on its loan by 1%, to 9.5%; at the end of June, the loan was extended, at a rate of interest of 11.5%.

In August, Dow Corning set a time-limit of the end of the year for purchase of A&W's 60% holding in MS. The Board's response was to approach ICI for a merger of the two companies' interests in silicones, but ICI's agreement with General Electric (of the USA) would not permit it to do that without the consent of GE, for five years. A&W had calculated that a 50/50 deal with ICI would financially be on a par with a sale of A&W's holding in MS to Dow Corning for £8 million - the valuation of the company was clearly falling. By the beginning of 1970, it was agreed in principle for ICI to lend A&W £3 million to enable it to buy out Dow Corning, following which ICI would acquire 40% of MS; if GE agreed, ICI would raise its stake to 50% and its silicone business would then be merged with MS. Dow Corning then indicated that it was agreeable to the sale of its holding, but rejected the offer from A&W. When A&W proposed to reorganise the Board of MS and to appoint John Hughes as Managing Director, Dow Corning would not agree. Relations between the partners deteriorated. In August 1970, Hill Samuel reported on A&W's financial position: it estimated that A&W would have an overdraft in the UK of £4 million at the end of 1970, rising to £10 million at the end of 1972, and recommended the sale of MS. To this the Board reluctantly agreed.

ICI and Bayer (the other main European producer of silicones), when approached to buy A&W's 60%, replied that they were not interested. Hill Samuel then notified Lazards (Dow Corning's merchant banker) in November that A&W's holding was on offer at £4.75 million (excluding some minor non-silicone operations). In December, Dow Corning was told that A&W required an offer of not less than £4 million. Finally, in February 1971, A&W agreed to sell its holding for £3.525 million.

The Chairman's Statement in the annual report for 1970 explained the sale as follows: "For some years Midland Silicones has been operating within an international market which has become progressively more competitive. The nature of the business has also been suffering the characteristic change from an innovative one, with many new and potential applications, to one with reduced prospects of growth and a declining rate of return. At the same time, the need for new and replacement plants has increased the future cash needs of the business. After careful examination, we concluded that the very substantial new investment in plant and equipment that would have been required in the near future would not have been sufficiently profitable".

Yet in February 1970 the A&W Board had approved a statement of corporate objectives and strategies for the next ten years that was based on a shift away from phosphorus and its derivatives, in favour of chrome chemicals, silicones and the BBA business. And Dow Corning in the next twenty years invested some £40 million at Barry. For A&W, it was a sad (though perhaps inevitable) end to an involvement in silicones that had begun nearly 25 years earlier.

Tenneco

In view of the severe difficulties being experienced by A&W and the interest expressed by several companies in acquiring some or all of the Company, one of the studies made by the Short Range Planning Group towards the end of 1968 consisted of an analysis of possible predators and the likely consequences of acquisition by them. The general conclusion was that acquisition would be followed by submergence, with at best a limited degree of autonomy. If unavoidable, there was a preference for acquisition by a UK company - ICI (but believed unlikely) or one of the oil companies, Shell, BP or Burmah, with Burmah thought to be the most acceptable.

In June 1969, soon after he had become Chairman, Sir Richard Powell reported to the Board that he had been invited by Robert Fleming (one of the leading merchant banks in London) "to meet a representative of Tenneco Corporation who was interested in the Company". Tenneco was absent from A&W's list of possible predators and nobody in Albright & Wilson had heard of the company.

A history of Tenneco

Tenneco's origin was the Tennessee Gas and Transmission Company (TGT), which was founded in April 1940 by a group of speculators who had the idea of building a natural gas pipeline to serve Tennessee. They lacked gas reserves, however, and the financial backing necessary to obtain approval from the Federal Power Commission. In September 1943 they therefore sold out to the Chicago Corporation, a company formed when the passing of the Glass-Stegall Act forced the Illinois Merchant Trust Company to separate its investment banking and commercial banking operations. One of the activities of the Chicago Corporation in the 1930s and early 1940s was "work outs" (reconstructions or liquidations) of businesses that in the years of the Great Depression had proved to be bad investments by the bank. Among their investments was TGT and a gas plant at Agua Dulce in Texas.

One of the Vice-Presidents of the Chicago Corporation at that time was Gardiner Symonds, a remarkable man, one of the great entrepreneurs of his time and a financier of genius. Born in Pittsburgh in 1903, Gardiner had graduated as a geologist at Stanford before going to the Harvard Business School, where he graduated no. 1 in his class in 1927. He joined the Illinois Merchant Trust Company in Chicago and became engaged in the work-out operations of the Chicago Corporation. He was directly engaged in the acquisition of TGT, and in the application to the Federal Power Commission for consent to build a pipeline from South Texas to West Virginia. It is said that Gardiner's plan for TGT was formed around the kitchen table of his house in Corpus Christi.

Gardiner saw the need to move gas from Texas (where people were being paid by the oil companies to take it because they were not allowed to flare gas) to the Appalachian area of West Virginia (where war production was seriously in need of natural gas). It was first necessary to persuade the Federal Power Commission to allow a private pipeline to carry the gas for which the government was the customer. Fortunately, the War Production Board stated that "A new transmission line must be built as an essential part of the war program" and a certificate was granted in September 1943. Under Gardiner's direction, the first ground was broken in December 1943 and the first pipe laid in January 1944. By the end of October 1944, a 1,265-mile pipeline had been completed, despite shortages of materials and relatively primitive techniques.

In September of the following year, Gardiner was able to persuade the Chicago Corporation to let him see what he could do with the business and, with financial assistance from Stone & Webster and White, Weld, formed a syndicate to buy the bank's interest. The syndicate soon after sold the stock to the public and so what was to become Tenneco (the name Tenneco Inc. was adopted in 1966) came into being, with Gardiner as its president and chief executive.

From that starting point, capacity was increased. In the 1950s and 1960s the pipelines were extended to New York and New England, into new areas of the eastern United States, to the Toronto area and to the Midwest. The Company became the largest US natural gas transporter.

At the same time, Gardiner embarked upon a programme of diversification. During the first twenty years of the programme, the diversification was linked with the original business, starting with oil and gas production in 1946. In the background, the pipeline provided a solid cash foundation, both in the revenues from transmission and in the facility for raising capital through pipeline bonds. The company also acquired interests in insurance, as part of Gardiner's financial plan, through the creation of Tennessee Life Insurance Co. in 1952, initially to deal with employee insurance plans; in 1967 Tennessee Life was merged into Philadelphia Life Insurance, giving Tenneco a 25% holding in that major insurance company. An investment in the Tennessee Bank & Trust Company in 1961 and its merger into the Houston National Bank in 1964, giving Tenneco a 37% holding in the merged company, was part of the same strategy.

There were real-estate operations, primarily relating to the premises required by the Company; thus in 1955 the subsidiary Ten-Ten Travis Corporation (named after the address in Houston) built a multi-storey garage in the centre of Houston, which was claimed to be the largest in the southern USA. Later, there was substantial investment in offices in downtown and outer Houston.

The direction in which the business operations were developing was indicated by the extraction of hydrocarbons from gas, which began in 1950. 1955 was a year of high activity: the assets of Bay Petroleum Corporation were acquired, including oil and gas production in the USA and Canada, two oil refineries and retail outlets; and Petro-Tex Chemical Corporation was formed, jointly owned by FMC (Food Machinery and Chemical Corporation), to purchase a government-owned plant in Houston manufacturing butadiene (one of the two chief ingredients in synthetic rubber). In 1956 a new subsidiary (Tennessee Products Pipeline Company) purchased a 50-acre site on the Houston Ship Channel for the manufacture of petrochemicals from liquid hydrocarbons transported by pipeline, including a 240-mile line from one of the Company's natural gas processing plants. The Company had thus entered into chemical operations, albeit very different from those of Albright & Wilson.

Three years later the foundation for expanded petrochemical operations was laid through the purchase of another site of nearly 800 acres on the Houston Ship Channel and in 1961 Tenneco Chemical Company was formed to build and operate plants on that site. Initially acetylene was made from methane and processed into vinyl chloride monomer(VCM) for shipment to Cary Chemicals, a company in New Jersey making polyvinyl chloride (PVC) and other derivatives of VCM; the Company acquired a 48% holding in Cary. In the next few years ammonia and methanol were added to its manufactures. At the same time Petro-Tex was expanding the range of its petrochemicals into maleic anhydride, fumaric acid, isobutylene and other intermediates for the plastics and chemical industries.

Of more relevance to A&W was Tenneco's acquisition in 1963 of Heyden Newport Chemical Corporation, a publicly-quoted company with annual sales of $65 million, assets of $75 million, ten manufacturing sites in the USA and 2,150 employees. The company had been built up over a period of 60 years from the amalgamation of a number of small units distinguished by their diversity rather than by a major position in the chemical industry. There were four divisions. The Heyden division had two sites in New Jersey. Garfield manufactured benzoic acid and derivatives including sodium benzoate and salicylic acid - its product range was similar to that of A&W at West Bank, Widnes; although the factory was old and on a constricted site, it was superior to West Bank in efficiency and working-conditions. Fords made benzyl chloride but also maleic anhydride and other organic chemicals. The Newport division produced rosin (the residue of turpentine distillation), pine oil and turpentine and derivatives; these products, based on the processing of tree stumps, were generally described as "naval stores" from their historical application to the timbers of naval vessels. (BBA's involvement in synthetic aromatic chemicals derived from turpentine provided a further point of relevance.) The Nuodex division manufactured speciality chemicals, primarily paint driers and fungicides, plasticizers and stabilisers for plastics, and additives for food processing, metal finishing and paper-making. Again there were points of relevance. The fourth division, American Plastics Corporation, was a custom moulder of plastic articles (bottles and other containers), with a factory in New York State.

Tenneco's chemical interests grew in the years after 1963. In 1965, Tenneco Chemicals Inc. was created, with a headquarters in New York, to manage Heyden Newport, Tenneco Chemical Company (later renamed Tenneco Hydrocarbon Chemicals) and Cary Chemicals (renamed Tenneco Plastics). There followed numerous small acquisitions in colours, plastics, paper sizing chemicals and other chemicals.They included Butler Chemicals, on a site at Avonmouth (near Bristol, England), manufacturing organic phosphorus compounds and a customer of A&W for its principal raw material. Companies were formed in Mexico, the Netherlands, Germany and South Africa, and a 40% share was taken in a phthalic anhydride venture with US Steel Chemicals. By 1969, there were 12 divisions and subsidiaries, with 42 plants in America and 15 in other countries. Sales of chemicals in 1969 were nearly $250 million (£100 million) and profit before interest and tax was $20 million (£8.3 million); the corresponding figures for A&W in that year were £120 million and £5.3 million.

Meanwhile Tenneco had broadened its diversification. First, in 1965 Packaging Corporation of America was acquired. The 1965 annual report described the strategy in the following words: "Natural gas transportation, integrated oil, chemicals and packaging - these are the result of a planned program to broaden the profit base of the Company through entry into new but related fields. All rely at least in part upon natural resources, and all have product relationships which offer remarkable potential for future growth". After that acquisition, with more than half of the sales and profits not from gas transmission, the name of the company was changed from Tennessee Gas Transmission Company to Tenneco.

The acquisition of greatest long-term significance, of the Kern County Land Company, took place in 1967. Tenneco's sales were thereby increased by more than 40%. The annual report for 1967 commented: "Tenneco, already broadly diversified, acquired new dimensions as a major diversified industrial complex". The acquisition took place following an approach by Kern County, seeking a "white knight" to rescue it from a bid by Occidental Petroleum. The battle between Tenneco and Occidental was fierce and led to colourful reports in the Press of some of the means alleged to have been adopted by both sides before Tenneco won.

Kern County Land Company (KCLC), named after the area of California from which it originated, owed its creation to the key importance of water in that part of California; control of water sources led to the ownership of large tracts of land. The company in 1969 operated 900 miles of canals, taking water from the Kern River and selling water to private and public customers. In 1969, the company owned 1.8 million acres and leased a further 700,000 acres; of the total (three times the size of Rhode Island, the smallest of the United States), 400,000 acres were in California, and over 1 million acres in each of Arizona and New Mexico. The land was used by KCLC for agricultural crops, including citrus fruits and almonds, cattle ranching, undeveloped grazing and urban developments - the last-named being in the form of communities including commercial and industrial property, residential property, schools, parks and churches. The scope for enhancing the value of the land was considerable.

KCLC was also engaged in oil and gas production and was receiving royalties from other producers on its land in California, Texas, New Mexico, Louisiana, Canada and Australia. While those operations added usefully to Tenneco's similar operations, the activities that were to prove of greatest significance to Tenneco were in manufacturing. KCLC owned the Walker Manufacturing Company, a supplier of exhaust systems, filters and other items to the automobile industry, with sales of nearly $90 million and headquarters in Racine, Wisconsin; the automotive operations were to prove a profitable long-term interest for Tenneco.

KCLC also had a 54% interest in J.I. Case Company, a manufacturer of agricultural and construction equipment, established for 125 years. Case had plants and sales offices in England, France and Australia and sales subsidiaries in Brazil, Japan and Hong Kong. In 1967, two-thirds of Case's sales of $340 million were of agricultural equipment but faster growth was expected in construction equipment, particularly backhoe loaders. Soon after Case came under Tenneco ownership, there were two acquisitions of manufacturers of construction equipment, namely

Drott Manufacturing and Davis Manufacturing. In 1967, however, Case made a loss, because of the softness of the market in farm equipment and the effects of what was described as an aggressive drive for increased market share in a domestic market where Case ranked fifth or sixth by size. In the years ahead, Case was to have a disproportionately important impact on Tenneco; some of the reasons for that were present when it became part of Tenneco.

A further important step in Tenneco's diversification was taken in September 1968 with the acquisition of Newport News Shipbuilding & Dry Dock Company, the largest privately-owned shipyard in the USA. The annual report for 1968 portrayed the acquisition as an expansion of Tenneco's manufacturing interests, created through the acquisition of the Walker and Case businesses within KCLC.

It was also said to be a result of Gardiner's wish to enter into a business largely supplying government, one of the major sectors of the US economy. Newport News's principal activity was the building of aircraft carriers and submarines for the US Navy: in 1968, the aircraft carrier John F. Kennedy was commissioned and work was started on the second nuclear-powered carrier, the Nimitz, while two nuclear attack submarines were delivered and a further two launched and eight Polaris submarines were undergoing overhaul. The yard was also building naval cargo ships and guided missile frigates. At that time there was also substantial activity in building and overhauling commercial vessels; later the commercial activity virtually ceased, as shipbuilding in other countries became more economical. Newport News continued to be the only builder of aircraft carriers and one of only two companies building submarines for the US Navy. In 1968, its revenues were about $300 million, giving a profit of around $20 million before interest and tax.

In the 1968 annual report of Tenneco, the Letter to Stockholders opened with the words: "Corporate growth comes not only from the identification of profit opportunities, but from the planned and purposeful development of the potential which they provide. This is the motivation that permeates Tenneco's long-standing program of diversification". The preamble to the report was in similar vein: "Building businesses is our business - those five words sum up Tenneco's point of view about diversification. Diversification, of course, is something Tenneco believes in. And always has. But in our dictionary diversification is quite different from conglomeration. Meaning that we don't believe in just collecting companies, but in making them grow". At that time there were several major US companies, such as ITT, classed as conglomerates. It was not for many years that there was a general reversal of the trend towards diversification and adoption of the principle of "Stick to your knitting" (Peters & Waterman, "In Pursuit of Excellence").

Gardiner Symonds had been remarkably successful in creating a major US corporation in the 25 years since he started with Tennessee Gas and Transmission

Company. The results for 1968 compared with those for 1945, the first year as a publicly-owned company, show the progress made:-

	$ million	
	1945	**1968**
Operating revenues	14	2,063
Net income	4	167
Income per average common share (dollars)	0.48	2.21
Total capitalisation	65	3,136

Tenneco's approach to Albright & Wilson

There were several reasons for Gardiner's interest in Albright & Wilson. Urged on by Si(mon) Askin, Vice-Chairman of Tenneco and in charge of its chemical operations, he was seeking to expand Tenneco's chemical interests, particularly outside the United States, to get a wider window on the world. He considered investing in Laporte and Courtaulds but A&W appeared a more suitable target.

A&W's shares in mid-1969 were looking relatively cheap. They had risen well from around 14 shillings in December 1966 to over 22 shillings in September 1968, despite a cut in dividend for 1967 from 21% to 15%. There appeared to be general optimism that A&W would show a substantial improvement in 1969. The Daily Telegraph wrote of a "quietly reassuring picture" and The Sun wrote that "the following year should be a year of wonders". The Times, however, had reservations: "Unless the chairman is more forthcoming in his statement, the share price will be dictated more by the recent history of management disputes and by falling profit margins than by improved outlook". The half-year statement published in September 1968 announced a further cut in dividend. The Times attacked A&W for a "second apparent dividend cut without a word of explanation". Thereafter the share price declined. When the results for the full year 1968 were published in March 1969 and the dividend cut was restored, the share price recovered some ground, until the announcement of the fish-kill in Newfoundland caused the price to plummet to a little over 11 shillings (55p.) in June 1969.

One of Gardiner's sons, Taft, was working at that time in London, for the merchant bank Robert Fleming. Gardiner asked him for his analysis of Albright & Wilson. Taft confirmed that the company had had problems and had fallen out of favour with the stock market; the banks were edgy, the company was not making any money and the situation was probably getting worse. The company did, however, have potential and the stock was cheap (for a time falling below its par value of 25p.). Acquisition of A&W would therefore be a good move. The project was then given the code name 'Root Beer', after the beverage 'A&W', popular in America.

At the A&W Board meeting in July 1969, Sir Richard Powell reported that he had met Gardiner Symonds, who had visited London. With Gardiner was Sydney Ellis, who had been appointed a Director and Vice-Chairman of Tenneco after ten years as President of Petro-Tex. Gardiner told Sydney Ellis that he wanted to look at Albright & Wilson to see if it could be put right. He told Sir Richard that he would like to consider either a minority stake in the company or a "complete link". Sir Richard, however, said that A&W was too busy to discuss the proposal then but would revert to it "if we were interested".

Shortly after that the Managing Director of Burmah Oil expressed a wish to acquire A&W; his plan was for FMC to acquire Long Harbour and some or all of the rest of Erco and for Burmah to build a phosphorus plant in the UK, based on power from surplus fuel oil. Sir Richard responded that no help was needed. Burmah then agreed that further discussion could be delayed until the Spring of 1970 and that they would not involve FMC.

In October Gardiner Symonds and Sydney Ellis met Kenneth Keith and Bob Clark of Hill Samuel and arranged to buy just over 10% of A&W's Ordinary shares in the market at a price of 37.5p.. (Sydney Ellis recalls that Gardiner then said that he should perhaps telephone Dick Freeman, the Chief Executive and President of Tenneco, who was chairing a Board meeting of Tenneco in Houston that day, to tell him that he had spent £5 million of Tenneco's money.) Soon after, Sir Richard and John Hutton-Wilson lunched with Gardiner, Sydney Ellis and Dick Freeman and were told of Tenneco's investment. Gardiner told Sir Richard that Tenneco had no present intention of increasing their holding and that they wished to have talks to discuss cooperation in non-competitive fields. The reaction from Sir Richard and John Hutton-Wilson has been described as at best coldly polite.

The view taken by the A&W Board at its next meeting was that A&W wished to remain an independent company but that it was realistic to suppose that Tenneco would not be prepared to remain a 10% holder. The Board agreed that if A&W needed to merge with another company, Tenneco was not the best partner and that ICI should be sounded out to see if it would maintain its non-interventionist stance if Tenneco or anyone else bid for control. Nothing came of that approach. There seems to have been a special reluctance in A&W to accept control by Americans. It is not clear why that should have been so, particularly in the light of the very human and non-aggressive attitude of Gardiner and Sydney. Robert Clark, of Hill Samuel, described Gardiner as a typical American Chairman but someone who had great charm and got on well with Europeans. It may be correct to assume that there would have been a similar reluctance towards any non-British bidder.

The Press statement issued by A&W concerning the Tenneco shareholding stated "in existing circumstances Tenneco has no intention of materially increasing this holding". Sir Richard issued a statement to employees saying "It is clear from public comments made by Tenneco that their prime concern is technological cooperation, and that it was with this in mind that they acquired their shareholding. They also regard their shareholding as an investment in a company which, despite the difficulties of the immediate past that are now showing their effects on current profitability and on the share price, has excellent prospects in the longer term. The Board therefore regard the acquisition of these shares as a mark of confidence in the company...The Board see no reason to think that the unity and autonomy of A&W will be jeopardised by the acquisition of this holding by Tenneco or by any action that A&W may decide to take to develop cooperation with Tenneco where this could be shown to be advantageous".

There was an exchange of visits to chemical plants and some conversations between the parties but no appreciable cooperation. When Bayer, in April 1970, proposed a link with A&W in chrome chemicals, flavours & fragrances and silicones and a link with Hoechst in phosphorus chemicals, the A&W Board agreed to explore the possibility, believing that there was little attraction in a wider association with Tenneco. (Nothing came of the idea.) When it became necessary to sell the holding in MS, Tenneco said that they hoped A&W would not sell without prior reference. Hill Samuel, however, advised that nothing should be said to Tenneco until agreement had been reached with Dow Corning. As A&W's financial situation deteriorated, there were several approaches to purchase parts of the company: British Oxygen for chrome chemicals, American Cyanamid for the Port Maitland dicalcium phosphate business, RTZ for sulphur chemicals. A&W tried unsuccessfully to interest ICI in ACC's fertiliser operations.

Towards the end of November 1970, the seriousness of the situation was marked by the issue of a letter from Sir Richard to all stockholders. It started "I regret to have to inform you of circumstances that have arisen since the issue of the Interim Statement for 1970 that have invalidated the forecast of improved profits in the second half of this year". The adverse circumstances listed in the letter were the problems at Long Harbour; production difficulties at Whitehaven in the sulphuric acid/cement plant and the decline in profitability at MS. It was expected that A&W would make a loss in the second half of 1970. (In the event, a profit was shown for the second half, but only because provisions against the value of the investment in BFL and against redundancy costs were excluded from the profit & loss account; no final dividend, however, was declared for 1970, the Ordinary shareholders' total dividend for the year being a token 2%, against 7% in 1969 and

15% in 1968.) The letter to stockholders caused the price of the shares, which had been in decline in 1969 and 1970, to fall from 7 shillings (35p.) to 4 shillings (20p.), which was below the par value of 5 shillings (25p.).

John Hutton-Wilson, as Managing Director, sent a letter to all employees a week after the letter to the stockholders. It repeated the account of the reasons for the decline in profits and went on to list measures being taken to improve the cash situation: redundancies, cuts in capital expenditure, reductions in inventories, etc.. The Albright Magazine reported that steps were being taken to reduce the cost of its production and commented "Albright & Wilson is struggling". Nearly 600 redundancies were declared at the end of 1970, the hardest hit functions being research & development and engineering; it was accepted that that could be damaging for development.

Also in November 1970 Tenneco proposed to sell its chemicals operations, excluding plastics, hydrocarbons and General Foam, to A&W in exchange for shares in A&W; that would have added about 50% to A&W's sales. Tenneco would also buy more shares in the market, would have two seats on the A&W Board and would find capital for development. Kenneth Keith (of Hill Samuel) persuaded Tenneco not to buy more shares in the market until more thought had been given to the idea of merging the chemical interests. Gardiner Symonds agreed to defer action for 90 days.

The first response of the A&W Board to the proposals by Tenneco was to institute a study of other potential partners. Then in January 1971, the A&W Board agreed not to give Tenneco any more information and not to allow Tenneco staff to visit Long Harbour. They were to be treated no differently from any other shareholder. Sir Richard, however, explained that he had doubts about the Company's ability to continue independently. It would be difficult to promote the necessary growth from its own resources. He regarded Tenneco as a safety net, to which the Company could turn if things went seriously wrong in Newfoundland. Although that view was discussed, other Directors expressed the view that A&W's shareholders would benefit more if the Company remained independent and that it was in their interest to delay any merger or bid for as long as possible to allow time for the share price to recover.

Tenneco's response in February was to make known their disappointment at not receiving the information they were seeking or being allowed to visit Long Harbour. They dropped the idea of merging chemical interests and said that they were keen to bid for the whole company. Sir Richard asked what Tenneco would do with A&W if acquired. In March, Tenneco said that they would not accept further delay and that if the A&W Directors would not acquiesce Tenneco would buy shares in the market. Reluctantly, A&W agreed to negotiate and to allow visits to Long Harbour and other sites. After visiting Long Harbour, Tenneco reported that they were satisfied that the plant could be made to work at its rated capacity. They indicated a price of 6 shillings per share for all the shares not held by them. That was unacceptable to the A&W Board.

The answer then put forward by Tenneco and accepted by A&W was for Tenneco to provide funds in the form of a 15-year convertible Debenture. The amount of the Debenture was determined by the conversion price; negotiation started with the par value of 5 shillings (25 pence) and ended with agreement on 32.5 pence for conversion before the end of 1976, 37.5 pence in the next 5 years and 42.5 pence in the final 5 years. Hence Tenneco lent £17.5 million, which would give a majority holding (just over 50%) after conversion at the lowest price. Sir Richard said at the Board meeting in March that he regarded Tenneco's offer as an opportunity not to be missed: it would provide an injection of cash that would transform the business and remove the strait-jacket caused by the cash shortage; there had been very little cushion against setbacks such as in Newfoundland, a severe recession or a prolonged strike. David Livingstone eventually alone opposed the proposal but said that he would not sustain his objection.

In his speech to the Annual Meeting in June 1971, Sir Richard said "before they decided to recommend the proposal, the Board reviewed all other possible courses of action with their advisers, and satisfied themselves that the Tenneco proposal was the only practicable one available to them. The directors would in my view have been imprudent and culpable if they had rejected it in the light of the circumstances that I set out in the Annual Report and have elaborated today; and despite some natural and nostalgic regret over this change in the status of a long-established British company, I am firmly convinced that it is in the best interest of all affected by it....Whatever we may feel about it, the day of the international company is already here and the activities of such companies will become an increasingly dominant influence in the economics of the industrial companies...I expect great gains to Albright & Wilson from forging this stronger link with Tenneco, which is a large, powerful and internationally-minded corporation. Opportunities can be opened up to us in the greatest market in the world, the United States".

It is interesting to note that at the end of 1971 the total of cash and short-term investments held by the A&W Group was nearly £22 million (including the £17.5 million injected by Tenneco) and that, apart from a dip to £15 million at the end of 1972, the figure was in excess of £22 million every year until 1978. At the same time, borrowings were reduced every year after 1971. The principal value of the Tenneco investment was thus not the cash injected but the security and stability provided by Tenneco's power to acquire majority control of the company. Predators were kept off, while Tenneco did not attempt to submerge A&W in a way that would have been likely if the company had been acquired by ICI or one of the German successors of I.G. Farben (Bayer, BASF and Hoechst).

In his letter to the stockholders of A&W accompanying the notice of the Extraordinary General Meeting called to approve the deal with Tenneco, Sir Richard wrote: "The Chairman of the Board of Tenneco has confirmed that it is the intention of Tenneco that A&W should continue to be directed in the interests of all its stockholders...Mr Symonds has also given assurances that it is Tenneco's intention that A&W will continue to be operated as an autonomous unit under its present management; and that not only will the interests of the employees be fully safeguarded but also their prospects will be enhanced by A&W's association with Tenneco". In an interview for the Albright Magazine, John Hutton-Wilson said: "full thought was given by the directors to other partners, including those in EEC. After carefully considering all the potential choices we were satisfied that Tenneco would bring to us what we most needed to strengthen and develop the company...we will have a great deal of independence and initiative within a very big organisation. We shall enjoy to some extent, I think, the benefits of both worlds".

At the Extraordinary General Meeting in June the deal with Tenneco was approved but only after a long and at times angry meeting in a very full room. The stockholders, most of whom opposed the deal, had seen their dividend cut severely and the share price down to a fraction of what most had paid, directly or through take-overs. For some time, the price would be held down by the prospective dilution of the equity through conversion of Tenneco's debenture. The possibility of an offer for its shares by another company had disappeared.

One of the conditions of the deal with Tenneco was that three Tenneco representatives would be appointed to the A&W Board - Gardiner Symonds, Sydney Ellis and Ray Marks (President of Tenneco Chemicals Inc.) - while John Hutton-Wilson would go onto the Board of Tenneco Chemicals. Just before the Tenneco representatives were due to go to London for the EGM, Gardiner Symonds secretly (telling only his secretary) went into hospital in Houston, because of an increasing problem with his heart. There he died, from a major heart attack, at the age of 68. Sydney Ellis, after he had arrived in London, learnt of Gardiner's death and telephoned Dick Freeman, who became Chairman in succession to Gardiner, and asked him to come to London to vouch for Tenneco. He did so and joined the A&W Board, but could not bring Gardiner's vision to the affairs of A&W. Sir Richard recalls a meeting with Gardiner when he said "Let's dream a little". He was irreplaceable.

Chapter 5

THE YEARS OF RECOVERY

1971 - 1978

"Albright & Wilson has proved to be a text-book example of recovery from a period of poor trading caused by a critically large capital project which went sour" (Investors Chronicle September 1974)

Overview

The 1970s were a period of economic turbulence, internationally but particularly marked in Britain. They were also a time of recovery for Albright & Wilson, from a position of near-disaster to a peak of profit.

Economic & political background

- China was admitted to the UN General Assembly in place of Taiwan in October 1971
- BP's interests in Libya were nationalised in December 1971
- the UK, Ireland and Denmark became members of the European Economic Community in January 1973; a referendum in June 1975, after terms were renegotiated, confirmed membership by 2 to 1
- the war in Vietnam ended in January 1973 and the last US soldiers left in March 1973; the country was reunified in June 1976
- the Berlin wall was partly opened in March 1972 and a treaty between West and East Germany was signed in December 1972
- Israeli athletes were killed at the Munich Olympics in September 1972
- the 16-day Arab-Israeli "Yom Kippur" war in October 1973 was followed by a cut in Arab oil supplies
- Harold Wilson succeeded Edward Heath as Prime Minister in March 1974 and governed with a minority until October 1974; he resigned in March 1976 and was succeeded by Jim Callaghan
- Margaret Thatcher became leader of the Conservative party in February 1975
- Turkish forces occupied Northern Cyprus in August 1974
- President Nixon resigned in August 1974 as a result of the Watergate affair
- the Khmer Rouge took power in Cambodia in April 1975
- the Suez Canal was reopened in March 1975, after 8 years
- the first oil flowed from the BP Forties field in the North Sea in November 1975
- in Northern Ireland, direct rule was imposed in March 1972, two months after "Bloody Sunday" in Londonderry; internment without trial was introduced in August 1971 and abandoned in December 1975; bombing continued in England throughout the period
- Concorde entered service in January 1976
- there were riots in Soweto in June 1976
- an explosion at the Nypro works at Flixborough killed 29 in June 1974 and an explosion at Seveso, in Italy, contaminated an area of 7 km radius with dioxins in July 1976
- Mao Tse-tung died in September 1976

- Jimmy Carter was elected President of the USA in November 1976
- Spain held its first free general election for 41 years in June 1977
- the Rhodesian Unilateral Declaration of Independence by Ian Smith was ended by agreement in March 1978 on majority rule
- Acts were passed in July 1978 providing for assemblies for Scotland and Wales but failed to secure endorsement in referenda.

At the beginning of this period, the main feature of the international economic scene was the balance of payments problem in the USA. With a fixed price for gold, of $35 an ounce, and fixed parities for the major currencies according to the Bretton Woods Agreement, the US deficits resulted first in the accumulation of dollar balances by the other members of the Group of Ten and then in the run down of the gold reserves of the USA. After revaluation of the deutschemark in May 1971, the USA in August imposed a 10% surcharge on imports and suspended the convertibility of dollars into gold. Then in December, the dollar was devalued against gold by 8%, the deutschemark and yen were revalued upwards and Britain and France maintained their exchange rates against gold, while for all currencies exchange rates were to be allowed to vary by 2.25% up or down. The new official rate for gold, of $38 per ounce, applied only to central bank transactions. The free market price of gold then rose to $70. After the official price was raised a further 10% in February 1973, the free market price continued to rise, reaching $180 by the end of 1974, at which point the official price was abolished. The process of realignment of exchange rates was carried further when the yen was allowed to float (upwards) and then by the agreement of the EEC countries to link their exchange rates in what became known as the "snake in the tunnel", floating against the dollar. Britain, Ireland and Italy had a modified form of floating, in recognition of their balance of payments difficulties.

The second major economic factor was the move by OPEC (the Organisation of Petroleum Exporting Countries) in October 1973, following the brief Arab-Israel War, to restrict supplies of oil and to increase its price. The price rose from $3.45 per bbl in September 1973 to $8.70 in January 1974. The surplus of the oil producing countries consequently rose from $13 bn in 1973 to $56 bn in 1974. This massive transfer of purchasing power was severely deflationary and in 1974-5 the industrial economies suffered from the worst recession since the war. Although recycling of the oil companies' surpluses developed in that period, there was instability because current account deficits were not necessarily matched by capital inflows. The increase in the price of oil, coupled with the abandonment of the gold standard, also led to inflation on a scale not previously experienced: consumer prices rose in 1974 by 11% in the USA, 14% in France, 16% in the UK and 23% in Japan. In the next two years, recession reduced the rate of inflation, except in the UK. Then from 1976 there was a gradual recovery from recession, assisted by an increase in oil production.

The Conservative government of Edward Heath, after coming to power in June 1970, started with the intention of cutting government expenditure and reforming industrial relations. After a prolonged and bitter battle in Parliament and several strikes, the Industrial Relations Act was passed in 1971, imposing some curbs on Union activity, which the Labour government had failed to do two years earlier when Barbara Castle's "In Place of Strife" was abandoned. In 1972, however, the Heath government was forced into an about-turn by trouble with the Unions and adverse economic circumstances. From then on the situation worsened, until Heath's defeat in the general election in February 1974. The economic trends in Heath's term as Prime Minister were:

- the balance of exports over imports fell from a surplus of £0.3 bn in 1971 to a deficit of £2.3 bn in 1973, leading to a deficit of £5.2 bn in 1974
- inflation in prices and earnings was high and rising; weekly earnings rose by 11% in 1971, 13% in 1972, 14% in 1973 and 18% in 1974, keeping about 2% ahead of the rise in retail prices
- Bank Rate (later Minimum Lending Rate), fell from 7% in May 1970 to 5% in September 1971 but then rose to 9% by the end of 1972, 11.5% in July 1973 and 13% in November 1973
- unemployment rose from 600,000 in 1970 to 1 million at the beginning of 1972 but a highly reflationary budget in 1972 led to an increase in production and employment, so that unemployment was back below 600,000 by the beginning of 1974.

Heath's attempt to reform industrial relations through the 1971 Industrial Relations Act led to disputes in the docks, Post Office and electricity industry and with local authority manual workers. At the beginning of 1972, there was a miners' strike, leading to power cuts and the lay-off of 1.5 million workers. The settlement brokered by Lord Wilberforce was inflationary. In November 1972, following the failure of an attempt at voluntary restraint, a 90-day standstill was imposed on wages and salaries, dividends, rates and rents and prices, with the exception of imported goods and fresh foods. Strikes, however, continued, involving hospital workers, train drivers, civil servants, gas workers, etc.. What became known as Stage I was succeeded in March 1973 by Stage II, when a Price Commission and a Pay Board were set up to operate a Price and Pay Code, regulating increases in pay, prices, rents and dividends. Stage III followed in October 1973; it introduced some flexibility in pay increases, notably providing for additional increases if the retail price index rose by more than 7% above the level at that time - a provision that was thought to be an important factor in the acceleration of inflation in 1974-5.

David Willmott Livingstone, Managing Director 1972-1986.
[photo: Baron (Rex Coleman)]

Albright & Wilson Board May 1976; l. to r back row:: Dick Robinson, Ray Marks, Bill Albright, Neil Peech, John Hutton-Wilson, George Ashford, Gene Anderson; front row: Nevil Wilson (Secretary), David Livingstone, Sydney Ellis, Tony Ward, Harold Kimberley.

Albright & Wilson Ireland's premises near Dublin c.1983 with l. to r.
John Hewitson (Managing Director, Ireland), Jim Ketelsen, David Livingstone,
Charles Suckling, Richard Wambold (Tenneco analyst) & warehouse manager.

Warley (Birmingham) office 1975, Head Office from October 1991.

The miners refused to accept a pay increase in accordance with Stage III, recognising that the oil crisis had strengthened their bargaining power. An overtime ban in November 1973 led to a State of Emergency, which was followed by a strike in January, a national 3-day working week to conserve fuel and finally Heath's calling a general election on the theme of "Who governs Britain?", which ended the period of Conservative rule.

The Labour administrations of Harold Wilson and Jim Callaghan inherited severe economic problems. The Industrial Relations Act was repealed and replaced by the "Social Contract", an agreement with the unions for voluntary restraint. The Pay Board and statutory controls on pay were abolished. Price controls, however, were retained and food subsidies were introduced. Nevertheless, the rise in weekly earnings accelerated, reaching an average of 27% in 1975, leading to an increase in consumer prices of around 25% in that year. The increase in earnings and prices was reduced in the following three years but opposition by the Unions grew in 1977-78 and culminated in the "winter of discontent" in late 1978-early 1979, followed by the return to power of the Conservative party in May 1979. Unionisation, especially among "white collar workers", progressed greatly in the period of Labour government.

Industrial production rose in 1971-2 and boomed in 1973, by more than 7%, but the whole of the rise in 1973 was more than lost in 1974-5, flattening out in 1976 before resuming growth in 1977. The UK equity price index, which had risen by two-thirds in 1971-2, fell again by 70% in 1973-4, to half the level of 1970.

While there were severe problems of inflation, labour relations and growing unemployment in the period, there was some recovery in the balance of payments, and of exports, helped by the fall in the value of the £, and paradoxically prices of manufactures within the UK benefited from regulation: there was sufficient flexibility in the allowance for increases reflecting higher costs and for increases required to support expansion, while prices were not driven down by competition and indeed customers were inclined to accept authorised price increases. The index of UK chemical industry prices, for example, which had remained stable in the 10 years to 1967, rose by nearly 20% in the next four years but then more than doubled between 1971 and 1977 and continued growing at an average of 10% per annum for the next five years.

Albright & Wilson's results

Seen against this generally unfavourable economic and political background, the results produced by Albright & Wilson may appear remarkably good but, of course, that is against a background of the collapse in profits in 1969-70 and the high inflation of the 1970s - between mid-1971 and mid-1978 retail prices in the UK rose by nearly 150%.

Progress 1971 -1978

£ million	1971	1972	1973	1974	1975	1976	1977	1978
Sales	**123.9**	**134.1**	**155.9**	**204.4**	**227.3**	**285.3**	**338.0**	**342.1**
Profit before interest & tax	6.7	6.9	11.2	27.6	22.0	34.5	43.1	33.6
Interest payable	3.8	4.1	4.4	4.5	5.5	5.5	4.7	5.3
Pretax profit	**2.9**	**2.8**	**7.5**	**22.8**	**16.5**	**29.0**	**38.4**	**28.3**
Tax	0.9	0.4	1.2	2.2	2.4	2.7	6.3	2.0
Profit after tax	2.0	2.4	6.3	20.6	14.1	26.3	32.1	26.3
Adjustments	-2.9	0.2	-4.2	0.3	0.7	-0.3	-0.4	-0.7
Profit after adjustments	**-0.9**	**2.6**	**2.1**	**20.9**	**14.8**	**26.0**	**31.7**	**25.6**
Ordinary dividend (net)	0.7p	0.7p	2.275p	3.52p	3.75p	4.13p	4.61p	5.29p
Capital expenditure	7.2	10.4	6.0	10.2	15.2	13.9	24.5	43.4
Disposals	-5.3	-1.0	-14.1	-6.2	-1.2	-0.6	-2.5	-2.9
Net cap. emp. (end of year)	**115.5**	**117.3**	**116.1**	**137.0**	**159.5**	**181.5**	**201.9**	**198.1**

The main adjustments were the loss on the exit from Belledune Fertilizer in 1971, already described, and a write-down of the investment in Long Harbour in 1973, treated as extraordinary items according to the accounting convention of the day. The first part of this period, from 1971 to 1973, was when the decks were cleared, leading to the good years. In real terms, profit in 1977 was the highest achieved by Albright & Wilson in the whole of the nearly 50 years covered by this history.

The first real signs of recovery were reflected in the results for 1974 (while 1973 appeared to show an upturn in profit, the large adjustments in that year cancelled out the rise). The Evening Standard, in reviewing the performance of shares in 1974 recorded that "The best performing Industrial share was Albright and Wilson, with a 63% increase" - but only from 23p. to 37.5p., still only a fraction of its previous peak. The Investors Chronicle said that A&W "stands out as a star performer for the past year" and pointed out that the pretax profit more than trebled since in 1974 £3.7 million was charged against profit to top up the UK pension funds. In the first two months of 1975, A&W's share price rose to 71.5p.. During 1974, A&W was described as "The company which came in from the cold" and reference was made to "The startling profits breakthrough". The

Financial Times ran an article under the headline "The smile returns to a fallen idol", previously referred to as "a bombed-out phosphorus company".

Although the 1975 profits were lower than 1974's, they were deemed "better than expected" in the recessionary circumstances and the share price early in 1976 was around 90p. The record results for 1976 earned the headline from the Investors Chronicle "all bright and breezy again". The Financial Times ran a major article starting: "A determined bid to demonstrate that Britain's chemical industry does not begin and end with ICI is currently being made by the second-ranked UK producer, the hitherto fairly retiring Albright and Wilson". Reference was made to the corporate advertising campaign recently embarked on with the slogan "A Force for British Industry". The 1977 results also pleased the Press, with predictable headlines: "Albright brighter", "All right at Albright", "Albright and beautiful" and the like, while The Times more soberly chose the headline "Bucking the chemical cycle". The share price rose to over 100p. but was restrained by the Company's forecast of unchanged profits in 1978 (which was to prove over-optimistic).

What were the reasons for the great improvement in profits during this period? Although one factor was better performance at Long Harbour, that was by no means the only reason; almost all operations showed large increases in profit.

- losses at Long Harbour were greatly reduced, helped by the write-down of the plant, but mainly through a long-drawn out succession of modifications in the running of the plant
- UK sales and selling-prices, especially of sodium tripolyphosphate, rose greatly and production costs were reduced significantly
- the flavours and fragrances business of BBA grew strongly from 1973, reaching a peak in 1977
- the pulp & paper sector of Erco, based on sodium chlorate, developed from virtually no profit in 1971 to a return of over 25% on sales in 1977
- Albright & Wilson (Australia)'s profit grew nearly sevenfold
- borrowing was reduced and cash resources rose to £40 million, contributing nearly £4 million to pretax profit in 1977.

The main developments underlying this picture are described more fully later in this chapter. First, it is appropriate to consider the influence of the management of the Company, in the seven years that followed Tenneco's acquisition of a (potentially) controlling interest in June 1971.

Tenneco and Albright & Wilson

The seven years of Tenneco's partial ownership of Albright & Wilson were a period when both were making good progress, with no great incentive for changes in direction. Tenneco advanced from sales of $2.8bn and a pretax profit of $245m. in 1971 to sales of $8.8bn and a pretax profit of $807m. in 1978. A&W's remarkable recovery encouraged Tenneco to support its management and then, when profit had reached a record level in 1977, to move to full ownership.

Management & organisation

The only immediate change in management resulting from Tenneco's position as potentially the holder of 50.6% of the Ordinary shares of A&W was the appointment to the A&W Board in 1971 of three non-executive Directors from Tenneco: N.W. (Dick) Freeman (Chairman of Tenneco Inc.), Sydney Ellis (an Executive Vice-President of Tenneco Inc.) and Ray Marks (President of Tenneco Chemicals Inc.). John Hutton-Wilson, then Managing Director of Albright & Wilson Ltd, was appointed to the Board of Tenneco Chemicals but in practice that had no significance. Sir Richard Powell remained the Chairman of A&W. One change, not dictated by Tenneco, was the appointment of David Livingstone as Deputy Managing Director of A&W, to be in charge of all current operations, leaving John Hutton-Wilson to concentrate on future development. In 1972 John Hutton-Wilson, whose health had deteriorated, moved to the position of Deputy Chairman and David Livingstone became Managing Director.

David Willmott Livingstone was born in 1926 and after going to school at Haberdashers' Askes (a public school) joined the Royal Navy in 1944, serving until 1947 and becoming a Sub-Lieutenant in minesweepers, based in Singapore. After taking a degree in modern languages at Christ Church, Oxford, he joined A&W in 1949. Starting in the sales department, he moved through publicity to market research and then in 1956 was appointed personal assistant to the Chairman, Sydney Barratt. In 1961 he became General Commercial Manager of the operating company, Albright & Wilson (Mfg), where he eventually became Managing Director in 1967. He was appointed to the parent Board in 1969 as Operations Director, in the shake-up (p.160) when Sir Owen Wansbrough-Jones and most of the long-serving Directors departed. David's experience within the Company and his personal qualities of intellect and command of language made him the outstanding candidate within A&W for the post of chief executive.

Sir Richard Powell in retrospect came to the view that an external appointment as chief executive would have been the best course for the company but there was a reluctance among possible candidates to take a position in a company beset with such difficulties. He also expected Tenneco to intervene in the management when it acquired the power to do so.

The principal player for Tenneco was Sydney T. Ellis. Born in 1913, he received a degree in chemical engineering from Virginia Polytechnic Institute in 1934 and went to work for DuPont for three years as a production engineer in synthetic fibre and film manufacture. From there he went to Wortendyke Manufacturing Company, a paper company (later part of Union Camp), as a sales and development engineer. In 1941 he enlisted in the US Army Corps of Engineers, serving in the Pacific and China-Burma-India theatres, engaged in the construction of pipelines, airfields and harbours, leaving in 1946 as a lieutenant-colonel. For the next five years he worked for W.R. Grace, in the USA, Europe and Latin America as a project engineer, analyst and trouble-shooter. In 1951 he was invited by a former colleague in Grace, Albert Woods, to join him in Commercial Solvents Corporation (later part of International Minerals & Chemicals) in New York, to help turn the company round. He joined as Vice-President, Operations, becoming Executive Vice-President. The company's interests were in pharmaceuticals, animal nutrition products, fertilisers, petrochemicals and industrial chemicals. For the next 8 years, he experienced battles with stockholders and takeover attempts, until in 1959 Al Woods was retired. He then joined Petro-Tex as President and Chief Executive; Gardiner Symonds and Paul Davies (Chairman of FMC) had bought the plant, making butadiene for synthetic rubber, from the War Production Board. Sydney Ellis spent ten years improving the profitability of the company and broadening its product range, in the difficult circumstances of a joint venture between two powerful and determined companies.

In 1969 he was brought into Tenneco as a Vice-Chairman of the Board and as President of Tenneco Chemicals; the other Vice-Chairman was Si Askin, who had been Chairman of Heyden Newport, the main constituent of Tenneco Chemicals. Sydney had the task of welding together a loose confederation of 14 low-performing businesses with 40 plants in the USA and Europe. When he became Chairman of Tenneco Chemicals he appointed Ray Marks as President and together they carried through a programme of reorganisation.

Early in June 1971, very soon after the confirmation of Tenneco's convertible loan, Sydney Ellis talked with David Livingstone about who was running A&W and how Tenneco could be injected into the decision-making hierarchy. He suggested an inner Board of two or three including himself. David did not agree and thought that Tenneco could not act as owners when they were not; indeed, he considered that Sydney's freedom of the offices should be curtailed - which, not surprisingly, was not well received. Later in that month, the Executive Directors and Divisional Managing Directors met to review the organisation. It was decided that the Board should meet every two months and that an Executive Committee, meeting monthly, should be responsible for managing the Company. Two of the Executive Directors, John Hughes and Peter Baines (reporting to the Managing Director), would be responsible for all the Divisions.

Over the next 12 months, progress towards recovery was slow. Output from Long Harbour did not increase and while there was some improvement in profit compared to 1969 and 1970 it was still well below the level of 1968. The share price remained below 30p. (against Tenneco's conversion price of 32.5p.). There was some clearing of the decks, as described later (See 'Divestments', pages 203-207).

Meanwhile, the relationship between A&W and Tenneco remained distant and uneasy. In May 1972, Sydney Ellis had tried to have Noel Poynton (Managing Director of Tenneco Chemicals in Europe) appointed an external Director of A&W but was rebuffed by Sir Richard. In July 1972, David Livingstone wrote to Bob Clark at Hill Samuel to ask whether he could see a way of getting rid of the Tenneco convertible loan, for example by selling BBA. He thought the A&W share price was depressed by the existence of the Tenneco convertible and feared a cheap bid by Tenneco for the rest of the A&W shares. He was also concerned that Tenneco might impose a large management fee, or attempt to purchase a part of A&W cheaply or to sell a part of Tenneco Chemicals (for example, Butlers) to A&W. David believed the A&W results had bottomed out but that would not be apparent until 1974. He aired the idea of increasing the dividend so as to improve the price of the A&W shares. Nothing resulted from that attempt.

In September 1972, Sydney Ellis met the Chairman of Prudential Assurance, the next largest stockholder, in London. He pointed out that Tenneco had been a stockholder for three years and a major lender with minor representation on the Board for more than a year, during which its investment of £22 million had come to be worth £14 million. The statement for the first six months of 1972 did not indicate any tangible progress, and indeed the outlook for phosphorus, detergents and BBA appeared less promising. Up to then, the Tenneco position had been passive and the Tenneco Directors had been continually reminded that Tenneco had no special position and would be treated very much as any other stockholder. Tenneco did not intend to continue in an impotent position and watch its investment going down the drain. It could use its influence and vote its stock to replace the A&W internal Directors and embark on a drastic turnaround effort, possibly involving disposals, write-downs and reduction of staff, or it could become much more active in monitoring at Director level, remove some of the internal Directors, resume restructuring and consolidation, introduce critical monitoring by the other external Directors and create a more tough-minded approach. Tenneco would prefer not to act without the support of the other main stockholders. The Prudential Chairman asked who would take the actions outlined and Sydney said he would. He was then given the backing of the Pru - they had no other choice, because they could not sell their stock to anyone else and no-one else would want to engage in a fight with Tenneco.

Sydney then saw Sir Richard and reiterated his concerns and intentions. Sir Richard in turn conveyed to David Livingstone Tenneco's sense of frustration and belief in the need for changes in organisation and management, including more devolution to the Divisions and reducing the central organization by outsourcing some operations. (Sir Richard was also a Director of GEC, which under Arnold Weinstock was well-known to have a very small central organisation running a company larger than A&W.) Sir Richard asked David to say what support he needed, what organisation was required and how any deficiencies were to be remedied, for consideration at the Board meeting in November.

At the Tenneco Management Meeting at Miami in October, Sydney talked at length with David. Sydney had decided that Sir Richard should cease to be Chairman and suggested that there should be an Executive Committee consisting of the two of them plus John Hutton-Wilson and George Ashford, who was due to retire from the Board of British Petroleum in February 1973 and had been Managing Director of BP Chemicals from 1967 to 1970. Although George Ashford joined the Board, in a non-executive capacity, the idea of the Executive Committee was dropped.

Sir Richard ceased to be Chairman during the course of the November meeting of the Board and Sydney became Chairman. It was announced that Sir Richard wanted to spend more time on his duties at Hill Samuel, and Kenneth Keith indeed extended his duties there; Sir Richard was quoted as saying "If someone wants to drive, then it is better to have him at the wheel than in the back seat" but he wrote to David saying "I felt as if I had lost a limb, so much part of me had A&W and everyone there become during the past four years". Sir Richard had been Chairman during a period of extreme difficulty and had steadied a ship that had nearly foundered. He was not an executive Chairman and never aspired to be so. He did not make any significant changes in the management of the Company and worked through exhortation rather than command, as when he suggested shortly before his departure that the Company needed "to move from a defensive mentality to one of rebuilding a profitable and growing business". "Let's think positively!" was the headline in an article by Sir Richard in the Albright News in October 1972.

Sydney Ellis & Management Changes

Sydney Ellis summarised his strategy for A&W as "feed the tigers, ride the horses and shoot the dogs". He classified Marchon as a tiger and was surprised that the best producer in A&W had never been popular and was treated as a step-child. The phosphorus-based business he saw as a necessary part of A&W, providing cash flow, and shedding Long Harbour he regarded as impracticable. The components of ACC he regarded as dogs, to be disposed of. He was concerned at the general cash situation: during 1972, cash fell by one-third while borrowing remained greater than shareholders' funds, and Sydney wished to have a cushion large enough to cope with the possibility of closing Long Harbour. The plans for capital expenditure were therefore cut severely, from £13 million in 1973 to an eventual £6 million.

His approach to organisation and management was not radical. As a non-executive Chairman, based in Houston, he was not in a position to impose fundamental changes. For some months, he had been engaged in a dialogue with David Livingstone about changes in organisation. There were some sharp differences between them, on Sydney's wish to extend the scope of Marchon's responsibilities and to decentralise some of the central functions. The changes that came into operation at the beginning of 1973 represented a compromise. There were four Divisions: Marchon (including UK agricultural operations and overseas companies except America), Industrial Chemicals Division (including the ACC industrial operations), Erco (including Long Harbour) and BBA. The four Divisions reported to David, Tony Ward continued as Financial Director, John Hughes was appointed Technical Director (responsible also for the New Ventures Division) and the remaining two executive directors, Peter Baines and Michael Peard, were to work on special assignments. Michael resigned in September and Peter in December. David's position was strengthened by terminating the Executive Committee and creating a Managing Director's Committee only advisory to him. Divisional authority for capital expenditure was greatly reduced.

At the same time, Sydney introduced - initially only as an alternate director for Dick Freeman and Ray Marks - Gene Anderson. C. Eugene Anderson, who was then 34, was at that time Director of Operational Planning for Tenneco Oil, based in Houston. Gene had joined Tenneco in 1961, after acquiring a degree in chemical engineering and an MBA at Harvard, as a process engineer with Tenneco Oil. In 1966, he moved to England and became Managing Director of Globe Petroleum Sales, based in Lincolnshire, whose business was in filling stations. He returned to Houston in 1969, to manage supply and transportation for the Oil Company and then planning. Sydney persuaded Dick Freeman (Chairman of Tenneco) to allow Gene to be taken out of the oil company, despite the resistance of George Meason (see p.191) and Wilton Scott, the head of the oil company (and later Freeman's successor as Chairman). In October 1972 Gene was approached by Sydney Ellis who told him the story of A&W and said that he was not happy with A&W's planning (too much emotion, not enough analysis) and would like Gene to develop an independent view of what was needed. He was offered the position of Vice-President of Tenneco International, based in Houston but assisting Sydney Ellis and focusing on A&W. Gene was pleased to have the opportunity to return to England. In December 1972 and January 1973 he toured the UK sites and then in the first half of 1973 went to the sites in Canada, Australia and South Africa.

Gene's impression of A&W was that it was an antiquated company without a coherent organisation that had not rationalised its acquisitions. BBA had not been welded together, there was warring between Marchon and Oldbury and ACC was no more than a hodge-podge of small companies. Gene was horrified at the serious environmental risks, especially in chrome chemicals. While Marchon had lived in a competitive environment and showed commercial awareness, the cosy monopolistic position in phosphorus chemicals in the past had led to a lack of technological improvements, which should have avoided the risks of the giant leap at Long Harbour; that had nearly broken the company and had bled it financially and emotionally. He believed that the company's founders had left a splendid legacy but succeeding generations had not perceived the changes in the world and the need for the company to be driven along with them. Because of Long Harbour, there had been insufficient focus on the rest of the company's operations.

During 1973, Sydney and Gene worked on plans for A&W. There was an obvious need to remove Long Harbour from the crisis list, weld BBA together, resolve the conflict between wet and thermal phosphoric acid proponents, tackle operations making an insufficient return on investment, get rid of cash drains, reduce staff and strengthen management, and make extensive disposals. Gene was optimistic - in his words "every rock turned over had money under it" - and bought a substantial holding of shares at a rock-bottom price of around 22p..

The relationship between Gene and David Livingstone was not easy: the difference in their experience and approach to business and David's antipathy to intervention were potential sources of conflict but Gene's smiling courtesy could dispel problems. In July 1973, David wrote to Sydney "Gene is being a great help to me and I am grateful for having so much of his time". In the same letter, David expressed concern at the consequences of the divisionalisation of the company: "Morale in London is dreadful; the pendulum has swung too far in favour of the Divisions in that it now quite often takes my personal intervention before they will disclose information we need to know to senior departmental heads...it is a natural desire of all the DMDs to run separate businesses totally without supervision".

In November 1973, the A&W Board agreed that Gene should become Director of Operations from the beginning of 1974. The impressive title, however, was not accompanied by direct responsibility for operations and Gene had no staff. David Livingstone did not want any American intervention in A&W's affairs and resisted any lessening of his control. Sydney, however, did not attempt to bring in more people to run A&W. Gene's role at that time was mainly to be an on-site channel of communications between Sydney and the A&W executive management, briefing Sydney and working with David in changing the direction of the company. There were battles between Sydney and David but they became good friends. Sydney appreciated David's intellectual powers and his stubborness, which combined well with Sydney's wish for change.

In mid-1975, Gene appointed Operations Analysis Managers as staff officers to assist in planning, business analysis and capital expenditure evaluation. The first holders of the position were Michael Winstanley (later a Director of A&W) and Giuliano Bossini (later head of Marchon operations in Italy and eventually of Surfactants operations world-wide). While the appointments strengthened Gene's position, it remained one of very limited powers. At the end of 1975, Gene returned to Houston to become Vice President of Development. He remained a Director and continued to attend A&W Board meetings, assisting Sydney Ellis, to whom he reported in Houston.

At the same time as the move of Gene to Houston was decided, an important reorganisation within A&W was announced. All operations other than BBA and Erco were brought together in the Detergent & Chemicals Group, headed by John Wills, at that time the Managing Director of the Marchon Division. David Anthony, the Managing Director of the Industrial Chemicals Division, the other main constituent of the new group, became General Manager, Operations & Corporate Development, taking over Gene's duties. Within the D & C Group, there were six Sectors: Phosphates (under Ray Naish, who had been deputy to David Anthony), Detergents (under Georgio Mira, who had been MD of Marchon Italiana and was succeeded there by Giuliano Bossini), Organics (under Jack McCoubrey, previously running the organic chemicals unit in the ICD Division), Specialities (under Harry Searle and comprising the speciality products within ICD, New Ventures and Albright & Wilson Ireland), Agriculture (continuing to be run by Bill Coates) and Australia (the company with ICI as minority partner, headed by George James).

The bringing together of the two main Divisions was explained in the Annual Report: "There had developed an increasing overlap of interests between the two former Divisions, notably in the field of phosphoric acid and industrial phosphates, and the re-organisation has enabled like activities to be put together under a single control". The move was advocated by Gene and reluctantly agreed to by Sydney Ellis. It was a remarkable step, in the light of the long-standing polarisation between Whitehaven and Oldbury, and undoubtedly was seen by its advocates as a way of bringing them together.

John Wills was the obvious choice for the key position. A chartered accountant, he had joined the Marchon accounts department from Price Waterhouse in 1961 and in his early years benefited from the leadership of Frank Schon. He became Chief Financial Accountant in 1965, Chief Accountant in 1967, Administrative Director in 1971 and Division Managing Director in 1973, at the age of 37. He had been the prime mover behind the change to the sulphur-burning route to sulphuric acid, from the anhydrite route on which Marchon's expansion had been founded. During

Danny Fagandini's period as Division Managing Director at Whitehaven, John had been responsible for rationalisation in the Agricultural sector and for a change in management in Australia (Dick Edquist's replacement by Mike Fearfield, previously with Marchon in Spain). He had vigour and determination and wide experience within Marchon. After the formation of the D & C Group, John took steps to bring together the separate operations and people, through a management committee, business unit committees, a unified engineering department and group directors for finance (Peter Salmon), commercial (George Pekarek) and production (Martin Rowe). When the Group was formed, it was announced that integration and restructuring would take place over 18 months - a reasonable aim in the light of the complexity and history of separation.

Yet within 18 months, in May 1977, it was decided to break up the D & C Group. John Wills was appointed to the Board of Albright & Wilson Ltd, to be responsible for commercial coordination, the Overseas Marketing Companies, planning, publicity and purchasing, but for none of the operating sectors. All the Sectors reported to David Livingstone (who added the title of Deputy Chairman to that of Managing Director), but with other members of the 'Managing Director's Office' as sponsors (commonly referred to as 'uncles') - Tony Ward (Finance Director) for Detergents, Organics and Specialities and Whitehaven site (a multi-Sector site), Harold Kimberley (Personnel Director) for BBA, and David Anthony (director of operations) for Phosphates, Agriculture, Erco and Australia. It was hard to avoid the conclusion that David Livingstone had come to realise that the formation of the D & C Group had created an over-mighty subject - the organisation had the look of a penny-farthing, with one part making 75-90% of the profit and taking much of the decision-making away from the Managing Director and the Board. The reversal in 1977 meant that many more years were to elapse before the A&W organisation achieved a real measure of integration.

Tenneco's move to full ownership

The years of Sydney Ellis's Chairmanship of A&W set the pattern for the whole of the period of Tenneco's involvement with A&W. Even when Tenneco acquired full ownership in 1978, A&W continued to enjoy a remarkable degree of autonomy. The reasons for this were: the conglomerate character of Tenneco, the fact that A&W, alone of the Tenneco divisions, was not a US business and had its headquarters outside the USA, the general lack of knowledge of chemicals and international business amongst the Tenneco management (Sydney was the most knowledgeable among them, but had other interests to manage as well), Sydney's general approach not to take drastic action and cause upset in a complex situation, and David Livingstone's resistance to interference. David told Sydney that there could not be an American chief executive of a British chemical company. David had 25 years' experience in A&W, was highly intelligent and eloquent to an extent unusual in Houston and capable of great stubborness and flashes of passion, but also able to be very charming, and so difficult to withstand. He also could show success in achieving a recovery in profits in the first five years' of Tenneco's investment that must have encouraged in Tenneco a reluctance to make further changes. Later, when Tenneco was facing serious problems, the emphasis was on divestment rather than changes in management. So Albright & Wilson maintained its identity, its name, its British management and to a large extent its ways of management. The results were published, as for a publicly-owned company, and it can hardly have been obvious that it was not.

It might have been thought that Tenneco should have put together its two chemical interests. Raymond H. Marks, chief executive of Tenneco Chemicals Inc., was critical of A&W and David Livingstone, and tried to make the case that TCI should take over A&W. When Noel Poynton (head of Tenneco Chemicals in Britain and a former employee of A&W) was made an alternate Director of Albright & Wilson Ltd, David saw it as part of an attempt to take over A&W. But Sydney Ellis, who was Chairman of both companies, told Ray Marks to sort out his own problems, which were numerous in a company formed by putting together many small units lacking in homogeneity. As Sydney put it "Two lemons do not make a pie".

As A&W's results improved, so the possibility drew closer that Tenneco would convert its loan into equity to give it a majority holding and would perhaps also acquire the rest of the shares. Towards the end of 1973, David discussed the likelihood of such steps with Sydney, who indicated that at that time Tenneco's covenants in its own loans prevented the consolidation of A&W's debt into Tenneco's balance sheet. David Livingstone then consulted Hill Samuel and Barclays Bank on the possibility of buying out Tenneco through the repayment of their convertible loan, but the figures provided no encouragement. In December 1974, in the light of the good results achieved in that year, Tenneco converted enough of its loan to give it a 49.8% holding, which avoided problems of consolidation but took advantage of the low conversion price (32.5p.) applying in the first five years of the loan. The move was strongly advocated by Gene Anderson. David Livingstone still hoped that A&W would remain independent; in February 1977 he wrote "I am determined that Tenneco shall never own A&W".

Not much more than a year later, however, Tenneco moved to acquire full ownership of A&W. The decision to do so was taken by Wilton Scott, then Chairman of Tenneco. It was supported by J.L. (Jim) Ketelsen, President of Tenneco, who succeeded Scott as Chairman in July 1978. Sydney Ellis was reluctant to move beyond conversion of the remaining loan stock, to give Tenneco a majority holding. So too was G.H. (George) Meason, who succeeded him as Chairman, also in July 1978. George Meason, who had graduated as a Chemical Engineer, joined Tenneco in 1956 after 16 years with Humble Oil (Exxon) and became President of Tenneco Oil in 1973 and an Executive Vice-President of Tenneco in the following year. He became concerned with Tenneco's chemical interests in 1977, in advance of Sydney Ellis's retirement.

In May 1978, Jim Ketelsen and George Meason informed David Livingstone of the intention to make an offer for the whole of the outstanding shares and handed over a letter offering 165p. per Ordinary share and continuation of the name and management. The Board of A&W (excluding the Tenneco Directors) rejected the bid and made approaches to ICI and BP, but neither company was interested in bidding for the Tenneco and public holdings. Tenneco, not wishing to have a prolonged contested bid, then increased its offer to 190p. per share, to which 5p. was added in lieu of dividend, and the offer was then accepted by the A&W Board unanimously.

Apart from the shareholder approval, it was necessary to obtain clearance from the Department of Industry and the Office of Fair Trading. Three of the Trade Unions asked the Government to refer the bid to the Monopolies Commission but, after Tenneco had provided assurances of continued employment, Government approval was given and a statement jointly from Tenneco and the Department of Industry was issued: "Tenneco have assured the Government that they will continue to support the active part which Albright & Wilson have played in the development of the Government's industrial strategy. They aim to strengthen A&W's competitive position in world trade by the infusion of capital where needed and by the maintenance of sound management practices, including in particular enlightened and progressive industrial relations. If this aim succeeds further employment and capital spending will follow. A&W will continue to operate as an autonomous subsidiary of Tenneco. The present name and management will be retained and Tenneco will maintain a majority of British directors on the Board...Tenneco have assured the Government that they have no intention of selling either equity in A&W or any of that company's major facilities. They have undertaken that if ever future events were to make this necessary or desirable they would consult with the Government beforehand".

David Livingstone in a statement to employees said "My personal belief is that the company will have as great a future as it has had a past, and that with the resources of Tenneco behind us we can achieve an even faster rate of growth". He interpreted Tenneco's investment of £117 million as a sign of confidence. In a letter to stockholders, David admitted "The UK directors view with sadness the disappearance of A&W as an independent UK company, as I know do many of our employees and stockholders". The stockholders' meetings at which the necessary resolutions were passed were thinly attended and lasted only a few minutes. An era had ended and a new era had begun. Yet, as will be shown in the next chapter of this history, there was remarkably little change as a direct consequence of Tenneco's full ownership.

Long Harbour

The problems of Long Harbour in the first two years after start-up have been described in the previous chapter. At the Annual General Meeting in June 1971, the Chairman said "we shall need a year relatively free from trouble before we can say with confidence that our difficulties are behind us". In the Annual Report for 1971, it was admitted that the improvement in output expected when the half-year's results were announced in September last was unfortunately not realised. Production in 1971, at 18,200 tonnes, was lower than in 1970 and losses from Long Harbour were higher. In November of 1972 (a year when production was better than 1971 but still below 1970) it was optimistically forecast that output in the next three years would rise from 36,000 tonnes in 1973 to 50,000 tonnes in 1975; in fact, less than 30,000 tonnes was produced in 1973 and 1974 and less than 5,000 tonnes in 1975. From 1977, however, there was a distinct advance, which was sustained in following years. Output of phosphorus in 1977 was 35,400 and in 1978 42,500 - still a long way short of the designed capacity of around 65,000 but sufficiently improved for Long Harbour not to be highlighted as a factor in the company's performance. Further improvements in the next four years led to a record output in 1983, of over 52,000 tonnes, in a year when there were no breakages of electrodes.

How was the improvement brought about? The short answer might be by trial and error. There were several ideas on what the problems were and even more on the solutions.

At the beginning of this period, in 1971-3, the main thrust was in approaches to other phosphorus makers, for possible assistance in remedying the defects at Long Harbour and perhaps also becoming partners in the plant. Although the original offer from Hoechst in 1966 to build the plant had been rejected, it was not long after the first problems with the plant that contact was made with Hoechst. In May 1969, a visit was paid to Hoechst to discuss effluent problems and in September 1969 there was a visit to the new plant at Flushing for a general inspection. In February 1971, David Livingstone suggested that Hoechst might take a 50% share in Long Harbour and in December of that year another visit was made to discuss the replacement of the preformed electrodes with Soderberg electrodes; it was concluded that the Long Harbour furnaces, without modification, were too deep for Soderbergs. In January 1972, the A&W Board, after ruling out closure of Long Harbour because of the cash required to pay off the Bonds and Debentures, decided to ask Hoechst to make an engineering survey. Hoechst visited Long Harbour in September, following which it estimated that it would cost around 50 million deutschemarks (£12 million) to rebuild the furnaces, install Soderbergs, and rebuild the precipitators and other items, plus sums for dismantling and training and a fee of 7 million deutschemarks. They would guarantee an output of 54,000 tonnes from two furnaces. A third furnace would cost a further DEM 50 million. They were not interested in a shareholding in Long Harbour, in view of their expenditure on a third furnace at Flushing.The Board also decided in January 1972 to ask Lectromelt to advise on modifications to their electrode suspension system; they estimated $0.5 million to reduce the height of the column by 1.5 sections - which was not pursued.

John Hughes (then the A&W Director responsible for phosphorus) visited FMC and Monsanto in November 1971. Monsanto was known to use a 3-electrode column, with rope suspension, and FMC a similar system. FMC's furnaces at Pocatello Springs, Idaho, were running at capacity, after trouble-free commissioning; they claimed to have spent many years on developing their system of feed preparation. Monsanto told John Hughes "Your system just won't work!" and said that the size of the furnaces would have to be reduced, with a redesigned electrode system, changed precipitators and tapping arrangements, changes in feed particle size and a reduced amps/volts ratio (Monsanto operated at a high voltage, whereas A&W had moved the other way earlier in the year). Monsanto would want a royalty of $1 million pa, on top of the costs of modifications of $10 million plus. Neither FMC nor Monsanto was prepared to guarantee a level of output. FMC withdrew when it was denied access to detailed records: it asked for detailed production, maintenance and financial records in order to assess the value of the FMC information to be transmitted, in terms of the improvement offered.

Discussions continued into 1973. A team from Monsanto visited Long Harbour and then offered to put the plant right, with a guaranteed output of 68,000 tonnes pa, for a royalty of $3 million pa for 10 years. Hoechst made a revised offer, to modify the two furnaces for $20 million, adding a third for $20 million, and charging a fee of $10 million, reducible if the furnaces failed each to make 33,000 tonnes pa. Mobil was also invited to visit and to make proposals for remedial action; they decided within six months, however, that they could not tackle the Long Harbour problems. They expressed interest in a joint venture if a third furnace were built, seeing Long Harbour as a cheaper source of phosphorus than their furnaces in South Carolina, which were not competitive with those of FMC and Monsanto in Idaho.

Tenneco's involvement in the problems of Long Harbour predated the time when their investment in the £17.5m. convertible loan was under consideration. A report was given to them at the beginning of December 1970 and in the next few weeks revised three times. In March 1971, Dr S.R.(Stan) Sheeran, senior engineer of Tenneco Chemicals, visited Long Harbour with two others from Tenneco

Chemicals. They had experience in electrochemical processes but not in phosphorus production. Tenneco's conclusion at that time was that Long Harbour would never become an economic producer of phosphorus. Sydney Ellis told the A&W Directors "our conclusions seem so very different from yours". Tenneco thought the technical problems would take longer and cost more than A&W believed and that the forecasts of output were over-optimistic. There were fundamental problems in the location. David Livingstone contested Stan Sheeran's assessment and said that he was sure that in 1972 Long Harbour would be able to produce at 59,000 tonnes pa, working for 80% of the available time. Sydney Ellis suggested that it might be best in the end to walk away from the investment, of $55 million.

A further visit to Long Harbour by Stan Sheeran took place in June 1972. He was accompanied by Sydney Ellis, Ray Marks and H.E. O'Connell, who had been on the previous visit. Points made in their report included: the timetable for reaching production of over 60,000 tonnes appeared highly optimistic; air and water pollution required urgent remedial action; furnace upsets were causing serious power surges throughout Newfoundland and the Premier was unhappy at the power contract granted by his predecessor; Varennes operations were much simpler and its cost of phosphorus lower than Long Harbour, highlighting "the unfortunate built-in technical and operating complications at Long Harbour"; a realistic projection of phosphorus manufacture from Long Harbour and Varennes was needed, taking into account the worldwide supply and demand for phosphorus, including the effects of the growth of competitive wet phosphoric acid and the decline in demand for phosphates in detergents; and there should be a strong general manager responsible for the manufacture, use and sale of phosphorus. David Livingstone's response claimed awareness of the points made but did not comment on the forecast output.

A month later, Stan Sheeran went to the Tennessee Valley Authority (TVA). His discussions there led him to conclude that A&W should no longer seek help from Hoechst or consider Soderberg electrodes. A&W should produce proposals for rope suspension of the electrodes in place of the Lectromelt system, which was said not to work well in phosphorus plants and to have been removed by Monsanto. The pelletisation plant (providing the phosphate feed for the furnaces), which had cost $15 million, was thought to be possibly a worse problem than the furnaces. Consideration should be given to engaging Dravo (US consulting engineers) to prepare a technical-economic feasibility study of Long Harbour and Varennes and to continuing consultation (free of charge) with TVA. The possibility of a third furnace at Long Harbour and modifying one of the existing furnaces, leaving the other as a standby, should be studied. TVA attributed the shutting down of some phosphorus plants to the economic advantages of wet acid and said that the only viable plants in the USA were those of FMC and Monsanto.

David Livingstone then explored the possibility of appointing Sheeran to run the

Long Harbour operation but Sheeran's commitments in Tenneco Chemicals did not allow that, or indeed regular visits to Long Harbour. Studies of the viability of Long Harbour continued, with David Livingstone continuing to argue that the least bad course, in cash terms, was to continue to operate, with an output of 30,000 tonnes pa as the break-even point. In December 1971, John Hughes (then the Director overseeing phosphorus operations) analysed alternatives and proposed that a final decision on whether or not to continue should be taken in June 1972. In October 1972, at the request of Sydney Ellis, Tony Ward produced a paper recommending that the programme of improvements, involving capital expenditure of $12 million in the next three years, should continue, although even with a hoped-for output of 55,000 tonnes by 1975 Long Harbour would make only a small profit (measured against the expected cost of purchasing phosphorus). The costs of phosphorus from Long Harbour were still expected to be above those of Varennes. The first shipment of phosphorus to Japan (in July 1972) had a cash cost of over $800 per tonne and a selling price of less than $400.

In February 1973, Gene Anderson produced a report in which he concluded that the contract with Japan should be cancelled, that more work should be done on purified wet acid and that the furnaces should be rebuilt in 1973-4. The figures indicated that it was better to run the furnaces than close the plant. He concluded, however, by saying "There is an overriding consideration as to whether we have the management talent, technical ability, and resources to survive five more years of Long Harbour".

There came a time, however, when a combination of the improvements achieved by A&W and advice from TVA and other US sources led to the conclusion that the best course was to rely on the in-house efforts. These may be divided into three periods, which may be described as the pre-Medves, Medves and post-Medves years, i.e. 1969-72, 1973-78, 1979-89.

1969-72

The first Plant Manager at Long Harbour was Ken Bradley, who reported to Stan Panaoti, the General Manager, Industrial Phosphates, who was based in Toronto. In mid-1969, Stan Panaoti decided that he could not manage Long Harbour as well as the rest of Industrial Phosphates and so Maurice Laperriere replaced him as the manager in charge of Long Harbour (reporting to Lloyd Lillico), where he became based. Maurice had joined Erco in 1959 as a plant superintendent at Buckingham and was transferred to Varennes as Production Superintendent in 1963, moving two years later to Port Maitland. In March 1970, Ken Bradley moved to Buckingham as Plant Manager and was succeeded by Jim Medves as Production and Maintenance Superintendent. Jim, when Plant Manager of Port Maitland, had been seconded to

Long Harbour in 1968, to head the commissioning team for the furnaces and then worked on a variety of special assignments for Maurice.

In October 1970, it was decided to divide the Canadian operations into a Chemical Division, under Lloyd Lillico (President of Erco) with its headquarters continuing at Toronto, and a Phosphorus Division, under C.A. Vessey as President, with a headquarters office in St John's, Newfoundland and an executive including F.M. (Mike) Cussons, the Engineering Director of Marchon, who was seconded to Newfoundland and based in St John's. Clifford Vessey, a chemical engineer, had joined British Chrome Chemicals (one of the constituents of what became ACC) in 1955 as General Manager of its Glasgow works and when ACC was formed he became head of research and then Technical Development Manager, before being appointed General Manager of the Industrial Chemicals sector of ACC in 1968. Clifford, a man of sharp intelligence, an inventive mind and enduring optimism, inspired confidence (described by an Erco source as "spellbinding") and was regarded as the person most likely to solve the problems of Long Harbour, despite his lack of experience in phosphorus manufacture. David Livingstone, who was resident in Newfoundland for the last three months of 1970, wrote to John Hutton-Wilson to say he was impressed with Clifford's expertise in everything and that he knew more about the plant after a few weeks than Maurice Laperriere. Ray Marks, in his report of June 1972, expressed serious doubts whether Long Harbour would attain the output projected for 1975 without the "conviction, determination and technical expertise of Cliff, or an equally competent replacement".

A month later, however, Clifford confirmed his wish to return to the UK and in October 1972 he did so, to head the New Ventures operation. His replacement was Maurice Laperriere. David wrote to Sydney Ellis to say that he was concerned at Clifford's departure from Newfoundland but that Laperriere's appointment was the "best use of the resources available". With Clifford's departure, the 2-Division split in Canada was ended, with Laperriere reporting to Lillico. Maurice Laperriere's period as head of phosphorus operations was brief. Not long after Gene Anderson's appointment to A&W at the end of 1972, he visited Long Harbour; the presentation to him by the Long Harbour management went very badly (Maurice did not possess Clifford's self-confidence) and very shortly after that Maurice left the company, in January 1973. Jim Medves, who had returned to Port Maitland in June 1971, was invited to return to Long Harbour temporarily, while a search was made for a permanent manager.

Progress up to the end of 1972 did not achieve a real increase in output, with tonnage in that year a little less than in 1970. In 1970, there had been an ice-storm which brought down power-lines and put the plant out of action for two weeks. The total of lost time in 1971 totalled over 45%; 1972 was better, despite time lost for replacement of mild by stainless steel, with the plant off for not much more than one-third of the time. There were 27 electrode breakages in 1969, 28 in 1970 and 32 in 1971, with an improvement to 22 in 1972. Apart from the breakages, the main causes of downtime were repairs to the precipitators and gas mains. The time and effort required to cope with the problems inevitably delayed basic remedial action. The numerous visits by external parties also absorbed valuable time. The pressure for more supplies of phosphorus tended to encourage sticking-plaster action. The cash requirements for Long Harbour in 1971 and 1972 were over $10 million in each year, of which capital expenditure was around $3 million.

One positive action was the containment of liquid effluent, through ponding, for which Maurice Laperriere was particularly responsible. Mention has already been made of the unsuccessful work on Optimised Furnace Operation and of the limited contribution made by the upsprings introduced on the furnaces by Clifford Vessey. In 1970-71, the mild steel gas lines were replaced by stainless steel, which reduced the downtime caused by failures in that equipment but otherwise did not improve performance. The precipitators were rebuilt in a simpler and more rugged design but continued to cause problems, because of the variable gas temperatures and the carry-over of excessive dust. The variable feed to the furnaces and the continuing difficulties with the pelletising plant remained as unsolved problems. Jim Medves recorded: "Through late 1970 and early 1971 the conditions at Long Harbour continued to worsen. Electrode breaks continued; the physical condition of the precipitators worsened; fires and flooding became an everyday problem and working conditions were terrible".

1973-78

Jim Medves was asked to take charge of Long Harbour on a permanent basis within a month of his return there. The Erco Board decided to close the St John's office - it had involved driving 70 miles in each direction every day and had not contributed to good management. It was also decided that the number employed at St John's and Long Harbour, which had risen to over 500 by the end of 1972, had to be reduced by 100, partly by streamlining the organisation and partly by cutting back on the engineers engaged on capital expenditure projects (in practice, the total remained at around 500 until 1978). The Board minutes record that "The operating conditions for the furnaces as laid down by Mr C.A. Vessey were hard to conform to and the possibility of making some alterations to these operating conditions was presently being considered".

In 1973, the winterisation programme begun in 1972 was completed, the rebuilding of the precipitators continued, there was a modification to the electrode suspension system and steps were taken to reduce wildcat strikes. Output, at nearly 30,000 tonnes, was higher than in any previous year. It was not until the following year, however, that significant steps were taken to achieve a real advance. In February 1973, Gene Anderson wrote a review of the phosphorus position, which concluded by setting as an objective to rebuild the plant in 1973-4, learn to operate it in 1975 and reap the benefit in 1976-7. The timescale was optimistic but the general direction was roughly right.

In 1974, the Long Harbour Technical Committee was formed; with Jim Medves there were Ernest Brazier, Ted Lowe and Robbie Robbins from Oldbury and Alf Barnett (Manager of the Furnace Plant), Lyall Work (seconded to Long Harbour as Technical Manager, for two years), Kevin Ryan (Senior Process Engineer) and other Long Harbour staff as required. The Committee was a powerful aid, which accomplished a lot. Also during the year R.F. (Bob) Chalmers returned to Long Harbour as Production Manager on the Pelletisation Plant. (Bob, who moved from Long Harbour to Vancouver in 1977, took over from Jim Medves as manager of Long Harbour in 1979.) Lyall Work moved to the UK in 1976 but remained on the Technical Committee until 1979, when he returned to Canada as Industrial Relations Manager.

During 1974, the decision was taken to give responsibility for Long Harbour to the UK Industrial Chemicals Division, as its main customer with greatest resources of experienced people. Varennes remained within Erco's management. This arrangement lasted only until the end of 1975, when ICD became part of the Detergents & Chemicals Group and Long Harbour reverted to being part of Erco.

Towards the end of 1974, the precipitators - despite large capital expenditure on rebuilding - had deteriorated to the point where replacement was essential. It was decided to review an unsuccessful test made in 1972, to by-pass the precipitators, but with modifications to eliminate build-up points. The test, in 1975, was a resounding success, in improving gas flow and temperatures and contributing to fewer breakages of electrodes. The disadvantage of eliminating the precipitators was that more phosphorus-containing mud was produced, most of which was dumped in the ponds. The mud furnaces that were installed later, at Long Harbour and Varennes (where the precipitators were only dust-boxes and were later by-passed) distilled phosphorus out of the mud but were not able to cope with all the mud. That created problems many years later.

The second significant step was the rebuilding of no.1 furnace. Both furnaces were in poor condition by the end of 1974; weaknesses in the furnace linings were giving rise to "hot spots". Gene Anderson was seriously considering adding a Varennes-type furnace, to allow the furnaces to be rebuilt. In May 1975, an event occurred that was to prove fortunate: a militant union executive called a strike, rejecting an offer of a pay increase of 37.5% over two years. It was ironical that that occurred not long after a paper had been produced for Stauffer, which was approached to take a share in a joint venture to expand Long Harbour by adding a third furnace: the paper stated "The last two years have seen a real improvement in labour relations and in relations with the Unions". The strike lasted until September, when it was settled for a lower pay award than originally offered. The strike allowed time to think about how to solve the major problems with the furnaces, resulting in proposals from Jim Medves and Kevin Ryan which Jim claimed "led to the turnaround of Long Harbour", a view endorsed by Gene Anderson.

The recipe devised, in addition to by-passing the precipitators, consisted of:

- improving slag tapping, by adding a third tap-hole and raising the holes, so reducing the working height of the furnace, and tapping more frequently;
- reducing coke in the feed, to avoid the accumulation of unburnt material, while accepting that there would be a greater loss of phosphorus in the slag;
- reducing the amps/volts ratio (i.e. a reduced current but a higher voltage, as recommended by Monsanto), with different ratios on each electrode, to give lower gas temperatures and greater furnace stability;
- modifying the technique for adding electrode lengths, under a method devised by Ernest Brazier;
- bringing the electrodes closer together so that they no longer operated independently;
- using a computer to measure electrode positions;
- improving feed to the furnace by introducing a carousel system for mixing the ingredients; and
- improving monitoring through the setting of limits on all factors and the requirement for all changes to be approved by the technical department.

No. 1 furnace was rebuilt along the lines advocated and came on stream eventually in December 1975. No. 2 furnace remained out of action. The rebuilt furnace operated better than ever before and in 1976 produced nearly 24,000 tonnes of phosphorus, despite some electrode breakages. In March 1976, Jim Medves wrote a memorandum detailing 31 items that had made the operation of the rebuilt furnace successful. The A&W Board was initially cautious and at the beginning of the year took out options for purchases of phosphorus from FMC and Hoechst, but by December the Board was satisfied with the furnace's performance and agreed that no. 2 furnace should be rebuilt. David Livingstone argued "ceasing to be a basic phosphorus producer would greatly reduce the credibility of the global strategy" and the Board agreed to spend $17 million over the next three years on the rebuild and other improvements. The annual report for 1976 stated "our employees...are justifiably proud of their part in resolving the technical problems which have dogged this plant since its commissioning in 1969...The reliable manufacture of phosphorus underpins an important part of Company's profitability and for the first time since 1969 we can look forward with confidence to an assured supply of this raw material".

No. 2 furnace restarted in June 1977 after its rebuild and in 1977 Long Harbour produced over 35,000 tonnes of phosphorus. Working conditions and morale on the plant were greatly improved. The A&W Board met at Long Harbour in July - its first meeting outside England. The site completed 1 million manhours without a lost-time accident, a record for A&W. Shipments of phosphorus to Japan were resumed. There were, however, some problems. The pelletisation plant proved inadequate to cope with the higher demand from the furnaces and working conditions within it were very bad. With the help of Allis Chalmers, the manufacturer of the balling pans (which also contributed to the cost of the modifications), the problems were largely overcome. The storage capacity for rock and pellets was also substantially increased, so reverting to the original specification before the cutbacks at the design stage.

With both rebuilt furnaces in operation, production in 1978 increased to 42,500 tonnes. Two mud furnaces began operating and expenditure was authorised on additional rail cars, for supply to the Canadian mainland, which had started in 1977. Production by Varennes, which had peaked at around 25,000 tonnes pa in 1972-5, was cut back as Long Harbour's output grew, to only 14,000 tonnes in 1978. Expenditure was also authorised for control of fluoride emissions after the Canadian Public Health Association, at the request of the provincial government, set up a task force to study the impact of fluorides in the neighbourhood of Long Harbour - which had led to an absence of vegetation in some areas. In general, however, the plant had settled down to a tolerable level of output, albeit well short of the designed capacity. The Annual Report for 1977, issued in April 1978, stated: "the better operation of this plant ensures the viability of our phosphorus chemicals business in the UK and Canada and removes the last significant loss-maker from our portfolio". In 1977, Long Harbour showed an operating loss of over $2 million; there is no equivalent figure for 1978 since it was decided then to charge the consuming divisions with phosphorus at full cost rather than at a price related to market prices (a change advocated by John Wills despite opposition from George Meason and David Livingstone).

1979-1989

From 1979 to 1984, when Bob Chalmers was in charge of Long Harbour, there were further important improvements. A computerised control system was installed, which calculated the required proportions of the materials fed to the furnaces and determined the position of the electrodes within them; that was the work of Bob

Croft, an engineer from Oldbury, who went to Long Harbour in 1977 as a senior engineer, and became Technical Manager; he returned to Oldbury in 1983. He described the control system as the key to the whole success. He was also responsible for the design of the mud furnaces. As a result of conversations with FMC staff in Chicago, he also increased the proportion of silica in the furnace feed, with what Bob Chalmers described as an astounding result: the furnaces were able to operate stably at high loads and with low gas offtake temperatures.

The other significant change in this period concerned the electrodes. Ernest Brazier as early as Easter 1969 had found that the machining of the electrodes supplied by Union Carbide was not sufficiently accurate, so that the fit between the nipples and the electrodes they joined could be as low as 10%. That caused overheating when a current was applied, opening of the joints and breakages. The length of the electrode stack and the method of suspension exacerbated the problem. Other users suffered breakages, but not so many, because of their different method of suspension and better conditions within the furnaces. For years, the Lectromelt suspension system was blamed for the breakages at Long Harbour, even to the point where an unsuccessful suit was brought against Lectromelt, but the system was retained with only minor modifications and eventually worked satisfactorily. In about 1979, sonic testing of incoming electrodes was introduced at Long Harbour, which led to the rejection of about 5%; Monsanto was reported to reject a proportion of the electrodes supplied to them. In about 1980, Ernest Brazier, then acting as a consultant to Bob Chalmers, persuaded him to spend a relatively small sum ($65,000) on buying and overhauling a piece of equipment for re-machining electrodes. About 200 electrodes were re-machined, constituting most of those currently supplied by Union Carbide, plus discarded electrodes dug out of the ground. The furnaces ran for almost a year without any breaks and with no purchases. Ernest Brazier then went to Union Carbide and talked with the technical staff there, with the result that they invested in a similar machine for $1.5 million and invited him to its commissioning.

While progress was made on these fronts, and on lesser items such as tapping and fume control, adverse circumstances developed that were eventually to prove crucial. The least significant was a tap-out and fire on one of the furnaces in 1979, for which a claim was made against Factory Mutual, the insurers. The claim took years to bring to court, in 1983, and more time to go to appeal; Erco rejected an offer to settle out of court and then lost the hearing and the appeal. Some millions of dollars were involved and much time and money were spent on what Erco and A&W had believed to be a strong case but had not presented well.

Much more important was the price of power. The contract with the Province of Newfoundland was believed to guarantee low cost power at a fixed price of 2.5 mils (0.25 cents) per kwh. As early as July 1972, however, Stan Sheeran had overheard a conversation while he was waiting at Halifax airport, which led him to join a discussion with two men who turned out to be the Newfoundland Minister of Mines, Agriculture & Resources and the Deputy Minister for Agriculture. They said that the power contract with Erco was costing the Newfoundland Government $10,000 pa subsidy for each of the 400 employees at Long Harbour; power was costing the Government 11 mils, including delivery to the plant. Probably because of Erco's and A&W's difficulties, the issue was not raised until mid-1976, when David Livingstone reported that he expected the price of power to double. In August 1977 the Premier of Newfoundland called for a joint working-party to look into costs of power and said that he expected a higher price once Long Harbour's costs were competitive. In February 1979 the Government said that it was looking for a substantial increase from January 1979, if necessary by legislation. In September, the Premier (Peckford) asked to meet David Livingstone and two months later there was a Press report of an increase of 300% in the price. The terms proposed by the Province in February were 8 mils rising by 2.5 mils annually, up to 15 mils; six months later the end-point was raised to 35 mils. The final terms agreed in November 1980 were 8 mils rising to 30.13 mils by 1993.

Long Harbour's costs had not been competitive before the increase in the power price. The situation was later made worse by the imposition of a tariff on imports into the UK (the common external tariff of the EEC) and by the weakening of sterling against the dollar. The closure of the rail link from Newfoundland to the Canadian mainland put Long Harbour at a disadvantage against Varennes for supplying Erco's requirements. A project to supply crushed slag to the USA for use on roads, on which $5 million was spent, failed when the material was rejected because of its radioactivity (naturally present in phosphate rock).

The final factor militating against Long Harbour was the development of purified wet acid (PWA), which is described later. As the quality of acid produced from the non-thermal route was improved, so the applications for it increased, while it had a cost advantage. Thus in 1984 A&W's Phosphates Division was complaining that Canadian phosphorus was too expensive and advocating further development of PWA to enable as much as possible of its requirements of phosphoric acid to be sourced from it. So after 1983, when over 52,000 tonnes of phosphorus were produced at Long Harbour, output was reduced, until in August 1989 the furnaces were finally shut down. Varennes continued to produce until 1992. After 141 years, Albright & Wilson had ceased to produce the material on which its prosperity had been founded and had become dependent on purchases from the USA, Germany, China and Kazakhstan. David Livingstone always contended that the concept of Long Harbour was sound but the execution was at fault. In the light of the developments in the 1980s that have been described, it is surely arguable that even if the plant had performed well from the start it would eventually have been uncompetitive with the producers that survived up to that time. If A&W had concentrated on having efficient plants at Varennes and in the UK, a great deal of money would have been saved, in capital and running costs, which might have enabled the company to grow faster, rather than shrink. But it could be argued that without the "poison pill" that Long Harbour represented Albright & Wilson would have lost its identity through divestment by Tenneco in the 1980s, as the history of those years may suggest.

Divestments

While the 1960s were for A&W a decade of acquisitions, the 1970s were characterised by a series of disposals - what Sydney Ellis would have termed "shooting the dogs". The sale of the holding in Midland Silicones in 1971, described earlier, was forced by pressure from A&W's partner, rather than the need for cash, but subsequent disposals were primarily prompted by A&W's financial situation.

The first disposal occurred in July 1971, when Wm E. Marshall, based in Hull and engaged in the compounding and sale of animal feeding stuffs, mainly in Yorkshire and Lincolnshire, was sold to J. Bibby & Sons Ltd. With it went the merchanting companies C. Hammond & Co. and J. Jordan & Sons (Kendal) Ltd and the lighterage business of W.H. Barraclough (Hull). They were small units within the conglomeration of Associated Chemical Companies, peripheral to A&W's operations, and the £850,000 realised was welcome feed for the appetite of the losses in Canada.

The Annual Report for 1972 stated "the Company intends in 1973 to review critically those operations which have unsatisfactory prospects and to direct increasing resources towards potentially attractive growth areas of the business". In April 1973, Sydney Ellis suggested that there were two alternatives to attempting to continue with all existing activities: sell Long Harbour, the rest of Erco and most of the Industrial Chemicals Division; or retain those and sell other parts. He favoured the former, believing that Marchon, BBA and the non-phosphorus parts of ICD would constitute a viable company. David Livingstone argued that Long Harbour should be retained if it was capable of production at over 30,000 tonnes pa. The Board then decided to seek to dispose of non-core businesses.

ACC provided an obvious seam to be mined further. The absorption of its agricultural operations into Marchon and its industrial operations into the Oldbury Division led to the closure of its headquarters at Harrogate and the sale of the extensive buildings there, early in 1973. Later that year, there were much more significant disposals, of most of the former industrial operations of ACC. Sydney Ellis argued that they would not do well, even with the injection of a lot of money, and that they diluted management that was already over-stretched with the problems in Canada.

After the acquisition of ACC by A&W, major steps had been taken to rationalise and expand the chrome chemicals business, by closure of the Glasgow and Bolton factories and the building of large kilns at Eaglesliffe for the production of the basic material, sodium dichromate. Production problems were, however, encountered and heavy capital expenditure, with large overruns, continued in the late 1960s and early 1970s. With over 500 employees at Eaglescliffe, fixed costs were high and margins were under pressure from imports from the USSR. There were also environmental problems in the production processes and from residues. The plan for 1972 showed capital expenditure of nearly £3 million on remedial and improvement projects and a further £2 million on expansion. In the event, the money was not spent. The Board concluded in April 1973 that the chrome chemicals business be sold, for not less than £10 million. In August, a sale to Harrison & Crosfield (a plantation company, interested in building up a diversification into chemicals) was agreed and the sale was concluded in November. The sale realised £8.2 million, less than the target sum but yielding a profit of £4 million over book value; included in the sale was Albright Chemical Co., a small Canadian subsidiary. Clifford Vessey moved to Harrison & Crosfield as managing director of chrome chemicals (a move that angered David Livingstone when he learnt of it). At the same time, A&W's 50% interest in Chrome Chemicals (South Africa) was sold to its partner, Bayer, for £400,000.

Another ACC unit sold at that time was the Brotherton sulphur dioxide business, with a factory at Bromborough, near the Lever Brothers home at Port Sunlight, Lancashire. The Board had set a target of £2 million; the business was bought by British Oxygen, which was interested both in industrial gases and in adding to the range of products in its Chemicals Division, for £1.85 million.

While the largest divestments were of former ACC units, there were numerous other disposals in 1971-5. The old Stafford Allen headquarters and spice processing building at Wharf Road in London was sold in July 1971 for £300,000 and the former Bush headquarters at Ash Grove, Hackney, was sold to London Transport in 1973 for £1,625,000. Bush's Mitcham (Surrey) site was sold in March 1972 and leased back for a short term while the operations were being set up elsewhere. Erco's interest in Ercona Adhesives was sold to the Dickinson, Robinson Group (primarily in paper products) in September1971 for $57,000 and assumption of a $100,000 guarantee to a bank; the company had never made a profit and there were disagreements with the partner, Evode. The remaining shares in Occidental Petroleum were sold in the same month for $1.8 million. The 25% holding in Polyfos (South Africa) was sold in April 1973 for its original cost of 150,000 rands (£30,000), to Amcor, the holder of 51%. Stafford Allen New Guinea was sold to the local administration in September 1973 for AUD192,000 (about £150,000).

In April 1973, the Board agreed that the aryl phosphates business (i.e. trixylenyl phosphate, etc., used primarily as plasticisers in applications where fire retardancy was important) should be sold to Ciba-Geigy. The business, based on the Rainham plant, had been created by Boake Roberts and the technology was superior to that of Ciba-Geigy, the principal competitor. The most important raw material was phosphorus oxychloride, made at Oldbury and supplied to Rainham and to Ciba-Geigy. The Oldbury Division had taken over the Rainham phosphates from BBA in 1967, much to the regret of the Boake Roberts staff who had developed the technology and sales, and the proposal to sell out to Ciba-Geigy (with a commitment to continue buying the oxychloride) was deeply disappointing to them. In the event, the proposal to sell was withdrawn in July 1974. (Eventually, in September 1983, the sale took place, in circumstances described in the next chapter.)

In accordance with Stock Exchange requirements, a letter was sent at the end of 1973 to all stockholders from the Chairman and Managing Director to explain the Board's policy on disposals, which up to then had raised £14 million. The letter stated that £40 million was to be spent over the next three years on flavours & fragrances (BBA), pulp & paper chemicals (Erco), organic chemicals, detergent raw materials, phosphate chemicals and Newfoundland.

Divestments continued in 1974 with the sale of Erco's Port Maitland fertiliser business to International Minerals & Chemicals (IMC) in February, realising £6.2 million and disposing of a business that had made a small profit in 1973 for the first time, as a result of a boom in fertiliser demand in North America. In February 1975, the former ACC 40% holdings in Swan Chemical Co. and Lancashire Chemical Works were sold for £200,000 and in May the foam fire extinguisher operation (a former Boake Roberts venture) was sold to Chubb - which provided the raw materials and was the sole customer - for £425,000. The land at Clevedon, near Portishead, from which clay for making phosphate briquettes had been extracted, was sold to Wimpey for house-building in July. In September, the Wakefield site and ammonia derivatives business was sold to the Green's Economiser Group for £875,000 and in the same month operations ceased at Mitcham, after 227 years. The undeveloped land at Kirkby was sold in November for £437,000.

There were also proposals for the sale of Erco's industrial chemicals operations, ICD's phosphorus-based operations and the phosphorus factories, which were worked on in 1972-5. After an appeal by David Livingstone to Sydney Ellis and the rest of the A&W Board, they were abandoned, because of the withdrawal of possible purchasers and the improvement in the cash and profit situation.

The divestments that were completed not only realised a substantial amount of cash but also reduced the dissipation of managerial time and attention, which was largely a by-product of the acquisitions of the 1960s. In October 1972, at a Tenneco management seminar, David Livingstone spoke of the reduction in the number of A&W's sites in the UK from 26 in 1971 to 21 by then, with a target of 15 in 1973. That was still a relatively large number for a chemical company of A&W's size and the reduction was to continue over the following 20 years, though mainly through divestments of businesses, rather than rationalising continuing activities.

Merger

With the ending of the period of divestment and with A&W restored to favour in the stock market, David Livingstone's thoughts turned to the idea previously pursued by Sydney Barratt (who had died in August 1975, at the age of 77), for the formation of a second ICI. In November 1976, David wrote to Sydney Ellis: "It is now some time since I gave you anything to think about in your bath, and I want to make amends. 'The last infirmity of noble mind' in all my predecessors as Managing Director of Albright & Wilson has been the concept of creating a second ICI in the UK, and true to type I have been toying with the idea again. Suppose we could put together BP Chemicals, A&W, Fisons and Laporte (for starters), how would Tenneco react? This would give us a company with a turnover of about £1,000 million, more broadly based between organic and inorganic chemistry, and so complicated to organise and rationalise that it would probably make no money for five years. The British government would have to be prepared to accept a holding of about 25% (through its stake in BP) and Tenneco would have to be prepared to accept a shareholding, I would guess, of between 8% and 15%....In some ways the climate for this kind of amalgamation is better now than it has ever been before, in that it would give government an opportunity of showing that it is not hell bent on nationalisation, but believes in a fruitful industrial strategy, and also because the people heading up the concerns in question contain fewer prima donnas than they did ten years ago".

David then put in hand the collection of information, for discussion with Sydney during his forthcoming visit to London. Michael Winstanley (see p.399), one of the analysts at Knightsbridge, produced a paper comparing A&W and Fisons: both companies had a market value of around £80 million, around 10,000 employees, derived about 60% of their earnings from operations outside the UK, with broadly complementary products within fields of common interest, and with A&W's profits somewhat ahead in the latest reported year (£18.5 million v. £16.7 million). The analysis also covered figures relating to Laporte and Croda (each with a market capitalisation of around £30 million). A meeting between David and BP Chemicals (estimated to be as big as the other four companies together) had a negative outcome: BP was not looking to hive off its chemical interests and was seeking to invest some of its cash flow from North Sea oil in expanding them.

David's discussion with Sydney was inconclusive. Sydney said that there had been some consideration within Tenneco of buying out the minority in A&W and that an approach from RTZ to buy Tenneco's holding in A&W had been rejected. Tenneco was expecting a large inflow of cash in the next five years and would be looking to buy RTZ rather than to sell A&W. Work then continued on the idea of a second ICI and in July 1977 a study was produced, of a possible group comprising Albright & Wilson, Fisons, Laporte, BP Chemicals and Glaxo, with a calculated market value of £1,000 million, against a market value for ICI at that time of about £2,300 million. Another possible member of the group was thought to be Solvay, a Belgian chemical company with a primary interest in chlorine/caustic soda, links with Laporte and a market value of over £300 million. Nothing, however, came of David's initiative. He marked the file "Nemesis - keep handy" but after Tenneco's acquisition of the whole of the share capital of Albright & Wilson and the subsequent events in Tenneco, the file was not reopened.

Developments

There were moves in 1972 that were directed towards development. In July, a 5-year strategic plan for 1973-7 was adopted by the Board. The main features were reported in the "Albright News" in September. It included not only short-term objectives such as achieving improvements in production from Long Harbour and the Eaglescliffe chrome chemicals plant but also maximising the ability to ship phosphorus in bulk, moving further into end-use markets, building on the bases established in Continental Europe, establishing a New Ventures activity and increasing expenditure on new project research. BBA was highlighted as an area of growth.

The New Ventures Division

The New Ventures Division was formed in 1972 to develop businesses not necessarily concerned with the chemical industry but making use of existing technical or commercial strengths. The small team was headed by Clifford Vessey, brought back from his stint as President at Long Harbour. His no.2 was Derek Johnson, formerly Technical Director of Midland Silicones and then of ACC. David Livingstone declared that the team would be given a free rein to develop projects for which they saw sound and rapid growth prospects. The NVD was expected to become self-funding quickly and to show a high return on capital - David Livingstone warned "we cannot pour in enormous quantities of money in the hope of a pay-off in the future".

It was hoped that one project would be under way in 1972 and two in 1973, with 4-6 then in process. The team considered a variety of possibilities. They included investing in a chain of riding stables, producing wine from sugar and BBA flavours (abandoned in the face of wine lakes on the Continent), using the Calder canal for continental barge traffic (abandoned when the British Waterways Board decided not to widen the canal), manufacturing organic fertilisers from sewage sludge and mushroom compost (several hundred tonnes made but not a bag sold), and marketing a process for pickling structural steel (abandoned after the envisaged joint venture went bankrupt). The one venture that became commercial was the marketing to janitorial outlets of a range of semi-domestic products (cleaning, hygiene and floorcare), through a separate company, Service Products Ltd. The products were manufactured at Wakefield until September 1975, when the works was sold and manufacture was transferred to Kirkby. At the end of 1975, the New Ventures activities, which were headed by Derek Johnson after Clifford Vessey left in October 1973, were absorbed into the Specialities Sector. Eventually, at the end of 1978, after Derek Johnson had left, the Service Products operation was sold to Diversey, for £173,000. The original concept, of creating a useful measure of diversification, had not been realised. Without substantial funding, and perhaps acquisitions, the hope of leapfrogging beyond more usual extensions of existing operations was unlikely to be realised. It also seems doubtful whether new ventures were needed, although at the time there was considerable pressure to break out of what was seen by some as a range of businesses without enough potential for development.

Research & Development

In the background, there was concern that the scale of research and development expenditure was inadequate. A paper of 1971 observed that "The technical function of the Company has probably borne the brunt of the recent economies in fixed costs". The technical plan for the company drawn up in 1969 showed R & D expenditure in 1971 of over £2.5 million, which two years later was reduced by a third, to £1.6 million, more than £300,000 lower than in 1970. The number employed in R & D was cut by 20% in the same period; at Oldbury there was a cut of 40%. The Company Technical Plan for 1976, drawn up in 1975, reported that R & D spending in 1974 was equivalent to 1.2% of sales, against 2% ten years before; figures quoted for other chemical companies were much higher - 2.5% for Fisons, 2.9% for ICI, 3.3% for Laporte. The report stated "It seems probable that our level of spending is at as low a level as possible, consistent with maintaining our position in a technological industry" and forecast that there would be a "technology gap" in the late 1970s and early 1980s. A few months later, George Ashford suggested that someone should be engaged to make a survey of research in A&W, but David Livingstone said that he preferred to ask the Sector Chairmen to say what they needed. There followed a number of proposals for centrally-promoted research on programmes chosen by the Sector Chairmen, sponsored university research, a strategic development department, etc., but it was not for another five years, after the appointment of Dr Charles Suckling (p.256 - footnote), that there was any substantial change in the approach to R & D in the company.

Phosphoric Acid & Phosphates

In the long term, the most important direction of development in this period was in the production of purified wet phosphoric acid (PWA). As has been recounted in an earlier chapter, when the decision was taken to build a phosphorus plant in Newfoundland, work on the alternative route to purified phosphoric acid was suspended. By 1968, however, a team had been re-formed at Whitehaven, reporting to F.M. (Mike) Cussons and a small pilot plant was built in the old NCB pump house; one of the shift workers, under the plant manager, Bob Southwood, was Ray Cranke, who many years later was to become manager of the Whitehaven site.

The key to purification is the application of a solvent to the crude phosphoric acid for the extraction of impurities. The team was looking at solvents that could be used without first concentrating the phosphoric acid. At the end of 1970, however, when Mike Cussons had been seconded to Long Harbour, the team was again disbanded in the course of staff cuts; experimenting with acetone as a solvent, it had made no progress. Towards the end of 1971, when Danny Fagandini was Managing Director at Whitehaven, he instigated a resumption of work. At about that time, in October 1971, David Livingstone presented a paper to the the A&W Board demonstrating that a large part of the usage of phosphorus could be replaced by PWA and reporting that work was being done on developing a process. Four years later, he was forecasting a surplus of phosphorus because of the success of PWA.

Danny Fagandini asked Alan Williams to review previous work and restart it. Alan (T.A.) Williams had joined A&W in 1960, after a degree in chemistry, to which he added chemical engineering. He became involved in PWA in 1965 and was to be the key person in PWA for A&W for more than thirty years, receiving an MBE in 1997 in recognition of his remarkable work. He found some records at Oldbury of a small investigation in 1963-4, which had not been pursued. In 1965 he visited Israel, primarily to look at the use of salt and hydrochloric acid (instead of sulphuric acid) in the production of phosphoric acid and phosphates, and while there was given a demonstration of the IMI (Israel Mining Industries) method for solvent extraction, which was not at that time in commercial production. He converted the concept to a process (his flow-charts were used by IMI) but A&W then developed along different lines. In 1974, IMI claimed that A&W had infringed its patent, served a writ in 1976 and litigation continued until 1978, when there was an out-of-court settlement, involving the purchase by A&W of Israeli phosphate rock over the next three years.

Another pilot plant was built at Whitehaven in 1971 and the first process tried turned out to be the one adopted for commercial production. A larger pilot plant was built in 1972 and towards the end of 1973 a plant to produce 40,000 tons pa of PWA was authorised. It was termed 'MO', recognising that its development was a combined effort by Marchon and Oldbury. The process used as solvent MIBK (methyl isobutyl ketone), which was considered to show several advantages over the IMI method, which used IPE (isopropyl ether). The acid was of a quality suitable for industrial phosphates; thermal phosphoric acid was still required for food phosphates, metal treatment and other applications needing a higher degree of purity. The process produced an underflow of impure acid, of 20,000 tpa (against 40,000 tpa of PWA), which was supplied to the agricultural division's fertiliser plant at Barton on Humber. The MO plant came on stream towards the end of 1976.

For the next twenty years, work was to continue on cleaning the acid to the point where ultimately it displaced thermal acid in almost every application, including use in food phosphates and in soft drinks. A further important development was the elimination of the underflow, which was achieved in 1985 through the 'UFEX' (underflow extraction) plant, so maximising the value of the phosphoric acid and increasing the effective capacity of the plants. (The later story of PWA is told in the chapter covering the period 1986-95 - p.300). In September 1976, at about the time that the MO plant was coming on stream, the A&W Board agreed to exploit the company's know-how in PWA through joint ventures, including possibly in Morocco. That decision was not implemented at the time but was to lead to an important advance for A&W ten years later.

At the same time as the development of PWA was occurring in the 1970s, large sums were being invested at Whitehaven in the basic plants for the production of phosphoric acid and phosphates. The first sulphur burner started operating in mid-1973 and enabled two of the anhydrite kilns to be closed. Later in the year, a second burner was authorised, leading two years later to the closure of the remaining kilns and the anhydrite mine. So ended after twenty years the Solway route to sulphuric acid that had been the foundation of the phosphate business created by Frank Schon. The gaunt remains of the plant, chiefly the massive concrete foundations for the kilns, were to stay for many years, until funds were allocated for cleaning up the site.

The increase in the demand for sodium tripolyphosphate (STPP), for home and export markets, and the closure of the Kirkby plant at the end of 1972, led to the Whitehaven plant's being under pressure and to the authorisation, at the end of 1974, of a 50% expansion, from 170,000 to 255,000 tpa. Commissioning of 'DS4' was completed in September 1976 and enabled sales in 1976 to rise to nearly 180,000 tonnes. In the year 1976, profit on Whitehaven STPP and other

Purified Wet Acid: dark 'green' phosphoric acid compared with white purified acid.

1972 pilot plant for purified wet phosphoric acid, showing cascade process.

1976 MO plant for purified wet acid showing mixer settlers development of cascade.

1990 Aurora (North Carolina) PWA plant showing columns replacing mixer settlers.

Whitehaven kilns for manufacture of sulphuric acid from anhydrite (calcium sulphate) before supersession by sulphur burners in 1973.

HM the Queen with David Livingstone at the opening of the F5 phosphoric acid plant 1980; and the royal cars in the snow.

One of the spray driers at the Whitehaven sodium tripolyphosphate plant 1976.
[photo: Adolf Morath]

The 'brake' at Whitehaven used for hauling rail wagons from the main line up to the site, before closure of the site rail system.

phosphates made from wet acid exceeded £10 million, equal to one-third of A&W's total profit.

The next and most important stage in expansion at Whitehaven was in the capacity for phosphoric acid and PWA. The two plants in operation were F3 (i.e. Filter House 3), commissioned in 1961, and F4, commissioned in 1968. Their combined capacity was insufficient to meet the demand expected following the increase in STPP capacity and F3 was proving increasingly unreliable. It was therefore proposed to built a new acid plant (F5) with a capacity greater than F3 and F4 combined, close F3 and continue to operate F4, but at a reduced rate. At the same time, it was proposed to increase the capacity for PWA, by building a new plant, known as MMO (modified Marchon/Oldbury), with an output more than twice that of MO. PWA capacity would then be sufficient to supply all the requirements for upgraded acid (except for food quality, for which acid from phosphorus was required) and 60% of the quantity of technical grade material required for STPP. That would allow a corresponding reduction in the tonnage through the 'wet salts' plant; that plant, producing sodium orthophosphate (then converted to STPP) by a process that removed some of the impurities present in the crude phosphoric acid, had been built in 1962 and was notorious for its unpleasant working conditions.

The estimated cost of F5 was £11.4 million, while MMO was to cost £8.1 million. The total project was A&W's largest investment since Long Harbour. Authorised in March 1977, it was due for completion in May 1979. It was estimated to show an exceptionally high return (a discounted cash flow of more than 40% over a ten year period) and to repay the investment in less than two years. The MMO plant was similar to MO, using A&W's in-house technology with little scale-up and to be built by the same contractor; it caused no significant problems. F5, however, was to prove a major headache. The technology for the plant came from Fisons, which had two plants in operation, in Holland and Yugoslavia, using the 'hemihydrate' process, described in the project proposal as "new generation technology". The proposal included the statement "We believe that the process is as developed as the industry requires and that incentive for foreseeable changes of any magnitude does not exist". The plant was, however, to be more than three times the size of the Yugoslavian plant (which had been operating for about a year), itself a fourfold scale-up of the original plant built by Fisons at King's Lynn. The proposal stated that F5 "represents the largest practicable single stream plant, since it utilises the largest available tipping pan filter. A scale up of this magnitude does not involve significant technical risk...No major difficulties of commissioning are foreseen". It is interesting that an alternative proposal was submitted by Uhde (Hoechst), based on Nissan (Japanese) technology - so providing a further echo of the Long Harbour story.

An alternative that was rejected by the authors of the proposal was to import phosphoric acid from Morocco. "Our judgment is entirely against this. We should be putting at risk a major part of the Company's profitability in return for what even today is no better than a break-even cost situation...without the F5/MMO project we should inevitably have to close down much of the Whitehaven site (indeed it might be difficult to keep any of its operations open) and the result would be catastrophic for the Company". Yet whereas the MMO element of the project was to prove of longer-term importance, F5 was closed in 1992 and Whitehaven's requirements of phosphoric acid for purification and for the manufacture of phosphates were then supplied by imports from Morocco. That led five years later to the closure of the sulphuric acid plant. In the business environment of the 1970s, the retreat from basic chemical manufacture was not considered a strategic option, whereas twenty years later Albright & Wilson, like ICI, was concerned with moving from commodity to speciality chemicals, which for A&W included PWA.

The 1979 Annual Report breezily recorded: "The largest UK investment in A&W's history was successfully completed in good time for a royal official opening on 21 March 1980 by HM Queen Elizabeth II accompanied by the Duke of Edinburgh". That memorable occasion was slightly marred by an unusually heavy fall of snow. What followed was more serious. The 1980 Report stated: "our detergent phosphates results were adversely affected by prolonged difficulties in bringing into operation the large new phosphoric acid plant at Whitehaven. A programme of remedial work and modifications, continuing into 1981, has succeeded in raising throughput and reducing costs, and should lead to a substantial improvement in 1981". A year later it was reported "Commissioning problems with the major new phosphoric acid complex at Whitehaven have been largely overcome" but the 1982 Report stated only that "The performance of the F5 phosphoric acid plant at Whitehaven improved steadily throughout the year".

The plant thus took some three years after its official opening (four years after the date originally set for its completion) to operate with reasonable consistency. Problems arose from both the unfamiliarity of the process and the size of the plant. It was found that the hemihydrate (the material resulting from the action of sulphuric acid on phosphate rock) could set like plaster of Paris, which affected the main reactor and the settling tanks. Stirrers could not cope, material would not pass from one part of the reactor to another, the rails on which the rotating filter ran became distorted, etc.. After the closure of F3, the output from F5 became critical. Major customers were kept waiting and daily bulletins on F5's output were reported to the Managing Director and anxiously awaited by many others. In the first 12 months, £1 million of interest and commissioning costs were capitalised; thereafter they were charged against profits. The plant had no computer controls and was labour-intensive. The position was made more difficult by the attempt to bring cadmium levels in the effluent from the plant within prescribed limits, through varying the mix of phosphate rocks fed to the plant - the low-cadmium rock did not perform well in the plant. Although never a problem on the scale of Long Harbour, F5 absorbed an undue share of management time.

The tonnage of STPP never reached the level predicted when DS4 was authorised. The peak reached in the 1980s was just over 200,000 tonnes in a year. The main reason why sales did not continue to grow was the reduction in the phosphate content of household detergents in North America, parts of Europe and Japan as a result of pressure from environmentalists. In the 1960s, concern at the growth of algae in lakes, especially the Great Lakes, led to the conclusion that it was promoted by the presence of phosphates. To combat the phenomenon of eutrophication, as it became known, action was taken in parts of the USA to reduce the permitted level of phosphates in detergents, or to eliminate them altogether. Producers of phosphates failed to convince the authorities and the public that detergent phosphates were not the principal cause of eutrophication, that other nutrients and phosphates from fertilisers were more important and that the solution to the problem lay in proper treatment of sewage.

Attempts were made (not by A&W) to produce alternatives to STPP. In 1960, SNTA (the sodium salt of nitrilotriacetic acid) was introduced and was proved to be an effective substitute for STPP. Two of the leading US chemical companies, Monsanto and W.R. Grace, built plants to produce SNTA. In 1970, however, the US National Institute of Environmental Health Sciences produced a report suggesting that there could be toxicological problems in its use and the US detergent manufacturers agreed not to use it. (It continued to be used in Canada.) The main substitute that was developed for STPP was Zeolite A (sodium aluminosilicate), which was introduced in Germany in 1973 and rapidly became a significant factor. The UK market for STPP was little affected but there were restrictions, imposed or voluntary, in the USA and Canada, Western Europe and Japan (from 1976). There was still growth in consumption in third-world countries but export markets for A&W became more competitive.

The Chairman's Statement in A&W's Annual Report for 1969 gave as much space to eutrophication as to the problems in Long Harbour, mainly to attempt to counter the argument against phosphates. It included, in referring to possible substitute for phosphates, the words "we have been studying this question closely for some time and are now intensifying our research efforts". In practice, there was never any significant work in A&W on substitutes; the investment in research that would have been required was deemed to be beyond A&W's resources, with a doubtful pay-off. The possibility of manufacturing zeolites was debated from time to time but rejected because A&W would have no special position in producing a material that had become a commodity and did not wish to show that it was not backing STPP to the full. Much later, when heavy duty liquid detergents were developed, A&W decided to offer products containing zeolites, which were purchased, but not on a large scale.

Albright & Wilson did expend considerable effort over a long period to counter the arguments against STPP. The Chairman's Statement for 1970 again treated the subject at length, including quoting from the conclusion of the Minister of the Environment's Standing Technical Committee on Detergents that "it does not consider, at present, that a case has been made out for the replacement of phosphates by alternative materials". A year later, the Annual Report referred to the US Surgeon General's statement on SNTA and his undertaking to provide federal funds to encourage sewage treatment. A&W then decided to publish a quarterly information bulletin, "Detergents and the Environment" for distribution outside the company and Erco also published a "Eutrophication Newsletter".

Thereafter, there was a continuous effort in defence of STPP, including appointing staff to concentrate on the defence (first Albert Taylor and then Eric Hudson) and encouraging independent bodies to review the impact of STPP and of zeolites on the environment, which resulted in conclusions favourable to STPP. Nevertheless, in Canada and the USA, sales for domestic detergents declined sharply but other uses, principally in dishwashing powders and for institutional applications (especially hospitals), continued. In the UK, sales of STPP were halved by the early 1990s because the main soapers reformulated to come into line with continental Europe, using zeolites, but there was then some recovery through the use of STPP in private label (supermarket) detergents and in some of the soapers' heavy duty liquid detergents. In other countries, where there was adequate sewage treatment, phosphates were preferred to zeolites because of the problem of disposing of sludge containing insoluble zeolite residues. STPP remained an important item for A&W, although selling prices and margins were greatly reduced. After 50 years it appeared likely to become one of the longest-running products of the chemical industry.

The Detergents & Chemicals Group

A&W's UK operations, excluding BBA, in this period may be considered in five segments, which were briefly brought together in the Detergents & Chemicals Group (p.188): Detergents, Phosphates, Organics, Specialities and Agricultural. The phosphoric acid and detergent phosphates operations have been covered in the previous section of this chapter.

In 1971 the **Detergents** operations had three sites: in England (Whitehaven), northern Italy (Castiglione) and France (St Mihiel). In 1972 two more sites were opened: in Spain, at Alcover (near Tarragona, in Catalania), and in Italy, at Frosinone (40 miles south of Rome).

The Castiglione factory, which had opened in 1961, had become within ten years the leading supplier of liquid detergents to the Italian market and was selling also into central and south-eastern Europe and North Africa. From selling in bulk, Marchon Italiana had advanced to filling bottles for its customers. In 1973 a further important step was taken towards the domestic consumers through the installation of blow-moulding machines to make the plastic bottles for filling with liquid detergents, shampoos and bubble-bath liquids. The bottles were supplied mainly for supermarkets, with lesser sales for industrial use. In 1973 over ten million bottles were filled by three machines. In 1974, a further three machines were installed and output was over 20 million bottles. The ability to provide a complete service to customers was an important factor in winning market share and persuading the suppliers to supermarkets to cease doing their own bottling. The basic manufacturing plants were expanded in 1972-4 to support the increased volume of sales; chief of them were sulphonation (see p.317) plants, using up-to-date (purchased) technology based on sulphur trioxide, for which additional sulphur burners were installed, and an ethoxylation (see p.318) plant.

The decision to build a factory in the south of Italy was based on the presence there of some of Marchon Italiana's main customers - Colgate Palmolive, Procter and Gamble, Henkel, Annunziata Squibb, SNIA and Mira Lanza. Another important factor was the generous grants and tax incentives given for development in the Mezzogiorno area. A site of 150 hectares was purchased (later expanded to 190 hectares), on which initially was built an ethoxylation plant for the production of foaming control agents for detergents, which came into operation in June 1972. In 1976, after an investment of £1.3 million, bottle-blowing and -filling on a scale similar to Castiglione's began. Plants were also installed to make and blend products for liquid detergents, shampoos, shower gels and floor cleaners for supply to supermarkets, using concentrates supplied from Castiglione. In 1978 further expenditure of over £3 million was authorised for a sulphonation plant, making Frosinone independent of Castiglione, and for expansion of the bottling operations. The growth of bottled products was to be maintained, with almost continual plant expansion, until the late-1980s, when a trend for customers to install their own bottling facilities developed.

Marchon France began trading in September 1968, merchanting surfactants from Whitehaven and Castiglione. The factory at St Mihiel, about 20 miles from Verdun in the Lorraine region of north-east France, started up at the end of 1969, manufacturing intermediates for detergents and for foundries. Capacity was increased by 50% in 1971 and by a further 50% in 1974, when an ethoxylation plant was also brought on stream. A bottle-filling line was installed and a second line started up at the beginning of 1975. Surfactants for industrial uses grew to account for 50% of output, supplying products for plastics and textiles as well as foundry catalysts. Exports were made to

Germany, Benelux and West Africa. Sales were taken over from agents in 1972, when an office was opened in Paris. Profits up to 1972 were disappointing but grew in 1973 and were at a high level in 1974 before improving again at the end of the 1970s. A continuous sulphonation plant costing £2.4 million, more than trebling capacity for detergent, toiletry and industrial surfactants, was authorised in June 1976 and was commissioned at the beginning of 1978.

Marchon Espanola was formed in August 1970 and a 17-acre site acquired at Alcover, about 15 miles from Tarragona and 60 from Barcelona. The area had been designated for chemical industry and among companies nearby were the German majors BASF and Bayer, Shell and Dow Chemical. At that time the Spanish market was protected by high tariffs and there were good rewards to be secured from local manufacture. Construction began in August 1971 and production started in December 1972, at a cost of £0.5 million. Plants included sulphonation reactors and drum driers, enabling a full range of detergent and toiletry materials to be produced. Within a year a doubling of capacity was authorised, which was completed at the end of 1974. Additional land was purchased to double the size of the site. In September 1976 a bottling plant was authorised, taking Marchon Espanola along the road travelled in Italy and France. Following the start-up of the first bottling lines at the beginning of 1978, a larger installation was authorised. While sales continued to increase, Espanola's profits were affected by adverse economic circumstances in Spain. Following the death of General Franco in November 1977, there were political uncertainties leading to economic problems. In 1978 inflation exceeded 28% and controls on prices, imports and exports posed problems. There was also the prospect of membership of the European Economic Community, leading to the removal of tariffs against the other members and so to competition from larger producers. Eventually, nearly 20 years later, A&W was to be forced into substantial rationalisation of its operations in Spain.

At Whitehaven, bottle-blowing was introduced in August 1975, following its success in Italy, to replace bottles purchased for supplying liquid detergents and toiletries for supermarkets, although it never reached the scale of the Italian plants because of greater self-sufficiency among the major producers of detergents and toiletries. At Whitehaven, however, alone among the detergents sites, packed powder detergents were produced, mainly for sale by supermarkets (Sainsbury, Tesco, Woolworths, Coop, Fine Fare, etc.) but also for export to continental Europe, especially Denmark. The possibility of "private label" powders had been discussed by the A&W Board as early as September 1964, when there was a division of views on whether that would alienate the "soapers" (Colgate Palmolive, Procter & Gamble, Unilever), who were the main customers for STPP, or be acceptable to them. There was pressure from the supermarkets for supply from A&W. Then in 1967 the Monopolies Commission launched an enquiry into the supply of domestic detergents, which concluded that the two main soapers met the definition of monopoly suppliers and that there should be an alternative source of supply. A&W started supplying private label powders in 1968 and installed its first automated machine in 1969. Since the existence of the supply from A&W was a mitigating factor in the criticism of the soapers' position, there was no conflict with A&W's customers. In 1972, a second packing machine was installed at Whitehaven and by the end of 1973 A&W's market share had grown to 5%. In 1977, machinery was installed to enable the full range of standard EEC pack sizes to be supplied, which led to a further increase in market share to around 8%.

The other direction of development at Whitehaven was into speciality surfactants. In 1977 plants were commissioned for the manufacture of tertiary amines and their derivatives. Demand for these products, first produced in the early 1960s for dishwashing and toiletry formulations, grew through the demand for ingredients imparting skin mildness to shampoos and foam baths; they also came to be used in sanitisers and cleaning formulations and in the 1970s sales were extended into the pharmaceutical, textiles, rubber, plastics and other industries for use in emulsifiers, corrosion inhibitors, biocides and antistatic agents. There were also plants for sulphosuccinimates (the foaming agent for the latex foam backing for carpets) and imidazolines (mild surfactants for baby shampoos and personal hygiene products). Another important development was in more highly concentrated surfactants. The manufacturing processes and some of the products were developed in the Whitehaven laboratories.

Overseas, there were investments in South Africa and Singapore. In 1976 a 50% holding was acquired in Paragon Chemical Holdings, A&W's distributors of detergents in South Africa, which had plants in Johannesburg and Pretoria manufacturing dodecyl benzene sulphonic acid, one of the basic surfactant materials. The company, renamed Marchon-Paragon, was to serve as the vehicle for a wider range of locally-manufactured detergent products. Some years, however, were to elapse before problems of ownership and management were overcome. In 1979 A&W's partner in Marchon-Paragon withdrew and there was a merger with Akulu Chemicals, a South African detergent manufacturer jointly owned by Akzo (a major Dutch chemical company) and Chemical Holdings (a South African company), to form Akulu-Marchon, in which A&W had a 50% holding. At the beginning of 1980, Akzo's share was acquired by Chemical Holdings. After that move became known, David Livingstone expressed the view that A&W's capital should be withdrawn from South Africa as quickly as possible, commensurate with continuing to support the operations of Akulu-Marchon. A&W, however, maintained its investment in Akulu-Marchon until the end of 1989, when through pressure from Tenneco A&W's shares were sold to Chemical Holdings, at a price that did not adequately reflect the company's profitable trading.

In 1977 A&W acquired, for £315,000, a 45% holding in UIC Organics, a subsidiary of the United Industrial Corporation of Singapore (UIC), which was founded in 1964 to manufacture detergents. UIC Organics was formed in 1976 to build a sulphonation plant at Jurong (on Singapore Island), which was commissioned in September 1977 with the assistance of A&W. The Technical Manager, Dr Roger Dunhill, was seconded from A&W (Australia). The company was renamed UIC-Marchon; its Chairman was Lee Kim Yew, brother of Lee Kuan Yew, the Prime Minister of Singapore. In 1978 its operations were extended to the manufacture of a range of Marchon products for shampoos and liquid detergents. UIC-Marchon was A&W's first major investment in South East Asia, soon followed by investment in Malaysia (see below). The initiative for expansion into South East Asia came largely from John Wills (see p.188) and George Pekarek. George emigrated from Austria in 1938 at the age of 14, obtained a chemical degree at Manchester and joined Marchon in 1953, becoming Sales Director and then Commercial Director of Marchon and later of the Detergents & Chemicals Group. In 1977, when John Wills joined the A&W Board as Commercial Director, George became International Marketing Manager and responsible for the Overseas Marketing Companies (which he had been largely instrumental in creating).

The organic detergent operations in the UK and continental Europe in the 1970s were profitable, reaching a peak in 1974. In that year, from sales of £46 million, profits (before interest and tax) of £7 million (equivalent to £46 million in 2000 money) were recorded, with £3 million contributed by Italy, France and Spain and £4 million by Whitehaven. (Although there was some argument over whether the overheads of the Whitehaven site were fairly apportioned between the organic detergents and phosphates operations, it may be noted that the phosphates operations there were also highly profitable, making £7 million profit in 1974.)

In 1971 the **Phosphates** sector operated through three factories: Oldbury, Widnes (Ann Street) and Kirkby. Oldbury, the headquarters and research centre, was the site for manufacture of phosphorus chlorides and other phosphorus derivatives and some of the industrial and food phosphates. Kirkby's STPP plant ceased production in 1972 and the factory was finally closed in 1980. The carbon tetrachloride plant at Widnes also ceased production in 1972, when the production route became uneconomic and the return on the £4 million needed for a new plant would have been insufficient. The closure of Kirkby, however, led to the move of ammonium phosphates production to Widnes and Calgon (water softening phosphate) production was transferred there from Oldbury.

While the troubles at Long Harbour were at their height, capital expenditure was kept to a minimum but by the beginning of 1974 it was possible to announce a programme of expenditure of £17 million in the three years 1974 to 1976, out of a programme of £40 million for the whole Company. That included extensions and improvements to the phosphates plants, several of which were operating at capacity.

Other developments in the Phosphates sector included the introduction of Kalipols (liquid potassium polyphosphates for detergents and food additives) and expansions of capacity for SMFP (sodium monofluorophosphate for toothpastes containing fluoride), phosphorus pentasulphide (used in lube oil additives and pesticides), disodium pyrophosphate (one of the long-standing aerators for baking) and phosphorus tri- and oxy-chlorides (basic intermediates for organophosphorus chemicals).

In October 1974 the Industrial Chemicals Division (as it then was) moved its offices to a newly-constructed building in Warley, on the western outskirts of Birmingham, three miles from the Oldbury works. Housing about 350 staff, it brought together departments from Oldbury, London and Walsall (where engineering staff had moved from Oldbury). The six-storey building, originally called Lenton House but renamed Albright & Wilson House, was leased for 25 years. The move was generally welcomed by the staff, although there were some who deplored the separation from the production operations and technical departments at Oldbury. Fifteen years later, when the end of the 35-year lease at Knightsbridge Green was looming, some Head Office departments were relocated to Birmingham, while the search began for an alternative location in London for a smaller Head Office. Eventually, in October 1991, the Head Office moved to A&W House, leaving only a pied-a-terre in London. The freehold of A&W House was purchased in 1997, thus confirming that A&W's centre would remain close to its birthplace. (Finally in 2001, A&W House was sold and the staff moved to Oldbury.)

Profits made by the Phosphates sector were at a peak in 1974, at £5.5 million, because of a rise in export prices and high volumes. They fell in 1975 to only £1.1 million, because of lower volumes and a failure to recover fully cost increases in higher prices, and then recovered to nearly £5 million in 1977.

In this period, significant progress was made in Asia in phosphoric acid and phosphates. A&W's longest-standing investment in Asia was in **India**, through Albright, Morarji and Pandit. In 1964, A&W was approached to participate in a venture to manufacture STPP in India. At the time, there was no domestic manufacture and manufacture was subject to government licensing. A licence to make STPP had been granted to Mrs Sharda Mukerjee, the widow of a former Air Minister, who had died through choking on a fishbone at an official banquet in Japan. Mrs Mukerjee, who became a member of Congress and subsequently Governor of two of the Indian states, belonged to the Pandit family. The family decided to form a joint venture with the Dharamsi Morarji Chemical Company (DMCC), manufacturer of sulphuric acid at Ambarnath, on the outskirts of Bombay, and an overseas manufacturer of STPP. The shareholdings initially were 46% for A&W, 27% for DMCC, 3% for the Pandit family and the balance for the public. A&W's shareholding was reduced to 39.9% in 1973 to comply with government legislation.

Plants, close to the DMCC factory at Ambarnath, for phosphoric acid (wet acid produced by the Prayon process) and STPP were opened at the beginning of 1968, at a cost of £1.5 million. The licence was for the production of 12,500 tpa of STPP and for 20,000 tons of phosphoric acid, of which 12,000 tons were sold to DMCC for fertiliser and for the clarification of sugar cane juice. The licence was subsequently increased to 25,000 tons pa of STPP and in November 1974 a second STPP unit was completed but power restrictions prevented its operation. In 1977 it became necessary to import STPP, which led to consent for power supplies to enable the second unit to come into production. Duty on imported phosphate rock was also removed. The other constraint on output was a shortage of sulphuric acid, supplied by DMCC. AMP therefore obtained government consent for building a sulphuric acid plant, but not at Ambarnath. The site chosen was at Roha, in an underdeveloped region 75 miles south of Ambarnath, where DMCC also built plants for some of its lower-tonnage products. The sulphuric acid plant, which cost £1.5 million and was built by DMCC, came on stream in April 1979, with a capacity of 45,000 tpa, to match the STPP capacity at Ambarnath.

While AMP's profit in 1978 was a record and its STPP output was close to capacity, there was a severe threat to the company's viability. About two years earlier, the Indian government banned the use of edible oils in soap and granted licences for the manufacture of STPP to four other companies, in anticipation of a surge in demand. One of the licences was granted to Hindustan Lever, customer for nearly half of AMP's output. A 30,000 tpa plant was built at Haldia, about 50 miles from Calcutta, with know-how supplied by A&W for a substantial fee, project management by DMCC and operational assistance by AMP for a 10-year period. The demand for STPP, however, did not expand as expected and after the Haldia plant had come on stream at the end of 1979 and some market share was lost to a third manufacturer of STPP, AMP made losses for several years. Following the appointment of Ishwar Khandelwal (p.360) in 1983, the company returned to profit, through product and market diversification, a gradual expansion in the market and improvement in prices.

The next development in phosphates in Asia was in **Malaysia.** In October 1972 Jagjit Singh Kaurah, an entrepreneurial Punjabi, incorporated Josen Chemical to make superphosphates and phosphoric acid on a site at Port Klang, about 20 miles from Kuala Lumpur. Production of superphosphates started in 1974 and a thermal phosphoric acid plant started up in 1976. The phosphoric acid was to be used in the refining of palm oil; palm oil production had become one of the leading industries in Malaysia, with production expanding from 1 million tonnes in 1973 to 1.7 million in 1977. A&W naturally was very interested in a new producer of thermal phosphoric acid and in December 1976 the Board agreed to acquire the company, for £600,000 - with Gene Anderson and George Ashford dissenting because of what they saw as a diversion of management effort on a relatively small investment. The acquisition was agreed to by Jagjit because the company was making losses. The fertiliser operation was uneconomic because of the high cost of materials and low selling prices and the small scale of production. The phosphoric acid plant was built to an ingenious compact design, by Chia Siang Ee (who was to become a senior executive for A&W first in Malaysia and then in Singapore) but the acid was not acceptable to the palm oil refiners because of Josen's failure to develop an adequate dearsenication process, essential for food grade acid.

A&W took over the operation in July 1977 and installed a dearsenication unit developed at Oldbury. Sales to the palm oil refiners then built up and eventually, with the advantage of a road tanker for bulk deliveries, Josen secured the market against competition from imports. The company was renamed Albright & Wilson (Malaysia) in 1979, when the capacity for phosphoric acid was doubled by modifications to the unit. The fertiliser operation was closed when A&W took over the company. It had been expected that the company would diversify into phosphates but, apart from a joint venture in sodium metaphosphate several years later, A&W Malaysia remained essentially a one-product company. Customers included rubber processors, sugar refiners and paint and metal finishing industries. Protected by a tariff, the company was very profitable.

The **Organics** Sector had plants at West Bank (Widnes), Dan's Road (Widnes), Rainham (Essex) and Canning Road, Stratford; the last three were on shared sites, with BBA and with Specialities.

The West Bank works, previously part of W J Bush, manufactured organic chemicals, derivatives of toluene, a benzene chemical. The products were used in soft drinks, perfumery compounds, pharmaceutical intermediates and general chemicals. In the period 1971-8, there was considerable expenditure on modernising and extending the plants on the site, which was congested through haphazard development. Several of the plants were old and there were problems with effluent. £1.5 million was spent in 1974-6 on plants for the chlorination of toluene, phenylacetic acid (used as a precursor for penicillin), benzyl cyanide and acyl chlorides. Capacity was extended and safer and more efficient processes were introduced. A long-standing effluent problem was tackled, with an overhead effluent system. A new road system was devised, involving the demolition of buildings - previously, access to some of the buildings was impossible for any vehicle larger than a forklift truck. There were much-needed improvements in working conditions and labour practices were also reformed. A further £1.2 million was spent in 1977-8 on expansions, including a 50% expansion in benzyl cyanide, making it the largest plant in the world for that chemical. The transformation of the site in this period was remarkable.

At the beginning of 1978, negotiations started for the purchase of De Laire, a French company with a factory at Calais, one of the main competitors of West Bank (the other was Prom, in Denmark). The acquisition would have been highly important for the West Bank business and would have given A&W a foothold just across the Channel, which might have been of use for other sectors. Although consent of the French government was obtained and the management of De Laire was in agreement, the bid was abandoned in September 1979 when the results of De Laire for the first 6 months of 1979 showed an unexpected fall in profit; it was decided that there was not a valid commercial case for the acquisition and that there should not be a re-negotiation at a lower price. The three brothers who owned De Laire then sold out to another French company.

In the long term, the most important Organics product was phosphorous acid, produced at Canning Road, Stratford. Early in 1974, the Board authorised an expansion of capacity from 900 to 2,400 tpa, making A&W the largest producer in the world. At that time, the principal customer for the product was Monsanto, for a sugar cane growth regulator; other uses were in pharmaceutical and laboratory chemicals and in the manufacture of phosphites, including stabilisers for PVC (polyvinyl chloride) plastic. The next major use was in herbicides, in the manufacture of glyphosate, the key ingredient in Monsanto's "Roundup", a herbicide particularly successful in killing persistent weeds while leaving no active residues in the soil. The most important new application was in the manufacture of phosphonates, specialised ingredients for detergents and water treatment chemicals. In 1981, these products were given the name "Briquests", reflecting their sequestering property (the ability to extract and hold dirt, etc.) and British origin. The phosphorous acid plant was expanded again in 1977 but outgrew the congested 4-acre site at Stratford and so the decision was taken to move production to Oldbury, where a plant with three times the capacity of the Stratford plants was opened in 1983. Oldbury was already making an allied product, ADPA (acetodiphosphonic acid), for which a plant was commissioned in 1977. The Briquests, which then became a Phosphates Sector product group, continued to grow in importance and became a significant profit-earner for A&W.

The other Organics products were principally for supply to the plastics industry. At Rainham in Essex, which was shared with BBA, phosphate plasticisers were produced, for which the main raw material was phosphorus oxychloride, produced at Oldbury. Annual sales were around £2.5 million but with only about 100 employees, one-third the number employed at West Bank. At the beginning of this period, there were production problems and a sale of the business to Ciba Geigy was under consideration. That course of action was, however, abandoned in 1974. There were improvements to the plant in 1977 and in 1979 it became the first A&W plant with microprocessor controls, the Diogenes system developed by the Rosemount Company of the USA, which was grafted on to the 1958 analogue control system. Computer control gave the plant a flexibility that increased its effective capacity, while improving safety.

At Dan's Road, shared with BBA, phthalates were produced. The problems with phthalate plasticisers have already been described (p.75). A&W had no advantage in raw materials, technology or market position and the products were persistently unprofitable. Eventually, in March 1979 A&W withdrew from phthalates and the buildings and usable plant items were taken over for BBA's fragrance chemicals.

The largest plant at Canning Road, Stratford, in the early 1970s was for the production of organotin compounds, used as a stabiliser for PVC (dibutyl tin oxide) and as an antifungal agent (tributyl tin fluoride) in antifouling paints. As already mentioned (p.28), A&W had been interested in organotin compounds since 1953 and had obtained a licence for their manufacture from Metal & Thermit Inc. in 1954. Initially, products were made from purchased intermediates, until a new plant was built in 1965. Although the plant was expanded by 50% in 1973-4, the process was not competitive (A&W's Grignard process was made obsolete by the aluminalkyl route) and A&W's profits on the organotins were disappointing. Early in 1980, the stabiliser side of the business was sold to Lankro Chemicals, part of Diamond Shamrock (one of the US major chemical companies). The remaining operation was uneconomic and so the plant was closed.

The **Specialities** Sector in the 1970s and for many years after included three main activities - metal finishing, water treatment and flame retardancy. In addition in this period there were the Xylok resins and Albright & Wilson Ireland. The Sector was moderately profitable but not large. In 1977 the Sector, excluding Ireland, accounted for about 2% of A&W's total sales and about 1% of operating profit. The main distinguishing feature of the Sector was the emphasis on selling effect or performance, rather than chemicals, and so there was a closer relationship with the customer. That was shown in the measure of technical service and in the Company's investment in equipment to reproduce the effects required by the customer, in the application of flame-retardant chemicals to cloth, or the plating of metals, or in descaling water systems. The specialities units had always been associated with the phosphorus-based side of A&W, which was understandable, given the nature of the Marchon and BBA businesses, which were inherently more oriented towards the final customer.

Most of the profits of the Sector in this period were made by the metal finishing activities. They originated partly from phosphoric acid and partly from the chromium-based treatments acquired with Associated Chemical Companies, which were retained when the chrome chemicals business was sold in 1973. The activities included chemical polishing, anti-corrosion treatments, electroplating and pretreatment of surfaces before plating or painting. Characteristic of what was offered were improvements in toxicity and effluent, through trivalent chrome plating (in place of the traditional hexavalent plating), alternatives to cyanide and the elimination of chemicals in effluent. Products launched in this period were Accomet C (pretreatment), Alecra 3 (trivalent chromium plating), Supalex (nickel plating) and Super Pyrobrite (copper plating). Income from licensing the processes in the UK and USA provided a large part of the profits.

The water specialities business, covering industrial water treatment, including softening, descaling and service to desalination plants in the Middle East, was long-established and modestly profitable but not a major growth point.

The flame retardancy business mainly consisted of the Proban process for application to textiles. Proban Ltd had been formed in 1955 (p.30) but even after 20 years had not become a significant contributor to profits. Some publicity was generated by the use of Proban-treated fabrics in motor racing and in railway seating, the process was licensed to a US textile company and the introduction of ammonia curing speeded up the treatment of textiles and extended application to some synthetic materials. It was not until the 1980s, however, that sales grew significantly.

Xylok resins (based on xylene) were developed by Midland Silicones as materials that were cheaper than silicones and possessed some of their properties, of stability at high temperatures, mechanical strength and electrical insulation. They were retained by A&W when MS was sold in 1971 and the team working on them, which had been set up in 1967, was moved from Barry to Oldbury. In 1974, British Rail adopted xylok resins for traction motors on their electric locomotives and manufacturing capacity was trebled. A few months later, an agreement was made for xylok resins to be marketed in the USA by Ciba Geigy, who were "very optimistic that this new group of high performance plastics will contribute substantially to the growth of our resin business". A full-scale plant for the intermediate Mimex was built at West Bank. Another application announced in 1974 was for injection moulding for components used in motor vehicles, domestic utensils, street lamps, etc.. In 1976, xylok resins were introduced into printed circuit boards and compressor blades. Unfortunately, Xylok resins proved to be not competitive with epoxy resins in cost or with silicones in performance. They were never profitable and eventually the rights to manufacture and sale were passed to Japan.

Albright & Wilson **Ireland**'s sales grew in this period from £4 million in 1971 to £16 million in 1978 and profit also quadrupled. Uniquely in the Albright & Wilson group, the Irish company (p.4) was not primarily engaged in the manufacture and marketing of chemicals; in a small market, viability of the company depended on selling a wide range of products manufactured by third parties. Expansion was particularly marked in consumer products, including detergents (Procter & Gamble), paper products (Kimberly Clark), tea and Oxo (Brooke Bond Leibig), canned fruits (Del Monte), Ovaltine (Wander), biscuits (Associated Biscuits) and shoe polish (Kiwi). There were also numerous agencies for industrial products, including imports from A&W in England, and sales of products manufactured or finished in Ireland: firelighters, food phosphates and cleaning chemicals. There was an office and warehouse in Belfast, which continued to operate after damage by a car-bomb in 1972. From 1971 the Managing Director of A&W Ireland was John Hewitson, who had been the Administration Director at Whitehaven, after a period with Marchon Italiana; he was to continue as Managing Director during the whole period of A&W's ownership of the company. The company's progress was uninterrupted, even by the strike of Irish banks in 1976, when the supermarkets (A&W Ireland's main customers) effectively became the banks through circulating the money brought in by their customers. By 1977, it was becoming clear that the main premises at Dun Laoghaire (the ferry terminal for Dublin) plus the smaller premises at Ash Grove nearby were inadequate to handle the growing distribution activities. Agreement was reached with the Dublin authorities to acquire a site at Sandyford, a district in south-west Dublin; there, on a site of 11 acres, was built what was believed to be the largest warehouse in Ireland, at a cost of £3.8 million, to which operations were eventually transferred in 1981. Market leadership was maintained through same-day or overnight delivery, made possible by technology more advanced than elsewhere in A&W, including the use by salesmen of hand-held computers communicating by telephone. It was an oddity in the A&W group but retained because of its good record of growth and return on investment.

The **Agricultural** Sector was another somewhat anomalous unit. It was an irony that the part of Associated Chemical Companies that A&W was reluctant to acquire along with the industrial chemical operations remained in A&W after the industrial operations had been sold. There had been some rationalisation, including the closure of Brigg, the headquarters of The Farmers' Company, which had become part of ACC in 1962. The Farmers' Company had been established in June 1874 to supply the needs of farmers in north Lincolnshire and was one of the pioneers of manufactured fertilisers in Britain. Its main factory, at Barton-on-Humber, had started making fertilisers in 1873, initially from dried blood and bone meal (produced from carcases delivered by ship), mixed with potash. In the early days the cargoes were unloaded from ships in baskets balanced on wheelbarrows. The factory had its own power-station, fired by oil delivered in lead-lined wooden casks and by "esholt", cubes of treated sewage. Fertilisers were despatched in hand-sewn sacks. In the 1930s production of superphosphates was started, by treating ground bones (and later, phosphate rock) with sulphuric acid made from iron pyrites. Then in 1946 a plant was built to make granulated fertilisers, which had been developed during the 1939-45 war and were greatly superior in application. The concentration of fertilisers was increased in the 1950s and 1960s. New plant was, however, required to produce fertilisers of a concentration to match the competition.

Brief reference has already been made (p.92) to the Barton fertiliser project, authorised by the A&W Board soon after the acquisition of ACC in 1965. At that time, ACC had several small plants, at Barton, Misterton (Nottinghamshire) and Eaglescliffe (Durham) producing a total of about 200,000 tpa of medium to low grade fertilisers, with about 5% of the UK market in fertilisers. To survive in competition with ICI and Fisons, it was necessary to produce high concentration compounds of nitrogen, phosphate and potash. The original plan was to build a plant to produce granular compound fertilisers and a separate ammonium nitrate plant, following the pattern of ICI and Fisons (and later Shell), but that was ruled out on grounds of cost. A conventional granulation plant could not, however, safely produce both compound fertilisers and ammonium nitrate.

It was therefore decided to make ammonium nitrate as well as compound fertilisers using prilling technology. The process involved feeding liquid into a spinner at the top of a tower, which in descending became solid pellets - a technique similar to that once used for making lead shot. It had been used successfully by others for making ammonium nitrate but not compound fertilisers of the sort required. The possibility of using prilling for compound fertilisers was pursued by Bill Coates, who had joined British Chrome & Chemicals (the predecessor of ACC) in 1957 as a works manager, becoming head of engineering and development in ACC and eventually in 1975 Chairman of the Agricultural Sector. Bill found a team at Stamicarbon (Dutch State Mines) who were thinking along the same lines and they designed a plant for Barton, which was completed towards the end of 1967. Commissioning was prolonged because of caking of the prills and it was not until 1969 that the problems were largely overcome. By then, the plant had overrun its authorised cost of £2.1 million by £1 million.

The plant operated well from 1970 and at the end of 1972 there was a proposal to spend £2.7 million on a second prilling tower and nitric acid plant. The A&W Board, however, rejected the proposal and there was no substantial expenditure on the fertiliser plant until 1979. The Board's caution was understandable: there was a shortage of ammonia and A&W was at a disadvantage compared with ICI and Fisons, which had cheap supplies based on an advantageous contract by ICI for natural gas. (The renegotiation of the gas contract in 1977 led to an increase in fertiliser prices from 1st January 1978.) A&W's shortage of ammonia was overcome first by a contract with ICI and later by the shipment of liquid ammonia from continental Europe direct to Barton, but still at a price disadvantage. There was also the adverse effect of a reduction in fertiliser subsidies to EEC levels, from 1972 to 1975.

In 1974, however, there was a severe world shortage of fertilisers because of a shortage of raw materials and fertiliser prices rose sharply. A&W made a record profit from fertilisers in 1974, in excess of £2.5 million. In 1975, prices weakened and A&W sought to supply overseas markets, exporting 50,000 tons in the second half of the year. Profit fell to £0.5 million. In 1976 A&W made a loss on fertilisers of £1 million and although there was a partial recovery to a break-even position in 1977, and to profit in 1978, profitability of the fertiliser operations remained unsatisfactory.

By contrast, the pesticides operations of Farm Protection performed well. There was some uncertainty, when ACC was acquired in 1965, whether FP should be retained, since it was essentially a merchanting operation, dependent upon licensing the products of other chemical companies. Keith Piercy set a target for profit to be attained in five years, which was exceeded within two years. Farm Protection Ltd was founded in 1947 as an offshoot of Robt Stephenson & Son, a small fertiliser manufacturer at Beverley (Yorkshire). Its founder was Pat Cumming, who had joined his father-in-law's company in the previous year. Initially the company specialised in contract crop spraying, until in 1951, when farmers were starting to buy their own sprayers, he sold FP's machines to Pest Control Ltd, which was later acquired by Fisons. Some years later, the Contract Service Unit was formed within ACC, for spraying and the application of fertilisers, but it was not a part of Farm Protection.

FP was dormant until 1959, when Pat Cumming obtained sole sale rights for certain of Du Pont's range of crop protection products. Other distribution rights were obtained, from the US chemical companies Diamond Alkali, Velsicol, Cyanamid, Murphy, Monsanto and Stauffer, and from Shell and Bayer. The product range included herbicides (selective weedkillers), insecticides (to control eelworm, aphids, Dutch elm beetles, blight and other pests) and foliar feeds. FP moved on to develop blends of herbicides, the most successful being Di-Farmon, marketed from 1967, and increasingly to conduct field trials of its products. In 1970, its headquarters was moved from Harrogate to a former hotel at Glaston Park, a small village in Leicestershire. Bill Cowan, FP's technical adviser, when visiting the Glaston Park Hotel, asked the landlord if he knew of any large properties and was told "You can have this place if you want it - business isn't too good around here". The location was highly suitable since 60% of FP's sales at the time were in East Anglia and the larger premises were needed to meet the aim of doubling the sales and biological staff in the next 3-5 years.

In 1975 FP reported that sales in 1974 were more than double those in 1972. They remained buoyant in 1975-7 when fertilisers were experiencing a downturn. New products were introduced. Pat Cumming retired in 1976; his successor, Peter Jones, had joined FP as a biologist in 1963. A significant step forward was the authorisation in 1976 of a plant for the blending and packaging of FP's products. The plant at Barton, costing £500,000, came into operation in November 1977. In that year, Farm Protection made a profit of over £500,000, while the fertiliser operations could do no better than break even. Later, FP's profits rose to more than £1 million. It was a remarkable result within Albright & Wilson, being dependent on marketing strength rather than investment in chemical manufacture or basic chemical technical expertise.

Bush Boake Allen

Bush Boake Allen also depended for success largely on marketing strength, in close attention to customers' needs. The period 1971-8 was one of strong growth in sales. In the early part of the period important steps were taken in rationalising the Division. In 1973, the headquarters were established at Walthamstow, on the eastern fringe of London, where offices and laboratories were built over a three-year period, enabling the previous headquarters of Bush (at Ash Grove, Hackney) and Stafford Allen (at Wharf Road bordering the eastern side of the City of London) to be closed and the Boake Roberts headquarters at Stratford to become only a factory site. Walthamstow was chosen as the least unsuitable of the sites in the London area, where most of BBA's employees in the UK worked but the 9-acre site was cramped, the manufacturing areas were not well-designed for the expanded production of flavours and fragrances and road and rail communications were not good. The leasing of adjacent premises in 1977 and the purchase in 1978 of the freehold of the industrial estate including those premises improved the potential of the site but did not transform it. The other UK sites were at Witham, Essex (essences and juices), Long Melford, Suffolk (extractions and botanicals), Stratford (chemicals and chemical research) and Dan's Road, Widnes (perfumery chemicals).

Tony Allen, who had been Managing Director of BBA since 1968, was replaced in August 1973 by Dr Danny Fagandini, who had joined Marchon in 1951 and had become its Managing Director in 1972. Danny immediately set about reorganising the business. "What I saw", he said, "left me in no doubt that there was an immediate need to give the Division a new, cohesive structure". He set up a functional management structure, with Technical, Production, Marketing etc. Directors, replacing the previous organisation, which had been on business lines. Danny brought a background in chemicals and a flair perhaps attributable to his Italian parentage. Features of his time at BBA were the Mexican and Polynesian symposia in 1974-5, demonstrating BBA's ability to match national flavours, audiovisual presentations to customers and the visit of Princess Margaret to Walthamstow in 1975.

In mid-1975, there was a further reorganisation, to a business-unit based structure, divided into Flavours, Fragrances and Chemicals, accompanied by redundancies made necessary by cost inflation and a downturn in sales. Danny Fagandini, after a period of ill-health, moved from BBA to the A&W headquarters at Knightsbridge a year later and was replaced as Managing Director by Ron Mason, who had a background of chemicals in Boake Roberts. So BBA continued its history of changing Managing Directors and patterns of organisation - Ron Mason retired in May 1979 and his successor, Malcolm Clark, left after one year, with his successor Robin Gooch in the position for only two years.

In the UK the principal plant developments for BBA in this period were major additional distillation units at the synthetic aromatics plants at Dan's Road, producing perfumery chemicals from pinene (obtained from pine trees), expansion of the extraction units at Long Melford and a plant at Stratford for Trimbal (trimethoxybenzaldehyde), an intermediate used in the production of l-dopa, for the treatment of Parkinson's disease. In 1975, a joint venture with General Mills, GMB Proteins, was formed, to make textured vegetable protein, given the name Bontrae, by a new process; capable of making flavoured products ranging from beefburgers to candy bars, the material was forecast to sell at least 30,000 tonnes pa within five years but disappointingly never became important.

More than half of BBA's UK production was exported. 80% of fragrances were sold abroad, the largest-selling fragrance being Bint-el-Sudan (see p.80), one of a range of "franchise" products sold in Africa and the Middle East. The finished products, plus packages and labels, were sold to local distributors who marketed them through bazaars and other small outlets. The business was run by Tony de Reymonth, an enthusiastic and engaging character, who started it in the Sudan in 1970, after 15 years in fragrances. It was said that it was de riguer for pilgrims to Mecca to wear Bint-el-Sudan. In Ghana it was known as "Okomfo Anokye", a fetish god, and in powder form was thrown over chiefs at their installation and by relatives over those who were acquitted in the courts. In mid-1975, the perfume was introduced into the USA, where it was targeted primarily at black Americans and sold by the Lehn & Fink Division of Sterling Drug after market testing during 1974. Unfortunately the heavy fragrance never acquired the popularity enjoyed in Africa.

Altogether, two-thirds of BBA's sales were outside the UK, of which half originated from the overseas subsidiaries. The most profitable was Bush Nigeria, selling Bint el Sudan and other perfumes and cosmetics through the markets of Nigeria. In 1973, A&W's holding was reduced to 58%, through an issue of shares to prominent local interests, and in 1978 it was reduced to 40% to comply with legislation. Since the profit in 1975 was over £1 million, rising to £1.3 million in 1977, the loss of subsidiary status had a significant impact in BBA's accounts. Of more significance was the difficulty in remitting past and current profits, because of Nigerian exchange controls; increasingly there were also problems in maintaining operations, because of local obstruction in the provision of services, to be overcome only by what in US legislation were termed "grease payments".

The other main overseas earners for BBA were South Africa and Australia and New Zealand. All were originally Bush companies, mainly in flavours; they were market leaders in their countries and profitable. In Australia, rationalisation and improvement included the closure of a factory at Bridgetown in Western Australia, which had enjoyed an artificial existence: decolourised and deflavoured apple juice had been produced there for sale to soft drink producers (as a sugar substitute) because of a loophole in taxation giving relief for fruit juices, which was closed in 1974. A new departure for BBA was the purchase in 1976 of Parbury Foods, in Victoria, making dehydrated foods, which included a joint venture in Tasmania producing dehydrated apples and potatoes. Although complementary to BBA's successful Saromex (powdered spices), the idea was not pursued elsewhere.

BBA's efforts to build up a significant presence in North America, regarded as necessary to compete internationally with Flavours & Fragrances Inc., the world leader, made little headway in the period. Companies based in Montreal and New Jersey were not profitable and ideas for acquisitions in the USA and Brazil came to nothing. Elsewhere, however, BBA was extending its operations: in 1971-3 offices followed by a small plant at Cannes, in 1972 laboratories and offices in Singapore and Cologne, in 1974 an office in Tokyo and in 1977 the acquisition of Klevas Aromer, a Swedish flavours company.

There was much optimism about BBA's prospects. The strategic plan for 1973-7 produced in 1972 showed BBA as the largest contributor to increased profits and a letter to stockholders from Sydney Ellis at the end of 1973 gave first place to the plans for BBA. In 1977 the A&W Board directed David Livingstone to make recommendations for an acquisition in flavours. In that year BBA's profit peaked at £8.6 million, compared with £1.8 million in 1971. Almost every unit produced record profits, in a year of high inflation and booming trade, with selling-price increases exceeding cost increases and UK exports particularly strong. In the second half of 1977, however, trade began to slacken, sterling strengthened and margins narrowed. BBA's profit in 1978, partly through the reduction in ownership in Nigeria, was not much more than half that of 1977. The deterioration continued in the next three years, as will be described in the next chapter.

Pulp & Paper

The Pulp & Paper Sector of Erco Industries in this period became the most profitable unit in A&W. At the beginning of 1964 a Chlorate Division was formed within Erco, recognising the growing importance of the sales of sodium chlorate in the bleaching of paper pulp, after the collapse of the market for chlorate in the extraction of uranium. In the next seven years, the chlorate plant at Vancouver was expanded from two to five lines of cells (to a capacity of 44,000 tpa), while Buckingham capacity remained at 33,000 tpa.

During that period there were also very significant developments in Erco's activities in the design and marketing to pulp mills of units for the generation from sodium chlorate of chlorine dioxide, the gas used in bleaching; the instability of the gas required it to be produced at the pulp mill. The key figure in chlorine dioxide technology was Howard Rapson. When working for the Canadian International Paper Company in the 1940s, he developed chlorine dioxide as an alternative to chlorine in bleaching. The first chlorine dioxide generators were built by Olin-Mathieson Chemical Corporation from 1946 and became known as Mathieson generators. In 1953 Rapson became Professor of Chemical Engineering at the University of Toronto and a consultant to Erco. A new type of generator was developed and became known as the R2, which in the 1960s was superseded by the R3 and in the 1970s by the R4. The aim of these and subsequent developments was not only to produce chlorine dioxide economically but also to reduce or eliminate the residual chemicals, which originally included sulphuric acid, chlorine and sodium sulphate. Initially Erco shared the rights in the Rapson patents with Hooker (which had acquired the Columbus chlorate plant from A&W through the purchase of OECCo and had built a plant close to Erco's at Vancouver) but from mid-1964 Rapson was working exclusively for Erco. Erco benefited from royalties from licensing the processes and from the margins on the generators it built for the pulp companies; by the mid-1970s, annual profits from the ESG (Engineering Services Group) had grown to around $1 million.

In 1972 Erco formed a joint venture with Envirotech Corporation of the USA to develop and market a closed-cycle pulp bleaching process, i.e. one in which by-product chemicals were recycled so that only clean water was discharged. In 1975 the Great Lakes Paper Company, of Thunder Bay (Ontario), decided to use the Erco-Envirotech process to build the world's first closed-cycle mill, which came on stream in 1978. Erco-Envirotech, however, did not subsequently prosper. For Erco, the emphasis was rather on the modifications to the R processes, which by the 1990s in R9 and R10 had virtually achieved complete recycling.

It seems strange that Erco's technology for the manufacture of sodium chlorate had lagged behind its competitors. Erco's process used graphite electrodes suspended in large tanks and was costly in power consumption, usage of graphite, maintenance and labour. As early as the 1950s, the Belgian company Krebs had developed cells with metal electrodes, much more compact and cost effective. It was not until 1971 that the decision was taken to install a sixth cell line at Vancouver with metal electrodes; the plant came into operation in mid-1975, after delays while alternative courses were under consideration. Even then, when a $4 million expansion at Buckingham was authorised in mid-1976 it was decided not to use metal electrodes - "The new plant will be based on Erco's well-proven graphite cell technology". By the time that plant came on stream in 1978 it was clear that it was obsolescent. A year earlier, new plants had been authorised with metal electrodes, which were technically ahead of the Krebs technology used at Vancouver.

In April 1977, it was agreed to build a 25,000 tons pa plant at Monroe, Louisiana, to serve customers, in the southern USA. In May 1977, authority was given to build a plant at Thunder Bay, Ontario, close to the Great Lakes paper plant at the western end of Lake Ontario, with a capacity initially of 15,000 tpa, to be expanded later to 25,000 tpa (see p. 261). Erco was thus in this period maintaining its position as the leading Canadian producer of sodium chlorate. Although the business was capital-hungry, margins on sales were high and the return on investment exceptional - in 1977, before the large investment in new plants in 1978-80 trebled the capital employed, the return on net assets employed in producing sodium chlorate was over 40%. On top of that, the profits from chlorine dioxide technology were over $1 million, bringing the total return up to not far short of 50%. That was, however, the peak of profitability, as in the next ten years the growth of competition drove down margins while heavy investment in increasing capacity continued.

Safety and the Environment

One other noteworthy feature of this period was the growing concern for Safety and the Environment. The A&W Annual Report for 1971 included the statement "Our safety record, although excellent at many works, has caused us concern". Steps were then taken to emphasise safety, through setting up a safety committee under the Personnel Director, safety audits, competitions and awards (including Green Shield stamps at Letchworth) and from 1975 the Annual Reports included charts showing accident frequency rates. In 1974 there were two significant events: the passing of the Health and Safety at Work Act and the Flixborough disaster. The Act for the first time applied to all people at work except those employed privately in domestic service and covered the handling and manufacture of dangerous substances, the emission of noxious or offensive substances and excessive noise. The explosion in June at the Nypro chemical plant at Flixborough, Lincolnshire, which killed 28 and injured 105, focused public attention on possible hazards in chemical plants. A&W gradually improved its performance: several works achieved years without a lost time accident but the average for the whole company (about 1.5 accidents per 100,000 hours worked) was still a long way from the standard achieved by Du Pont in the USA and "Albright World" was still publishing photographs of plant operatives without protective clothing or safety glasses.

In parallel with efforts to improve safety steps were taken to improve the impact of the chemical industry on the environment. In April 1972 A&W appointed its first Environmental Officer (Dr James Farquhar, previously Research Manager for ACC). That followed the Deposit of Poisonous Wastes Act passed in the previous month, stimulated by a cyanide dumping scare. The Act introduced penalties, including imprisonment, for depositing poisonous, noxious or polluting waste. Although A&W had introduced several schemes for effluent treatment at its UK sites, there were problems at every site, which were to require an increasing proportion of future capital expenditure. Many years were needed for the achievement of a standard of zero pollution.

The EEC policy was for the universal application of fixed standards for discharge of effluent. That was resisted by the UK, which had a more pragmatic approach and argued that with more extensive sewage treatment and the dilution of effluent through discharge into the sea the expenditure that would have resulted from harmonisation would have been excessive. Not for the first time, other countries argued that the UK would have an unfair advantage if not required to conform to EEC standards. The chemical industry was particularly involved, through its manufacturing processes and its products, in the debate on environmental pollution. Winning its public relations battles became an objective of growing significance.

Chapter 6

SUBMERGENCE & RATIONALISATION

1978 - 1986

"We believe that we are now more efficiently manned and managed than we have ever been, and we are keen to realise fully the benefits of the advances we have been making in recent years" (1983 Annual Report)

Overview

The years from 1978 to 1986 were a period of economic and political turbulence, and of disappointments and divestments for Albright & Wilson and Tenneco, in the first eight years of full ownership by Tenneco. There were, however, several positive developments for A&W in the later years, during the final period of David Livingstone's leadership.

Economic & political background

1978
- the UK decided in 1978 not to join the European Monetary System (EMS)

1979
- the Shah left Iran and the Ayatollah Khomeni arrived (February)
- a peace treaty between Egypt and Israel was signed (March)
- Margaret Thatcher became Prime Minister (May)
- first elections to the European Parliament were held (June)
- Earl Mountbatten was killed by the IRA (August)
- OPEC (the Organisation of Petroleum Exporting Countries) increased the price of oil by 50%

1980
- through North Sea development, the UK moved into a surplus on its oil account
- the USSR invaded Afghanistan (January)
- Robert Mugabe became Prime Minister of an independent Zimbabwe (April)
- Ronald Reagan was elected President of the USA (November)

1982
- the Falklands war was fought (April to June)
- Helmut Kohl became Chancellor of West Germany (October)
- Leonid Breznev died (November); after Andropov and Chernenko, Mikail Gorbachev became leader of the USSR in March 1985

1984
- Indira Gandhi was assassinated (October)
- 2,500 were killed at Bhopal through leakage of dioxins from a chemical plant (December)

1985
- USA imposed sanctions against South Africa (September)
- OPEC ended controls on oil production (December)

1986
- European Court ruled on equal retirement age for men and women (February)
- Chernobyl reactor accident occurred (April)

- 'Big Bang' day in the City extended competition in dealing (October)
- OPEC re-imposed controls on oil production (October)

For a company with its principal interests in the UK, the most significant event was the election of Margaret Thatcher as Prime Minister in May 1979. Actions taken by her government included the abolition of price controls and restrictions on hire purchase, denationalisation of British Aerospace, Cable & Wireless, Britoil, British Telecom, British Petroleum, British Gas, British Airports Authority and British Airways, the 1980 Competition Act, strengthening the Office of Fair Trading and the Monopolies & Mergers Commission. The government also introduced Assisted Places in private-sector schools, repealed the requirement for comprehensive education, and made it possible for tenants to buy their council houses in some areas.

In the early years of the Thatcher government, there were sharp economic shocks. Inflation in the UK, which had averaged 14% pa in 1975-9, rose to over 18% in 1980. Weekly earnings rose by more than 15% in 1979 and again by more than 20% in 1980, but Britain's sharpest recession in 50 years struck in 1980-81, forcing reassessment; the rate of wage increase dropped to 6% by 1984. During this period the price of oil, which averaged $13 per barrel in 1978, rose to $19 in 1979 and $32 in 1980, peaking at an average of $36 in 1981.

Changes in the law on picketing, closed shops, strikes and Trade Union immunity were followed by the miners' strike from March 1984, which ended a year later without any concessions from the government. The power of the print unions, which had led to the suspension of printing of *The Times* for nearly a year (1979), was broken in 1986 through the introduction of new technology by Rupert Murdoch (who had bought *The Times* in 1981) at Wapping, under siege conditions. The rise in unemployment, from an average of 1.2 million in 1978 to 3.2 million in 1986 (over 13% of the work force), also weakened the unions' power; membership, which had risen markedly during the Labour governments from 1974 to 1979, declined steeply during the Thatcher years.

The impact of the recession on Albright & Wilson was felt from mid-1980, alongside the impact of higher oil prices which affected trade around the world. The downturn was sharp and sudden, customer industries slumped and many companies ceased to trade. In turn, high interest rates in the UK, its growing positive balance in oil and the recession-led fall in imports resulted in a rise in sterling from less than $2 in 1978 to $2.44 in October 1980, making exports from the UK less competitive.

From its peak in 1980, sterling declined to a low of $1.05 in March 1985. The reasons for this were the strengthening of the US dollar against all currencies, doubts about the sustainability of oil prices, and concern about the miners' strike, which ended in March 1985. Thereafter sterling rallied, assisted by increases in interest rates, with the Treasury Bill rate reaching 14%.

Albright & Wilson's results

The fluctuations in A&W's results in this period may be in part explained by the influence of the wider economic pattern, although the company was also affected by other significant factors, such as divestments, acquisitions and substantial interest charges arising from the capital expenditure programme, as will be described.

Progress 1978 - 1986

(£ million)	1978	1979	1980	1981	1982	1983	1984	1985	1986
Sales	**342**	**395**	**424**	**503**	**531**	**570**	**569**	**642**	**652**
Continuing businesses	259	294	317	375	421	479	525	556	540
Bush Boake Allen	52	65	65	74	*56				
Agricultural Division	28	36	41	54	54	#52			
Tenneco Chemicals Europe						^39	44	46	53
Albright & Wilson Inc.								@40	59
% of total sales in UK	*44*	*45*	*43*	*42*	*40*	*39*	*33*	*30*	*27*
Profit (before interest & tax)	**34**	**27**	**17**	**25**	**28**	**42**	**42**	**42**	**46**
Continuing businesses	27	22	17	23	28	38	38	38	39
Bush Boake Allen	5	3	-1	neg	neg				
Agricultural Division	2	2	neg	2	1	1			
Tenneco Chemicals Europe						4	5	3	5
Albright & Wilson Inc.								1	3
Origin of profits: UK	*17*	*10*	*-1*	*-*	*4*	*13*	*10*	*8*	*14*
rest of world	*17*	*17*	*18*	*25*	*24*	*29*	*32*	*34*	*32*
Interest payable	-5	-6	-12	-16	-16	-13	-12	-13	-13
Pretax profit	**29**	**21**	**5**	**9**	**12**	**29**	**30**	**29**	**33**
Tax	-2	-2	-4	-3	-5	-8	-7	-6	-9
Minorities	-1	neg	-1	-1	-1	-1	-1	-1	-1
Extraordinary items	-1	-1	-	1	*-10	1	neg	-3	-
Net available for equity	**25**	**17**	**neg**	**6**	**-3**	**22**	**22**	**19**	**24**
Dividends to Tenneco	4	18	4	1	4	8	10	-	10
Capital Expenditure	43	33	30	26	19	25	35	43	33
Net cap. emp. end of year	**198**	**242**	**249**	**275**	**238**	**224**	**267**	**289**	**289**

* BBA sold in April 1982   ^ Tenneco Chemicals Europe transferred to A&W January 1983
\# Ag. Division sold in November 1983   @ Mobil Chemicals acquired May 1985

The table shows the effects of the main disposals and acquisitions in the period (described later). In terms of profits before interest and tax, although it appears that for the continuing businesses recession was followed by recovery, the high rate of inflation and the doubling of the Retail Price Index for the UK between 1978 and 1986 meant that in fact there was little growth in sales and a real fall in profits. The high level of capital expenditure resulted in high interest charges, but no real growth in profits. Borrowing peaked at £102 million at the end of 1981 and was then reduced through the disposal of BBA (raising £43 million) and the 1983 disposals (Ag. Division, West Bank and aryl phosphates, raising £26 million). The acquisition of the Mobil Chemicals operations cost £33 million.

The eight-year period saw a marked shift in the pattern of sales and profits between the UK and the rest of the world, partly due to disposals (mainly in the UK) and acquisitions (mainly outside the UK), but also due to the majority of capital expenditure being outside the UK. Within the UK, there was increasing competition from imports, notably in the key product, sodium tripolyphosphate, leading to lower selling prices and some loss of market share. Moreover, the decline in UK manufacturing from 1980 onwards hit A&W's sales to the engineering, textiles and other industries. Losses of sales and shrinking gross margins, coupled with high wage settlements, led to a reduction in the number of employees. In 1980, 90% of the value added (sales minus the cost of materials) was absorbed in labour costs. In that year, redundancy payments in the UK cost £5 million; a further £5 million was paid in 1981-3. Between 1978 and 1986, disposals and cuts at all sites meant that the number of UK employees was more than halved to under 3,400.

But what was the impact of Tenneco's ownership at this time? For insight into the relationship between the management of A&W and its owner, it is necessary to examine the fortunes of Tenneco, which waxed and waned very significantly during these years.

Tenneco and Albright & Wilson

Tenneco's acquisition of full ownership in 1978 did not lead to a marked change in the relationship between the two companies: it is perhaps characteristic that A&W continued to regard itself as an essentially separate entity, rather than as a division of Tenneco. Towards the end of the period, however, the pressures on Tenneco and the lack of progress in A&W's profits led to a change in that relationship.

Tenneco's acquisitions, growth and rising profits

Up to 1981, Tenneco achieved increases in sales and profits year by year. After marking time in 1982, the company fell into decline, and started a process of shedding various operations that had been acquired in its 35 years of existence. It finally broke up just under two decades later, in 1999.

The 1978 Annual Report described Tenneco as "a growing energy company with other profitable diversified businesses," and boasted that the company was in the "best overall financial condition of its 35-year history". Out of total sales of nearly $9 billion, $4 billion was in oil and gas production and marketing and the original gas pipeline business: they accounted for almost 70% of the total income of $1,128 million (before interest and tax). There were 104,000 employees. The diversified businesses comprised construction and farm equipment (J I Case), Automotive (Monroe and Walker), Chemicals (Albright & Wilson and Tenneco Chemicals), Agriculture & Land Management (Tenneco West), Packaging (Packaging Corporation of America), Shipbuilding (Newport News Shipbuilding), Insurance (Philadelphia Life Insurance) and real estate (mainly in Houston).

In 1979 Tenneco extended its interest in energy by taking a 50% interest in a shale oil project in Colorado and a 49% interest in a venture to exploit the Athabasca Tar Sands. It also became a partner in a coal gasification project and formed a coal mining company, invested in the importation of liquified natural gas from Algeria, acquired interests in numerous offshore tracts and acquired uranium leases. Together with the sinking of wells onshore and offshore, these developments cost $1 billion out of the year's total capital expenditure of $1.5 billion. Profits from the energy-related businesses were over $950 million out of total income before interest and tax (IBIT) of $1,362 million. Dividends were raised, for the eighth successive year.

Growth continued in 1980, with sales over $13 billion and IBIT of $1.6 billion. Capital expenditure totalled $1.8 billion and further acquisitions were made: South West Life Insurance was acquired for $500 million, and Houston Oil & Minerals Corporation for $400 million. The continuing energy shortage gained Tenneco high prices for its oil and gas: the average for oil was $23.77 per barrel against $13.61 in 1979, while for gas it was $1.59 per million cu.ft against $1.26. The Annual Report predicted: "For the foreseeable future, Tenneco anticipates further growth in earnings from its oil and gas activities". Not all of Tenneco's businesses were prospering, however, because of the developing recession: lower profits were reported for automotive, chemicals and J I Case. A turn around was expected in tractor sales and $175 million was committed for a 50% share with the Cummins Engine Co. to produce a new line of engines.

Signs of decline

An article published in Business Week in November 1981 described Tenneco as "one of the last real success stories of the go-go days of diversification" and claimed that it was on the brink of much greater prosperity, expected to overtake ITT as the largest of the "old-line conglomerates". Oil and gas prices had risen sharply, to $30.57 and $2.13 respectively, Tenneco's land holdings were greater than those of Texaco and Socal (Standard Oil of California), it had succeeded for four years in adding reserves of oil in excess of production and gas deregulation was expected to double the value of Tenneco's gas reserves. It also had stakes in alternative forms of energy. Rather perceptively, however, the article cautioned that, "for all its bright prospects, Tenneco in some ways looks like a company in trouble". Its Canadian oil and gas operations were up for sale, as were some of its US chemical interests, austerity programmes had been introduced for the non-energy businesses and the dividend had not been increased, for the first time in nine years. Pressure came from the overwhelming cash requirements of the energy businesses which were essential if opportunities were to be developed. They included $500 million to upgrade the Chalmette refinery.

Tenneco had to borrow at very high rates of interest - up to 17% on long-term loans (including a 30-year debenture yielding 15%) and up to 20% on commercial paper. In 1981 $2 billion was spent on developing the energy businesses. Jim Ketelsen (Chairman and Chief Executive since 1978) admitted, "We are going to have to do some weeding out," and the 1981 Annual Report stated: "We are also carefully reviewing various segments of our businesses which we do not believe hold great promise. There are candidates for disposition". In 1981, disposals in the US chemicals and automotive divisions followed the move to sell Canadian energy operations. Tenneco was under pressure to sell more of its non-energy businesses, but argued that diversification was an advantage, drawing on history to support its argument - in the 1960s there was pressure to sell its energy operations before the rise in the price of oil transformed their economics. In fact, the energy businesses had another record year, and accounted for 80% of IBIT in 1981. The rest of Tenneco contributed $412 million to IBIT, $60 million more than in 1980, partly because of recovery from recession. Case's profit, however, remained at about half the 1979 level, even after significant foreign currency gains; sales of the construction and farm equipment industry were down and Case was operating at only 55% of capacity.

The results in 1982 were on a par with 1981. Weakening oil prices and a reduced demand for gas contributed to a standstill in IBIT. Sales and IBIT from oil were slightly lower but it was a good year for the pipeline operations, automotive and shipbuilding. Case's sales were down by nearly 20% because of depressed markets and no profit was made. The dividend was once again increased, on the strength of a strong cash flow and maintained profits, in adverse conditions. In addition to cash from the Canadian energy operations, the remaining US chemical operations were sold (to a management buy-out) and A&W's BBA division was also disposed of (see below). Debt was reduced by $500 million, partly through debt-for-equity swaps (which also contributed to profits).

In 1983, popularly regarded as the bottom of the energy recession (although the "gas bubble" was expected to last into 1985 or 1986) sales and profits of the energy businesses fell due to reduced oil prices and a surplus of natural gas. Tenneco's oil production fell 4% and the price was 10% lower. Most non-energy businesses increased their profits but Case's sales continued to fall – in 1981 a further drop of 13% resulted in a loss of $68 million before interest. In total, IBIT was down 13% and earnings per share fell by 17%. Dividend, however, was increased and the Annual Report claimed, "Tenneco is the premier example of a successfully diversified, energy-based company". It was the youngest corporation among the top 20 companies listed by the magazine Fortune.

In 1984 Tenneco achieved an increase in gas production, and record oil production. A continuing strong cash flow supported a further increase in dividend but the yield of 7.7% on Tenneco's shares indicated a lack of confidence among investors. Earnings per share fell by 15% in the face of depressed market conditions in petroleum refining and the agricultural and construction equipment industries and the Case loss (before interest) increased to $105 million. The division hoped for a return to profit in 1985. Petro-Tex Chemical Corporation, which was making losses, was sold but there were acquisitions in packaging, gas transmission and insurance. Tenneco also formed Tenneco Ventures Inc., a unit for extending into new fields; investments were made in biotechnology, factory automation, space technology, healthcare and telecommunications.

The most surprising and controversial move occurred at the end of 1984, when Tenneco acquired the agricultural equipment business of International Harvester for just under $500 million. Through the acquisition, Jim Ketelsen believed, "we have met the serious problems of this industry head-on". He described the problems as the recession in farm income, severe excess manufacturing capacity and excess product inventories resulting from years of declining sales. The acquisition added to Case's dealer network, increased Case's market share and cut capacity through the closure of an IH plant. But Case IH, the name of the merged business, was to continue to make losses or inadequate profits and to absorb excessive funds in its inventories.

There were no smiles on the faces of the Chairman and President pictured in the Annual Report for 1985, described as "a frustrating year". Profits from the energy businesses held up, despite continuing weakness in oil and gas prices and lower volumes of gas sales. Shipbuilding and packaging both had record years. The Case IH loss, however, doubled to $214 million before interest, largely through temporary plant closures to reduce inventories. The Annual Report stated: "we believe we are well on the way to contending for the leadership position in the farm equipment industry...we are confident that Case IH will prove to be the latest addition to a growing list of managed turnarounds at Tenneco". The termination of the unsuccessful shale oil and coal gasification projects involved a write-off of $240 million. In addition, $23 million was written off the PVC operation in anticipation of disposal. Earnings per share fell to only 75 cents and debt increased by $1.2 billion but the dividend was again increased, to a total of $2.95.

The picture worsens

The collapse in oil and gas prices early in 1986 was a devastating blow for Tenneco. Its average price for oil was $12.37 per barrel compared with $22.33 in 1985 (and the peak of $30.57 in 1981); gas averaged $1.71 per million cu.ft compared with the previous value of $2.48. Oil and gas sales fell by 37% and IBIT for energy fell to $153 million from $465 million.[1] Higher profits were made by automotive and packaging, and Case reduced its loss to $1 million before interest but after credit for a change in pensions accounting. Steiger Tractor was acquired, to add large agricultural tractors to the Case IH range. Towards the end of the year the Tenneco Minerals business was sold for $130 million, giving a net profit of $36 million, and the life assurance subsidiaries were also sold for $570 million net, resulting in a net loss of $240 million. There was a net loss per share of 72 cents against a loss of 43 cents in 1985 (after the accounting change).

Deterioration continued in 1987. The price of oil recovered a little but the price of gas fell further and IBIT for the oil and gas operations was down 40%. $300 million was provided towards settling disputes arising from Tenneco's deliberate breach of take-or-pay contracts following the fall in gas prices; by a Federal order, Tenneco was allowed to charge its pipeline customers with 50% of the compensation payable to gas suppliers. Case IH made a loss of $259 million (before interest) because of a weak agricultural equipment market, intense price discounting and the cost of plant closures. The agricultural and land development operations of Tenneco West were sold for $212 million, realising a loss of $86 million. Combined profits from the other businesses were $70 million higher, but that was well outweighed by the $220 million fall in oil and gas. Despite the loss of $1.81 per share, however, dividends were maintained at $3.04 per share; the Chairman's statement in the annual report concluded with the words, "Long term, we build value by managing major turnarounds in our various businesses...Short term, we increase the wealth of our shareholders by maintaining a generous dividend policy".

---

[1] A change in the method of accounting for exploration & development from 'successful efforts' to 'full cost' accounting for development costs, whereby costs of unsuccessful drillings had to be expensed instead of capitalised, reduced the 1985 and all preceding years' profits; cumulative retained earnings were reduced by nearly $1 billion, from $3,209 million to $2,221 million.

Attempt at recovery

Tenneco's bold step in 1988 was, for many, a profound shock. The oil and gas businesses were sold for $7.6 billion, an act described by Jim Ketelsen as "a difficult but necessary move that enabled us to unlock significant immediate value for shareholders and restore our flexibility to capitalise on growth opportunities". Tenneco had concluded that it could not wait for oil and gas prices to improve. Action to raise cash was essential and Case was not saleable. The company reduced its debt by $5 billion and re-purchased shares to a value of $1 billion. A profit of $892 million was recorded on the disposal. The rest of the company broke even, after interest charges of $888 million. Case's loss before interest was reduced. For a while, in 1989 and 1990, Tenneco reported results close to the level of 1984 but then moved back into losses, caused by Case's trading difficulties, restructuring charges and interest costs. The story of the 1990s is covered in the next chapter.

Results of Tenneco 1978-1988 (US$million)

	1978	1979	1980	1981	1982	1983	1984	1985	1986	1987	1988
*											
Sales	8762	11209	13226	15462	14969	41449	14890	15270	14529	15062	15707
IBIT +	1128	1362	1596	1954	1930	1699	1646	1274	1010	664	903
Interest payable	321	464	475	683	749	658	734	814	908	907	888
Pretax profit	**807**	**898**	**1021**	**1271**	**1181**	**1041**	**912**	**460**	**102**	**-243**	**15**
Net for											
Common stock	421	539	674	750	757	654	570	110	-105	-267	-70
Earnings/share ($)	4.53	5.30	5.95	6.01	5.74	4.75	4.01	0.75	-0.72	-1.81	-0.65
Equity	3180	3368	4164	5045	5474	5822	6153	5903	4412	3773	3161
Debt #	5447	4949	5950	7786	7521	7163	7486	10205	11025	10919	7519
Total capital	**9039**	**8692**	**10953**	**13438**	**13597**	**13576**	**14211**	**16801**	**16134**	**16127**	**10914**
Debt: total capital	60%	57%	56%	58%	55%	53%	53%	61%	68%	74%	69%
Oil price $/bbl	10.32	13.61	23.77	30.57	26.99	24.27	23.68	22.33	12.37	13.86	
Gas price $/m.cu.ft.	1.09	1.26	1.59	2.13	2.65	2.62	2.65	2.48	1.71	1.51	

+ income before interest and tax
* IBIT & earnings exclude $892 million profit on disposal of the oil & gas operations
# debt includes finance subsidiaries (mainly financing Case receivables), which before 1988 had been excluded from the balance sheet; at the end of 1988 that debt amounted to $3,566 million.

An analysis of the results by segment shows the rise and fall of the oil and gas business, the burden of the Case operations and the valuable contributions made by shipbuilding, automotive and packaging. The other segments' results were affected by disposals. (Note that all figures are as reported in the year concerned, not as subsequently reported by Tenneco after adjustments for disposals.)

Sales and IBIT in detail: 1978-1988 (US$million)

	1978	1979	1980	1981	1982	1983	1984	1985	1986	1987	1988
Sales											
Oil & gas E&M *	2015	2347	3185	4339	4114	4107	4149	3854	2773	3117	2473
Gas pipelines +	2013	2660	3372	4180	4645	4098	4216	3621	3139	2535	3003
Case	1985	2366	2420	2476	2014	1752	1741	2697	3358	3664	4306
Shipbuilding	733	730	891	1096	1324	1627	1826	1801	1641	1659	1671
Automotive	747	816	794	820	850	921	976	1074	1254	1484	1665
Packaging	533	539	586	n.a	n.a	n.a	n.a	851	944	1144	1298
Chemicals	827	1487	1639	1589	1104	n.a	n.a	841	952	1068	1065
Other #	-91	264	339	962	918	1944	1982	-269	468	391	226
Total	**8762**	**11209**	**13226**	**15462**	**14969**	**14449**	**14890**	**15270**	**14529**	**15062**	**15707**
IBIT											
Oil & gas E&M *	481	678	940	1208	1133	844	676	755	153	233	125
Gas pipelines +	293	279	304	334	422	383	424	423	394	92	114
Case	128	131	65	70	0	-68	-105	-214	-1	-259	-59
Shipbuilding	14	33	55	82	111	151	219	285	246	175	175
Automotive	78	60	33	58	83	111	143	134	179	195	203
Packaging	25	28	32	n.a	32	43	86	93	110	166	215
Chemicals	66	103	82	28	11	n.a	47	42	71	77	@18
Other #	43	50	85	174	138	236	156	-244	-142	-15	112
Total	**1128**	**1362**	**1596**	**1954**	**1930**	**1699**	**1646**	**1274**	**1010**	**664**	**903**

* integrated oil operation comprising oil and gas exploration, production, processing and marketing
# "other" includes Agricultural & Land, Insurance (profit but not sales), Minerals, financial operations and for some years packaging and chemicals where figures are not available. 1985 IBIT includes losses on discontinuance of the shale oil and coal gasification operations and 1986 losses on the disposal of the insurance companies.
+ gas pipelines profits in 1987 and 1988 are after provisions for settlement of take-or-pay contracts.
@ Albright & Wilson 1988 profit is after $58 million rationalisation provision.

The Management of Albright & Wilson

One of the most intriguing questions in the history of Albright & Wilson is what impact Tenneco made during the period of over 16 years when it was A&W's sole owner. Considerable changes in management and direction might have been expected. Yet, with one exception, no-one from Tenneco joined the senior management of A&W and interchange of staff at any level was extremely rare - and even then was instigated by A&W. The one exception was Gene Anderson, who returned to London in March 1979. Sydney Ellis wanted Gene to be Managing Director under David Livingstone but David objected and so Gene became Joint Deputy Managing Director in charge of operations, with the Divisional Managing Directors reporting to him. Tony Ward, the other Joint Deputy, who was in charge of finance and administration, acted for David in his absence. The conflict of personalities and philosophy between Gene and David made Gene's position difficult. David was reluctant to allow Gene as free a hand as he wished and maintained his direct contacts with senior operational staff. Gene's wish for A&W to become a significant international chemical company proved unrealistic. Bringing A&W and Tenneco Chemicals together seemed impossible, with neither David nor Ray Marks being prepared to serve under the other and with little in common between the two companies. In March 1981, just two years after his return to England, Gene left A&W and Tenneco to become President of Celanese International and a Vice President of Celanese Corporation. Four years later, Gene (a firm Anglophile) was back in England as Chief Executive of Johnson Matthey. Tenneco made no other attempt to introduce its staff in to A&W.

When the Board of Tenneco visited the UK in July 1979, Jack Diesel (then Chairman of A&W as well as President of Tenneco) said: "It is difficult to overstate the importance of A&W to Tenneco and its UK activities" - the latter perhaps being a reference to A&W's role as front for Tenneco's applications for North Sea oil concessions. Jim Ketelsen believed that the influence of Tenneco on A&W was considerable. He expressed his philosophy in these words: "the divisional chief executive officers run their own operations, but we set difficult targets for them, and we work closely with them to develop much tougher performance goals than an outside board would. We also provide our divisions with the financial strength to build their companies and to weather difficult times".

For several reasons, however, Tenneco's influence over A&W was limited: A&W was remote from the rest of Tenneco, geographically and in the nature of its business, David Livingstone's opposition to American interference was strong (as was his exceptional ability to express himself in speaking and writing) and Tenneco was preoccupied with its own major problems. Tenneco did not have people obviously suitable for drafting into A&W. There was a fundamental philosophy to let its Divisions run themselves, with control being exercised through budgeting, the authorisation of major capital expenditure and standard operating procedures. George Meason, soon after becoming Chairman of Albright & Wilson, declared, "It was never our intention to 'Americanise' A&W". On top of that, there was what Bob Blakely (Tenneco's Chief Financial Officer from 1981) described as "the disarming politeness of the British," in explaining eloquently why it was beyond their control to do anything about shortfalls in results.

Although capital expenditure budgets put forward to Tenneco were generally reduced, A&W underspent its approved budget in most years and it would be hard to maintain that more would have been spent without control by Tenneco. Interviewed by The Financial Times in March 1982, David Livingstone said that he would restrict capital expenditure without a directive from Tenneco, because of the heavy borrowings by A&W. In 1981 Tenneco rejected a proposal by A&W to make a major investment in US phosphate rock reserves on the grounds that it did not have sufficient capital but there were also doubts within the A&W management about the soundness of the project. The dividends paid to Tenneco were not excessive, being half the profit available in 1979-86.

The sale of BBA

In one respect, however, Tenneco did exercise an important influence, in this period and even more after 1986. The minutes of the Board meeting, in October 1981, the last attended by George Meason (Chairman of A&W since mid-1978), record his words:

> "Tenneco regarded the money invested in Bush Boake Allen Division as unsatisfactory, with little chance of improvement. A number of companies were interested in buying BBA and Tenneco had decided that the business should be sold ....The Chairman acknowledged that Mr Livingstone was not in favour of the sale and had consistently advised against it ... The Chairman explained that the compelling reason for Tenneco to sell BBA was its need to realise some of its assets at a time when interest rates in the USA had risen to levels at which Tenneco did not wish to undertake further long-term borrowing. This need to raise money had also led Tenneco to the conclusion that it should seek a purchaser for the remainder of Albright & Wilson Limited. Various potential purchasers had been contacted and those companies which had expressed interest would be examining the Company in the next few months. The Chairman regretted having to make this statement on the eve of his retirement from the Chair, but explained that similar decisions had been taken for other non-energy parts of Tenneco's business".

The decision on BBA, although strongly contested by several of the senior A&W managers, was hardly surprising. Since 1977, BBA's results had been deteriorating. The table over the page shows figures in £'000.

Operating profits BBA: 1977 - 1981

	1977	1978	1979	1980	1981
Flavours	2695	2155	1173	90	-450
Fragrances	1355	772	126	-141	450
Chemicals	2374	806	236	-2550	-2180
Overseas*	1265	1083	1828	1866	1170
	7689	**4816**	**3363**	**-735**	**-1010**

* excluding associated companies; A&W's share of their operating profits, mainly from India and Nigeria, in 1981 was £910,000

The overseas results had held up well, except for the USA, where BBA Inc. made a loss in 1981 of over £400,000, double the loss in 1980. At the end of 1978 Monsanto Flavour Essence Inc. was acquired for $9 million, which brought BBA's US sales up to nearly $20 million; although BBA Inc. made a profit in 1979, the costs of building its business in a highly competitive market led to losses thereafter.

The real disappointment was the performance of the BBA sectors in the UK, where in four years a profit of £6.4 million was turned into a loss of £2.2 million. For BBA, market leader in flavours, to make a loss was almost unthinkable. Contributing to the problems was the building of a £3 million plant at Long Melford to make dry and liquid onion flavour products: it proved to be a white elephant, making products that the market did not want. BBA also continued to suffer from changes in its managing directors - Ron Mason in 1978, Malcolm Clark in 1979 and Robin Gooch in 1980 - and changes in organisation. In the UK, the flavours and fragrances businesses lacked the customer orientation that was the basis of success in Australia, New Zealand and South Africa. BBA also included West Bank, the toluene derivatives chemical business, which was running at a loss of around £1 million pa (turned round into profit, however, after it was detached from BBA in 1982). The other part of its chemical interests, the synthetic aromatics at Dans Road, was also losing money, although this proved to be the real money-maker after A&W had sold BBA.

The sale of BBA, excluding West Bank and Rainham, was announced in April 1982, to Union Camp, a US manufacturer of forest products including paper, paperboard, packaging, building materials and associated chemicals. It had recently purchased the tall oil operations of British Oxygen and was looking to strengthen its position in synthetic aromatic chemicals derived from pinene (extracted from pine trees). BBA, Union Camp and Glidden were the three main manufacturers of these chemicals. Although there were plans to move into flavours and fragrances, Union Camp's principal reason for acquiring BBA was the chemical operation. Union Camp appointed John Dean, who had headed BBA's chemical operations from the beginning, to run BBA. Under him there was a gradual recovery, with increasing profits every year. The company obtained a quotation on the American Stock Exchange and by 1996 had a market value of $500 million.

Questioned about the sale of BBA, David Livingstone acknowledged that A&W had not recommended it. He said, "It is a decision which A&W accepts as the best in all the circumstances. Tenneco wishes to raise cash to reduce the high interest costs of its short-term borrowings and to fund essential investment, especially in its energy business ... In the last analysis A&W believes it best that BBA should have a new owner anxious to foster the business". The sale was completed in September 1987 for £43 million, resulting in a loss of £8 million against book value. Of the proceeds, £30 million was lent to Tenneco, £3 million was paid to Tenneco for BBA Inc. and the balance used to reduce A&W's debt.

Further sales considered

As George Meason had stated in October 1981, Tenneco was actively seeking a buyer for the rest of A&W from 1980 through into 1981. There were visits and discussions involving Monsanto and Hoechst, both likely purchasers because of their interests in phosphorus chemicals. Morgan Stanley was retained by Tenneco to handle the proposed sale. In February 1982 there was an outbreak of Press speculation that A&W was up for sale and that an announcement would be made within six weeks: Tenneco and Albright & Wilson stated that there was no substantiation for this. The Unions asked for assurances, pointing out that Tenneco's undertakings in 1978 required the Unions to be consulted before there was a disposal of the company or a major part of it.

In the event, Monsanto withdrew from the scene, and the price offered by Hoechst was considered too low. Interviewed in April 1982, David Livingstone stated, "Tenneco have reviewed the possible sale of many of their businesses, including A&W. They have concluded that A&W is worth more to them than it is likely to fetch in the market". Yet he added, "No company can be reasonably asked to abstain from selling its own property if circumstances require it".

At the beginning of 1984, David Livingstone approached A&W's long-term merchant bankers, to see whether it would be possible to float off A&W. The Company's profit performance since the low point in 1980 had been good and - provided that the price was right - it was thought that Tenneco would be prepared to divest this part of its non-core activities. Shortly after the first consultation with Hill Samuel, David Livingstone received an approach from another merchant banker, Robert Fleming & Co. but did not pursue it. Discussions with Hill Samuel continued. It was estimated that A&W would have a market value of about £225 million, against a value at the end of 1983 of about £330 million for Fisons and a little over £200 million for Laporte. In April, however, when David Livingstone put the idea to Tenneco, he received what he described as "a totally negative response". Two years later discussions recommenced but it was concluded that the recent record of flat profits would not be helpful in a flotation and that if divestment were aired with Tenneco the result might be sale to another company, to A&W's disadvantage.

Developments

Although hardly reflected in the financial results, this was a period of several significant developments, strengthening and adding to the Company's core businesses and shedding some peripheral activities.

Divestments

During the years 1978 to 1986 there were many divestments other than BBA. They were essentially decisions by the A&W management to rationalise and to eliminate parts without prospects of profitable growth.

In August 1978 A&W's 25% holding in Chipman Chemical was sold for a little over £300,000; two of the other three shareholders also withdrew from the small operation, which was mainly concerned with the application of sodium chlorate as a herbicide. The next divestment was in January 1979, when the Industrial Service Products business was sold to Diversey for £173,000 on the basis that it was better to supply the chemicals for the detergents etc. sold by Diversey to hospitals and other institutions than to invest time and money building up market share.

In January 1983 it was announced that the Canning Road (East London) works would be closed in 1984 because of adverse trading conditions and declining sales and profitability; the phosphorous and hypophosphorous acid plants were to be moved to Oldbury. Also in 1984 the Kirkby site was sold, for just £70,000, and in the same year marketing of the Domestic Products (Calgon, Micromet and other products for domestic use) was transferred to Benckiser, a major West German detergent company and distributor of Calgon since the 1930s. Another minor disposal was the land at Fobbing, on the Thames in Essex, which had originally been acquired for the dumping of gypsum from the wet acid plant proposed for the nearby site at Mucking, which was never built. Under a threat of compulsory purchase, the land was sold for £156,000.

Of much greater significance were three other divestments in 1983: West Bank, the Agricultural Division and the aryl phosphates business. In July, the **West Bank** toluene derivatives operations were sold to Marchem Ltd., a company set up by Marlborough Teeside Management, a small but aggressive company with chemical interests. The price obtained - £750,000 plus the working capital and leasing liabilities - represented small recompense for the capital recently invested in rationalising the site; although the operations had been moving into profit, the past profit record was poor and there were significant effluent problems.

An announcement in October 1983 opened with the words, "The sales of our agricultural and triaryl phosphates businesses announced today will enable Albright & Wilson to focus its capital investment and development programme on securing growth in its core businesses - phosphorus chemicals, detergent and toiletry materials and paper chemicals and processes - in which we are specialised, and have achieved international standing and recognition over many years".

It might at first seen surprising that A&W had retained the **agricultural** business for so long but it was in fact a useful outlet for the impure underflow phosphoric acid from the purified wet acid plants at Whitehaven. The Farm Protection (pesticide) side of the business was consistently profitable. The fertiliser side, however, was only intermittently profitable and A&W had only a 4% share of the UK market. The Barton on Humber prilling plant eventually worked satisfactorily and in 1979-80 nitric acid capacity was increased at a cost of £1.5 million. In September 1979 the agricultural chemicals sector was expanded through the acquisition for £860,000 of Midox, a company based in Kent marketing fungicides, herbicides, insecticides and plant nutrients. Midox had been established in 1950 as a subsidiary of Rentokil, which sold it to Philips and Guinness in 1964. In 1970 Philips became the sole owner but by 1979 had decided that it would concentrate on its electronics activities.

A&W Agricultural Operations Results 1978 - 1983 (£'000)

	1978	1979	1980	1981	1982	1983 (10months)
Sales						
Fertilisers	n.a	28417	31381	42201	42484	n.a
Chemicals	n.a	7405	9935	12062	11585	n.a
	27576	**35822**	**41316**	**54263**	**54069**	**51900**
Profits						
Fertilisers	n.a	1172	39	1353	111	n.a
Chemicals	n.a	612	765	931	609	n.a
	1641	**1784**	**804**	**2284**	**720**	**882**

At the close of 1982, the net capital employed in the fertiliser operations was nearly £15 million whereas the chemicals operations employed a little over £4 million. Thus although the return on chemicals was adequate, fertilisers provided a very poor return, even in the better years.

Approaches for the sale were made to Kemira and ICI. Kemira, the Finnish fertiliser company, was moderately interested; ICI at that time was making a lot of money from its agricultural operations and was concerned at the threat of competition from Kemira. Farm Protection would fit well with ICI's Plant Protection. So ICI agreed a deal at about the net book value, £20 million.

The **triaryl phosphates** business was sold to Ciba Geigy, competitor in these plastics additives, used to impart flame resistance and flexibility to PVC and in hydraulic fluids. Ciba Geigy, a Swiss company formed from the merger of Ciba and Geigy, wanted A&W's market share, its trade names, goodwill and technical know-how, but not the Rainham plant. There was overcapacity for the products in the UK and competition from functional equivalents. For the past year Rainham had operated at less than half capacity and the 40,000 tpa Ciba Geigy plant was adequate for the whole UK demand. The price paid was £5 million. A&W also required Ciba Geigy to enter into a contract for the purchase of phosphorus oxychloride, the principal raw material. The Rainham factory was closed and the site sold a year later. (Years later, Ciba Geigy decided to sell its triaryl phosphates operation at Trafford Park, Manchester; A&W would have liked to buy it but the funds were not forthcoming.)

The key A&W player in these and later divestments and in the acquisitions and joint ventures over a period of some 15 years was Peter Salmon. Peter joined A&W in 1955 as a trainee cost accountant at Oldbury, eventually becoming Finance Director of the Oldbury Division. After a brief spell in London, he went to Whitehaven in 1973 as Finance Director of Marchon. He returned to London, where he became General Manager - Economic Analysis in 1978, extended to Planning and Economic Analysis in 1981. In 1986 that evolved into Strategic Planning Manager with a strong team including Paul Rocheleau (later Chief Executive of A&W). While his involvement in the planning processes was important, Peter's uniquely influential role was as the individual engaged in almost all A&W's negotiations for acquisitions and divestments. In that, he displayed a sharpness of mind, persistence and judgment of the limits of negotiation that brought results in many difficult negotiations.

Paper Chemicals

When it became clear, in September 1982, that Tenneco intended to break up and dispose of Tenneco Chemicals (TCI), A&W made it known that it was keen to acquire the organophosphorus operations of TCI's subsidiary, Tenneco Chemicals Europe, based on its factory at Avonmouth (near Bristol). As has been described earlier, TCE had progressed farther than A&W in the development of products derived from phosphorus oxychloride (supplied from Oldbury) used in flame retardants, plasticisers, coalescents, metal extractants and ore flotation agents.

Tenneco, however, wished to dispose of the whole of Tenneco Chemicals Europe. At the end of 1982 it transferred the whole to A&W for £7 million (a figure determined by the tax position rather than by an assessment of the worth of the company). The unit that A&W acquired had sales in 1982 of £36 million and an operating profit of £2.8 million. It had over 350 employees, about 200 at Avonmouth and the rest in Blackburn and Aberdeen in the UK, Maastricht in Holland, Bordeaux in France and Toronto in Canada.

The origin of TCE was a tar distilling business founded in 1843 by William Butler, a foreman on the Great Western Railway, to make creosote for railway sleepers. In 1962 William Butler and Company sold the tar distilling business to the Gas Board. By then, the company had expanded into paper chemicals, principally rosin based sizes (materials used to bind together fibres in the manufacture of paper and reduce absorbency), with plants at Avonmouth and Aberdeen. It also refined and distilled lubricants and fuel oils, manufactured disinfectants and allied chemicals, merchanted other industrial chemicals and had a chain of oil distribution depots. The heating and fuel oil distribution was carried out by two companies, Butler Oil Products (dating from 1919) and Arndale Fuels (established in 1965), jointly owned with Petrofina.

Another strand of what became TCE was Transicol, a company set up in 1922 in Holland to produce paper sizes for Holland and Belgium. It had been taken over in 1960 by Heyden Newport (see p.165), which was acquired by Tenneco in 1963 and became part of Tenneco Chemicals Inc. in 1965. In that year the British Bewoid Company was purchased, with plants at Blackburn and in Holland. Tenneco acquired the paper chemicals division of Butler Chemicals in 1966 and merged it with British Bewoid to become Tenneco Malros. The name Malros was applied by Butler to its rosin soaps fortified with maleic anhydride but following the merger the rosin soaps were gradually replaced by rosin emulsions, under the trade name Roscol. In Holland Bewoid became a subsidiary of Transicol and in 1973 a new factory at Maastricht replaced the Bewoid and Transicol plants. In 1979 Transicol formed a branch operation at Landskrona, in southern Sweden, to supply the paper and board industry in Sweden and Denmark.

The remainder of Butler Chemicals was purchased by Tenneco in 1967. Plants were then built at Avonmouth for phosphate plasticisers. Tenneco Chemicals Europe was created in 1974, with two divisions in the UK, Tenneco Malros and Tenneco Organics. The latter included four product groups: organophosphorus chemicals, disinfectants, biocides and solvents (mainly white spirit).

In 1976, TCE acquired a French company making paper chemicals, La Societe Anonyme Industrielle de Resines (SAIR). The company had been founded in 1913 to acquire a business established in 1885 for the manufacture of products based on gum rosin and turpentine from the pine forests South of Bordeaux, and had begun producing Bewoid sizes in 1932 at a factory at Begles, near Bordeaux. A second plant was acquired in 1970 at Grenoble, in a major paper-making area close to the French Alps.

SAPCCO (South African Paper Chemicals Co.), 60% owned by TCE, was founded by TCE in 1962, with a factory at Pinetown, near Durban, to supply the South African paper and board industry with a variety of products. In 1984 SAPCCO moved to new premises at Isithebe in KwaZulu, to a site owned by TCE's partner, Chemserve, on which was located the detergent chemicals plant of Akulu-Marchon, jointly owned by A&W and Chemserve.

Tenneco Paper Chemicals Canada (TPCC) was formed in July 1982. A plant came into production in April 1983 to manufacture Roscol size, previously exported from Blackburn. It was very successful in replacing the less cost-effective rosin soaps previously used in the American market. Within a year a doubling of the plant was put in hand and the product range was expanded to include the Snowhite water-based adhesive tackifiers (for removable labels, etc.).

A&W had thus acquired a profitable and expanding company in the sort of speciality business that fitted well with its general objectives and its position as a medium-size chemical company. The performance of the components of the Resins & Organics Division, as it became in 1983 in its first full year in A&W, is shown in the table below.

Resins and Organics Division performance 1983

	Sales £m	Profit £'000	Return on sales %
UK	19.5	898	4.6
Holland	7.7	1146	14.9
France	5.8	761	13.2
South Africa	4.4	878	20.1
Canada	1.0	-55	-5.2
Sweden	0.8	31	3.7
	39.2	**3659**	**9.3**
Associated companies:			
Butler Oil Products		263	
Arndale Fuels		213	
Total profit		**4135**	

The relatively low UK return reflected the divisional administrative and technical costs not charged out to the subsidiaries. The return on net assets for the whole Division in 1983 was just under 20%. In the years that followed, TCE successfully produced a synthetic size (alkyl ketene dimer, trade name Keydime), but only after considerable difficulty, and opened a highly-automated plant at Kristinehamn, near

Stockholm, to make rosin and synthetic sizes and de-inking chemicals. There were also advances in organophosphorus chemicals and biocides, including MBT, a water-based material for wood and water treatment. Three more fuel distribution companies were bought. Tenneco Organics obtained a Queen's Award for its exports in 1984. In 1986 the Division made a profit of nearly £5 million, with particularly strong performances in Holland and South Africa.

Asia

Expansion in Asia was a prominent feature of A&W's progress in the early 1980s. Advances were made principally through joint ventures in the Philippines and Thailand and Singapore.

A&W's entry into the **Philippines** came in June 1980, when after some two years of discussions with Chemical Industries of the Philippines (Chemphil), A&W acquired a 40% stake in Polyphosphates Inc.(PPI), a subsidiary of Chemphil. That happened even though George Meason, the A&W Chairman, considered the prospective return of 16% after tax too small in view of the risks involved. PPI was the only manufacturer of sodium tripolyphosphate and tetrasodium pyrophosphate plant in the Philippines. PPI's plant near Manila, using imported phosphoric acid, was built to a design supplied by A&W (Australia). Under the arrangement with Chemphil, A&W provided the General Manager for the company; the first appointment to that position was Dr Steve Clarke, from the staff of A&W (Australia), who had been on secondment to A&W in the UK since 1978 as a project manager in the Phosphates Sector.

PPI's profitability was adversely affected by the need to import phosphoric acid. In February 1982 a surplus thermal phosphoric acid plant was found in Mexico, which was dismantled and shipped to Manila during 1983 and came into production in June 1984. With the protection of a heavy tariff barrier, PPI became very profitable: A&W's share of the operating profit was in excess of £1 million pa from 1984 to 1986, thereafter declining through competition and reductions in tariffs, but still providing a good return on the investment of 16 million pesos (about £1 million).

The next ventures were in **Thailand.** The first arose because the Birla group, a leading Indian industrial group with an interest in Thai Rayon, wished to establish a plant to make STPP and were looking for A&W to be a partner. Since Tenneco was not willing for A&W to invest any cash in the venture, it was eventually agreed that A&W would provide the know-how and engineering for the plant in exchange for a 30% share in the equity of the company, with an option to increase the stake to 50% with a cash subscription. Thai Polyphosphate & Chemicals Co (TPC) was formed in November 1981 to build an STPP plant south of Bangkok with a capacity of 20,000 tpa, to replace imports of that quantity. The plant was commissioned in

September 1984, at a cost of £11 million, and became a showpiece among A&W's STPP plants, proving to have a capacity well above the designed rating. Thanks to a 30% tariff protection and restrictions on imports, the plant was profitable after initial losses caused through dumped imports.

The second venture in Thailand was the formation in April 1984 of a joint venture with A&W's sales agent in Thailand, Adplan Ferrous-Chem Ltd. A&W's holding was 49%. The company, initially named AWAT-Adplan Ltd., later became AWAT Thai Ltd. (AWAT standing for Albright & Wilson Asia Trading). It expanded A&W's sales in Thailand but its activities were restricted because of difficulties in the relationship with TPC over sales of STPP in Thailand. AWAT Thai's operations were confined to sales until in 1993 it began production of acrylic emulsions at a factory south of Bangkok, owned by Adplan Ferrous-Chem Ltd (see p.313).

Meanwhile there were several developments in **Singapore**. In September 1981 A&W bought the 55% share of United Industrial Corporation in UIC-Marchon for £115,000, a modest sum reflecting the marginal economics of the plant (at Jurong, on Singapore island) at that time. The negotiations for the acquisition were presided over by Lee Kim Yew, Chairman of UIC-Marchon and brother of Lee Kwan Yew, the Chief Minister. The company was renamed Albright & Wilson (Marchon). While the company continued to struggle to make profits, because of the strength of the competition, the smallness of the domestic market and the scale of production, the Jurong operation provided the technical selling and administrative base for expansion in Asia.

In April 1985 Albright & Wilson Asia Trading (AWAT) was formed in Singapore to oversee all the Asian operations, which at that time comprised joint ventures in India, the Philippines and Thailand, the manufacturing subsidiary in Malaysia and sales companies or offices in China, Japan, Hong Kong, Taiwan and Korea. The first President of AWAT was Don Beck, who joined A&W in Ireland and became its Administration Director from 1974 to 1982, when he moved to South Africa as General Manager of Akulu-Marchon. Don's enthusiasm and Irish persuasiveness markedly increased the tempo of A&W's operations in Asia.

In April 1984 John Wills, the Director primarily responsible for Asian development, made a proposal for building an ethoxylation plant at Jurong to replace imported ethoxylates, one of the main detergent intermediates, at an estimated cost of $2.5 million. Charles Suckling[2] suggested that a better alternative

---

[2] Dr Charles Suckling FRS was appointed to the A&W Board in November 1981 as a non-executive Director with special responsibility for examining and reporting on R&D and engineering. He joined ICI in 1942, became Deputy Chairman of Mond Division, then Chairman of Paints Division, and finally General Manager - Research & Technology. In 1969, as research director for Mond, he had advised against the proposal by the government's Department of Trade and Industry for ICI to take over A&W. He was later approached by George Ashford to join A&W's Board when George was about to retire.

would be to build a plant on Pulau Ayer Merbau, an island near Singapore City, where an ethylene oxide plant was under construction. Not only would the economics be better; ethylene oxide was a hazardous substance and supply by pipeline would avoid problems of transportation. In September 1985 a joint venture was formed with Indonesian partners, PT Prima Inti Perkasa (in which the major shareholder was the Salim group, which was to become A&W's partner in Indonesia and Australia). It was not until 1988, however, that the ethoxylation plant of Ethoxylates Manufacturing Pte Ltd. (EMPL), as the joint venture company was named, came into operation (see p.322).

In **India,** Albright, Morarji and Pandit Ltd. began operations at Roha where a 45,000 tonnes pa sulphuric acid plant was commissioned in April 1979 (see p.220). For some years the only AMP operation on the site was for the supply of sulphuric acid to Ambarnath for the manufacture of phosphoric acid. Later a detergent plant was added and DMCC's detergent plants on the adjacent site were taken over by AMP (see p.323).

Although A&W had a sales office in **Japan** and was shipping phosphorus in bulk to that market, operations never progressed to the point of manufacture. Exports of sodium chlorate were assisted by a local repacking facility. At the end of 1985 approval was obtained at short notice for the acquisition of a 40% holding in Rinkagaku Kogyo (Rin), a customer for phosphorus and a manufacturer of a number of chemicals in A&W's range. Negotiations, however, foundered and the proposal was withdrawn in September 1986.

Australia

In December 1978 Albright & Wilson (Australia) opened a new factory at Wetherill Park, on the outskirts of Sydney, for the manufacture of surfactants. It had long been an ambition of the Australian management to establish production in the Sydney area, where the major customers for the products were located, by acquisition or new construction. It had proved difficult to demonstrate satisfactory returns until expanding demand had led to production at Box Hill (Melbourne) reaching capacity. An 11-acre site was purchased in 1977 and a plant was built within 18 months and opened in December 1978 by Neville Wran, the Premier of New South Wales. The plant, which cost AUD 6.5 million (£3.8 million) had a sulphonation capacity of 7,000 tonnes p.a., described at the time as "of world scale" but in fact smaller than the plants installed by Colgate and Lever & Kitchen, the two largest detergent manufacturers in Australia. The technology for the Baker Perkins units installed at Wetherill Park came from Whitehaven; eventually they were to be superseded by the Ballestra unit obtained from Lever & Kitchen (see p.324). The Chemithon sulphonation plant at Box Hill continued in production until 1989, supplying customers in Victoria and providing material for bottling, which was also then discontinued since it was not on a competitive scale.

Research & Development

One of the questions overhanging much of A&W's history is whether a lack of resources devoted to research and development had a significant impact on its profitability and long-term success. Certainly the financial crisis of 1969-73 led to a reduction in spending and there had been doubts about the adequacy of development effort before then. In January 1977 Dr Danny Fagandini was appointed General Manager of a new Central Development Department, concerned with long-term strategic development. In October 1978 he reported to the Board that technical strength, which had been severely cut back six years earlier, was "inadequate even to sustain the competitiveness of the main business, let alone to extend the frontiers of the Company's technical knowledge". David Livingstone, however, responded cautiously, saying, "we did not set out to be major innovators within the chemical industry".

At the second Company Council in April 1981, concern was expressed at the scale of development effort. (Meetings of the Company Council, while serving a purpose as a method of communication between senior management and Union representatives, rarely resulted in any change of course for the Company.) Danny Fagandini observed that the level of R&D expenditure had by then probably recovered to the 1968/9 level of 2% of sales, but its effect had diminished through the higher cost of technical staff and the increased attention to safety, toxicology and environmental demands. Harry Searle (head of the Agricultural Division) pointed to ageing products and plants, technical problems with new plants, slowness to adopt computer controls and the lack of new products. David Livingstone had a "gut feeling" that A&W should be spending more on R&D.

Charles Suckling reviewed A&W's technical effort and made a report to the Board in November 1982. In it he concluded that there was just enough effort to defend existing businesses, but that the Company was not innovating at the rate required, and drew comparisons with ICI where there was a correlation between new products and prosperity: if work on new products stopped there would be a slow decline but after about 15 years profits would fall by about 50%; if technical effort then resumed at three times the previous rate, there would not be full recovery until year 40. He commented that scientific and engineering staff were generally bright and competent, yet there were hardly any young people, some staff were on the ebb-tide of the academic work of earlier years, there was no effective research leadership at a senior level, no-one to enthuse and no intake of new people. In addition, technical efforts were not coordinated. He praised the process development work

The main site of Marchon Italiana, at Castiglione della Stiviere, near Lake Garda.

Marchon France's site at S. Mihiel, with effluent treatment plant in foreground (1993).
[photo: Cliché Imatec]

Ann Street, Widnes (1996).
[photo: Aaron Agencies Studios]

The ACC Fertiliser site at Barton on Humber, with the Humber bridge in the background.
[photo: David Lee Photography Ltd]

under Ted Lowe, technical director of the Phosphates Division, which led to innovations such as the phosphine plant at Oldbury and to important cost savings in production. He was, however, concerned at the level of competence in plant supervision and the lack of priority given to safety and environmental matters.

In February 1983 Charles organised a marketing and technology conference for 40 senior staff from all parts of A&W. At the conference, David Livingstone promised that the money would be found for good ideas; "I want to put fresh urgency into product development - and in the promotion of some younger people into senior management positions to keep us progressive". There was a large measure of agreement on the products, technologies and territories offering the best opportunities for growth. Three months later George James (head of Phosphates Division) was made Technical Director with a brief to improve the Company's technical base. Towards the end of the year two groups were set up - the Technical Resource Group and the Engineering Resource Group - to bring together divisional and central senior staff.

In mid-1984, at the second Technology and Marketing Conference, David Livingstone noted that 90% of the Company's profit came from products at least 30 years old. There was general agreement that development should be more market-led. In April the Executive agreed that George James should put forward proposals for engaging consultants to investigate opportunities for acquisitions in North America. The firm Innotech was hired and recommended in 1985 that the hydrological cycle (water treatment, etc.) was the area to enter. (Jack Diesel, A&W's Chairman, said that the consultants should not have been hired without Tenneco's permission, because of their strict rules on any expenditure that might constitute bribery.) In December 1985 two US companies in water treatment, Clow and Polymetrics, were proposed as acquisitions. Tenneco rejected the proposal early in 1986.

Meanwhile there were moves to market A&W's technical know-how. A small business unit was set up to sell process know-how and engineering expertise but the idea proved to be a non-starter since there was a reluctance to part with know-how that would have been saleable. Another move was to buy know-how. At the beginning of 1985 A&W (Australia) acquired world rights for the Apace process for the addition of methanol or ethanol to diesel. The licence required a minimum royalty of $78,000 rising to $120,000 per annum, but with the collapse in the price of oil in 1986 the process lost its attraction.

The third Technical & Marketing Conference, in 1984, focused on regeneration. There were signs that R&D activity was increasing. Charles Suckling was, however, still critical that technical effort was not sufficiently market-led and that there was minimal reporting of technical work to the Board. Short-term profit requirements inhibited a significant expansion in the resources devoted to R&D.

There was, however, still substantial scope for expansion by extending the application of existing process know-how and product technology, in surfactants, pulp bleaching and phosphates.

Surfactants

In this period capacity for sulphonation (see p.317), one of the basic manufacturing steps, was expanded. £5.5 million was spent at Whitehaven to double capacity with improvements in blending and filling units, commissioned in 1984. Before that, there had been expansion at Alcover in Spain and at St Mihiel in France, the start of sulphonation at Frosinone, in southern Italy, and the introduction of a new method of sulphonation, by a loop reactor, at Whitehaven. Another of the basic processes at Whitehaven, hydrogenation, was developed by the building of a new hydrogen generator in mid-1982, expanded two years later. The product range was enlarged by developing high-active surfactants, fabric conditioners and other speciality products. The variety of private-label powder detergents supplied to supermarkets was broadened to include enzymes, a low-temperature bleaching system, larger packs and a new brand name, 'Albrite'. Microprocessors were installed on the packing lines to increase capacity and reduce costs.

Of particular significance was the development of heavy duty liquid detergents (HDLs). The original work at Whitehaven on HDLs began in 1978, when in continental Europe sales of liquid detergents were growing, but without a builder such as sodium tripolyphosphate. A&W's aim was to develop a product containing STPP, which would not affect the sales of STPP through displacing powder detergents. In order to understand the structure of such a product, analysis was conducted at the Harwell nuclear laboratory. Patents were filed in 1984, which proved a key to later development. Phosphonates were added to remove bleachable stains without bleach and a small plant, with a capacity of about 5,000 tpa, was put together. Presentations were made to the 'soapers' (Unilever and Procter & Gamble) in September 1983 but 15 months later they rejected the materials. Selling was focused on supermarkets and volume quickly rose above the original plant capacity. Careful patenting of A&W's HDL system led to success in a patent dispute with Witco (the leading US supplier of private label detergents), resulting in a settlement of $850,000. A potential conflict with Unilever was resolved by cross-licensing with a payment to A&W. HDLs became a product group of increasing importance until the advent of compact powders whose intensified promotion checked their growth.

At the beginning of 1985 A&W acquired Tensia Surfac, based in Barcelona, Spain, manufacturing surfactants largely complementary to those produced at Alcover, some 60 miles away. Previously owned by the Belgian company Tensia, it employed 200 people and had plants for sulphonation and ethoxylation and a large number of speciality chemicals.

In this period up to 1985 the Whitehaven surfactants operation made little or no profit, with losses in five of the years. In Italy, however, there were profits of £2 million or more in each year, France was profitable from 1981 and Spain from 1985 made over £1 million each year. The Whitehaven profit was highly dependent on the price of natural alcohols, the main raw material; a downturn in the price in 1986 led to a profit of over £6 million in that year and profits remained high for the following two years.

Pulp and paper

As mentioned in the previous chapter (p.231), at the start of this period the return on pulp & paper operations was very high - a 40% return on net capital employed in 1977. From 1978 to 1986 over Can$100 million was invested in additional capacity for sodium chlorate. Operating profit, however, after rising from under $10 million in 1978 to nearly $15 million in 1981, declined to a low point of $6.5 million in 1986 before recovering strongly to new peaks in 1987-1990.

In 1978 Erco's capacity for sodium chlorate was 110,000 tonnes pa, all of it in the obsolete graphite cells except for 9,000 tonnes installed in Vancouver in 1975. The direct costs of graphite-based chlorate were more than double those of chlorate from metal cells (in 1986 the figures were $230 per tonne against $99). By 1986, capacity had risen to 213,000 tonnes, of which nearly two-thirds was metal.

In January 1979 a 25,000 tons pa sodium chlorate plant with metal cells opened at Monroe, Louisiana, at a cost of US$ 13 million. The plant was to supply the large papermaking industry in the southern United States, in particular mills operated by International Paper. Demand for sodium chlorate was forecast to grow rapidly because of the requirements for the chemical caused by increasingly stringent effluent standards, which were due to come into operation in 1983. The amount of chlorine used in the first stage of the bleaching process had to be reduced so as to reduce the chlorinated organic compounds in effluent. The processes developed by Erco for generating chlorine dioxide (the bleaching gas) from sodium chlorate were increasingly effective in reducing effluent from mills. Erco Envirotech (a joint venture set up for the purpose) designed a process for an effluent-free pulp mill which was installed by Great Lakes Pulp and Paper Company at Thunder Bay, Ontario.

It was at Thunder Bay that Erco opened its next plant, in March 1979. Costing CAN $10 million, the plant was built to supply Great Lakes Pulp and Paper Company and had a capacity of 15,000 tons pa. Almost immediately an expansion to 35,000 tons (32,000 tonnes) pa was announced to serve other mills in the area; it came on stream in 1981. Capacity was further increased to 47,000 tonnes in the following year. Thunder Bay used metal cells and improvements in design were introduced at each expansion.

Towards the end of 1979 IMC (International Minerals and Chemicals Inc.) offered Erco a new chlorate plant for US$6 million. Erco, which had a depot in North Carolina, considered locating the plant there, which would have cost a further $14 million, but the proposal was not taken further because of the lack of guaranteed customers.

The next major project was at Buckingham, where a metal cell line with a capacity of 33,000 tonnes pa was built at a cost of Can$27 million and started up in July 1985. 8,000 tpa of graphite capacity was retired but 55,000 tpa remained in operation. The decision was taken in mid-1986 to eliminate the remaining graphite capacity by building a 44,000 tpa metal cell line. That plant came on stream in November 1988, after expenditure of Can$44 million. The graphite cells were closed in 1987 and interim purchases of chlorate were made from Erco's competitor Kemanord.

Meanwhile in February 1984 consideration was given to the closure of the Monroe plant and removal of equipment to Vancouver. The key power contract had been abrogated by the supplier (with a rebate of $4.3 million paid in 1983) and production became uneconomic against larger chlorate producers in the area. The plant was eventually closed in 1986, involving a write-off of $4 million, and moved to Vancouver, bringing the metal capacity there up to 32,000 tonnes. The 47,000 tonnes' graphite capacity was kept in operation and it was not until mid-1989 that it was replaced with a metal line, after the Vancouver authorities had given an ultimatum for the graphite cells to be reduced or eliminated in the face of concern about the accumulation of graphite mud contaminated with chrome and arsenic.

In the period 1978-86, Erco was the largest producer of sodium chlorate in the world. As such, it attracted support for expansion from Tenneco. There were, however, some basic problems. The cost of capacity was high (Can$700 or more per tonne), including crystallisation (for economical transportation), while the netback on sales was only about $450. It was therefore necessary to have high margins on sales in order to achieve an acceptable return on investment. Although the market was expanding strongly, so too was capacity, including new entrants. The customers were large mills and if capacity for sodium chlorate exceeded demand the price of the product fell; as a result, prices tended to fall in real terms. In 1986, in the Eastern and Southern Canadian and US markets, sales of sodium chlorate were 447,000 tonnes against capacity of 563,000 tonnes. The netback at Buckingham at the end of 1986 was down to Can$331, against around $450 in 1982-5. Hence the collapse in the profit on sodium chlorate from over Can$8 million in 1985 to $1.6 million in 1986 (when Buckingham with its graphite cells was operating at a substantial loss). Thereafter, as demand for sodium chlorate accelerated and overcapacity diminished (in 1988 there was a shortage of capacity), profits hit new peaks.

Erco's dominant position in the supply of chlorine dioxide generators supported its sales of sodium chlorate and earned substantial sums in royalties and fees. Generators were sold not only in North America but also in Scandinavia. In 1986 Erco sold its 50th generator and was engaged in upgrading earlier (R3) models to the latest technology. In that year the profit on generators was nearly Can$5 million. Erco's only competitor for them was Kemanord, which in February 1983 purchased the share of Oxychem (formerly Hooker) in the R3 technology, as well as its plant at Columbus (originally OECCo's). Jack Diesel had dissuaded A&W from purchasing Hooker's share in the technology, in the expectation that it would withdraw from the field. In fact, Oxy continued in Canada and Kemanord went on to become the largest producer of sodium chlorate, though still relatively small in generators.

Phosphorus and phosphates

The improvement in the Long Harbour situation has been described in the previous chapter. It had ceased to be the dominant feature of A&W's phosphorus and phosphates business. Also described were the difficulties experienced with the F5 phosphoric acid plant at Whitehaven, which continued for more than two years after the official opening of the plant by the Queen in March 1980. With the building of F5 went a further stage in wet phosphoric acid purification, the 'MMO' plant (Modified Marchon Oldbury) which added 90,000 tonnes pa to the 40,000 tpa 'MO' plant (Marchon Oldbury) completed in 1976. The MMO plant produced acid of a purity sufficient for industrial (but not food) phosphates, in addition to STPP for which the MO grade was suitable. The underflow (impure) acid was mainly taken to Barton-on-Humber and used in fertilisers, with some being exported to continental Europe.

The next stage in purification, the "UFEX" plant (Underflow Extraction), came into operation in the latter part of 1984. Its purpose was to eliminate the underflow acid (following the disposal of the Agricultural Division) by extracting the phosphoric acid and neutralising the remaining sulphuric acid. The process employed a column (instead of the mixer settlers used in the earlier plants) and was to lead to the 'MOS' plant at the end of 1986. By adding a solvent extraction column, with equipment to remove fluorine and arsenic, acid pure enough to be used in food phosphates was produced, accounting for about a quarter of the 140,000 tonnes pa of purified wet acid. Through development of that technology, A&W was in a position to extend the production of purified wet acid into the USA, as will be described in the next chapter.

The sales of STPP from Whitehaven reached a peak in 1983 of just over 200,000 tonnes, worth nearly £75 million, yielding a profit of £5.5 million. The home market accounted for 150,000 tonnes. At that time, the alleged contribution of phosphates to eutrophication (see p.213) had not affected sales in the UK, but had a severe impact on North American sales. In December 1985, however, Henkel (a leading German producer of detergents) announced that it was eliminating STPP from its powder detergents.There were other pressures on A&W's home market sales. At the beginning of 1981, A&W was forced to concede a "temporary voluntary allowance" (TVA) to Unilever and Procter & Gamble to meet price competition from imports of STPP. That was followed by a dispute with Unilever concerning selling prices; it was referred to arbitration early in 1982 and decided in A&W's favour a few months later. In 1986 Unilever imported half its requirements of STPP from Hoechst in Germany. Prices in the UK weakened and exports fell as zeolites (silicates) replaced phosphates in detergents outside the UK. 5-day working was introduced on the plant in 1986. While STPP continued to be one of A&W's leading products, its relative importance declined.

Of growing importance was phosphine, THPC and other organophosphorus chemicals. The capacity for THPC (TetrakisHydroxymethylPhosphoniumChloride), used in the Proban flame retardant process, was doubled in August 1980 and again in August 1985. In November 1981 a new plant for the production of very pure phosphine (phosphorus trihydride), the principal intermediate for THPC, was commissioned at Oldbury. The microprocessor-based technology for the production of a highly toxic and volatile gas was developed by A&W. It was based on the continuous hydrolysis of red phosphorus by steam. The process was first investigated in the early 1960's but not developed to a full-scale plant until demand justified the investment of £2 million. The plant was the first A&W to be designed from scratch with computer control. The innovative technology was recognised by the receipt of one of the few Queen's Awards for Technical Achievement in 1983.

A Queen's Award for Export Achievement followed in April 1986, for an increase of 80% in exports of flame retardants over three years. The products concerned were Proban and the Amgard range made at Avonmouth by the Resins & Organics (R & O) Division. Two years earlier R & O had obtained a Queen's Award for exports of organophosphorus products (including flame retardants for polyurethane foams and resins used in building), biocides and disinfectants, which had grown by 145% in three years. It was a prolific period for Queen's Awards for A&W: at the same time as the award for Technical Achievement, Oldbury obtained an Award for exports of water treatment chemicals, especially for desalination plants in the Middle East.

Other developments in Phosphates in this period were the Briquest range of phosphonates and the opening of several phosphates plants at Widnes. Briquests were launched in 1981, for use in detergents, water treatment, oil wells and other applications. In April 1983 capacity at Oldbury was trebled and rapid growth continued, making Briquests eventually one of the most profitable product groups for A&W.

The site at Ann Street, Widnes, had not received any major investment for a long time. The first development was the opening of new plants for Calgon (sodium hexametaphosphate – used in water treatment) and mono- and di-ammonium phosphates (used in flame retardancy and other applications) in the second quarter of 1980, at a cost of £35 million, as replacements for smaller plants at Oldbury and Kirkby. In 1984 plants were opened for trisodium phosphate and for Kalipols, potassium polyphosphates with applications in detergents, water treatment, plant nutrients and flame retardants. Towards the end of 1985 a £4 million plant for food phosphates, replacing plants at Oldbury and Widnes, was commissioned. The site was transformed, ending local fears of closure.

Mobil

By far the most important development in Phosphates occurred in the USA. In February 1984 Ray Naish, the Director principally concerned with phosphorus and phosphates and with North America, raised the subject of the impending surplus of phosphorus, as purified wet acid replaced thermal acid in the UK and Long Harbour was achieving higher output more consistently. He suggested that the problem could be solved by acquiring a US user of phosphorus. A possible target was the Industrial Chemicals Group of the Mining & Minerals Division of Mobil Corporation. It included the plant formerly owned by Virginia Carolina at Charleston, South Carolina, where phosphorus production had ceased many years before and requirements were purchased from Monsanto. Jack Diesel made contact with Mobil, who were receptive because of the unit's relatively small size and their lack of a basic position in phosphorus. The acquisition was agreed in February 1985 and completed three months later at a cost of $40 million.

The unit acquired comprised plants at Charleston and Fernald (Ohio), with offices leased from Mobil at Richmond (Virginia) and access to Mobil's laboratories at Princeton and Edison (New Jersey). There were 200 employees. The Charleston plant produced phosphorus chlorides and speciality organophosphorus products, used in pesticides, biocides, corrosion inhibitors, pharmaceutical intermediates, metal extraction, flame retardants and other specialised applications. It also produced phosphoric acid, which was the main product at the much smaller operation at Fernald, a site of 13 acres compared with the 103 acres at Charleston. A&W once again had a manufacturing base in the United States and an outlet for phosphorus from Long Harbour and Varennes. It also acquired technology in organophosphorus products and an enthusiastic and market-oriented technical team.

The Mobil chemicals team welcomed what they expected to be a cheaper source of phosphorus than Monsanto. On the day that the deal with A&W was closed, however, they were informed of A&W's phosphorus prices - appreciably above Monsanto's price. That led the Mobil team to reactivate an earlier proposal to move to purified wet acid as the source of the phosphoric acid sold from Charleston and Fernald. Several years before, know-how had been acquired from the German firm of Budenheim and in 1983 there had been discussions with Olin, one of the leading US producers of STPP, on a proposal for a PWA plant at Pasadena, Texas, where Mobil had a phosphatic fertiliser operation. In 1986 a study group was formed, with representation from Erco (including its President, Claude Hollands) and the UK (Peter Salmon) to look into the possibility of building a PWA plant, probably in partnership with a major producer of fertiliser acid such as IMC or Texasgulf. David Livingstone agreed that the remit could include the possibility of closing the Long Harbour phosphorus plant since the quantity of phosphorus that would then be required for North America and the UK would probably not justify keeping it open. This decision would mean that the Mobil chemicals operation would not fulfil the main purpose for which it was acquired, which was to use excess phosphorus produced by Long Harbour. The outcome of the study is described in the next chapter.

The acquired operation became a Division of A&W, under the name of Albright & Wilson Inc.. Its President was Frank Kuhn, who had been General Manager of the Mobil unit. Of the six Vice-Presidents, three were transferred from A&W to strengthen the staffing and the ties with the rest of the Company. The separation of the Mobil chemicals division from Mobil was achieved by building a new headquarters at Richmond close to the Mobil offices. The building was opened in mid-1987 and included laboratories, so that Mobil's facilities at Princeton and Edison were no longer needed. It was to become A&W's headquarters for the whole of the Americas, and the acquisition of the Mobil unit changed not only A&W's operations in the Americas but also the international balance of the Company.

Organisation and management

It might be considered a truism that organisation and management is the deciding factor in commercial success or failure. Over a period of a few years, however, circumstances must have an important bearing. The background to the period 1978-86 already described - the influence of Tenneco, the disposals, the earlier difficulties at Long Harbour, the threats to STPP - imposed some constraints on actions by the senior management. There were numerous changes in organisation - some thought too many, others regarded them as sensible adaptations – as well as significant changes in management.

1979, the first full year of Tenneco's 100% ownership, heralded the first changes in management. As earlier described (p.186), in March Tenneco transferred Gene Anderson from Houston to A&W. As Joint Deputy Managing Director - Operations Tenneco hoped that Gene would be able to re-point the direction of the Company. Before Gene's appointment, all the operational heads (comprising 5 Sector Chairmen and BBA in the UK plus the heads of Erco, A&W Australia and Ireland) reported to David Livingstone. The executive Directors formed the 'Managing Director's Office', a committee advisory to the Managing Director, and some of them acted as 'uncles', an arrangement that blunted responsibility. It was thus an organisation very much centred on David. When Gene was appointed, all the operational heads reported direct to him. David Anthony, who had held the central staff position of Director of Operations (he had transferred to Oldbury from Australia in 1967 and was managing director of Oldbury Division from 1970-75), retired.

At the end of 1979 all the non-executive Directors of A&W retired, i.e. former executives Bill Albright and John Hutton-Wilson, non-executives George Ashford and Neil Peech, and the previous Chairman from Tenneco, Sydney Ellis. No replacement non-executives were deemed to be necessary in view of the formation of the Tenneco European Council on which several prominent European businessmen sat under the chairmanship of retired Admiral Ralph Cousins, former Supreme Allied Commander, Atlantic, and then heading Tenneco's London office.

Some further steps in tightening the organisation were taken in March 1980 when the Specialities and Organics sectors were merged into Phosphates, so that there were four UK Divisions (Phosphates, Detergents, Agriculture and BBA). Ray Naish, who had been in charge of Phosphates, was brought onto the Board on the retirement of Harold Kimberley as Director in charge of employee relations. George James was moved from Detergents to Phosphates, Mike Fearfield from Agriculture to Detergents and Harry Searle from Oldbury research to Agriculture, while Malcolm Clark replaced Ron Mason at BBA. So there was a "general post" at divisional level.

Addressing the first Company Council meeting in April 1980, Gene pointed out that sales had declined in real terms in 1978 and 1979 and that UK sales per employee had fallen 11%, while costs per employee had risen 46%. Numbers were reduced in 1980, at a cost of £4 million in redundancy pay. David Livingstone commented: "significant cuts in numbers have been achieved by natural wastage. The trouble about 'natural wastage' is that it tends to be the wrong people that get wasted". Compulsory redundancy was still regarded as too difficult in the face of Union opposition.

In June 1981 Gene Anderson left A&W and Tenneco (to join Celanese). He had become dissatisfied with progress in A&W. He was also unhappy with the general Tenneco situation, its deteriorating financial position, the continuing Case problem and the moves to dispose of A&W if a satisfactory price could be obtained. On Gene's departure, the Division Managing Directors reverted to reporting directly to David Livingstone.

In November 1981 Jack Diesel succeeded George Meason as Chairman of A&W, on the latter's retirement from Tenneco.[3] Jack Diesel's background was in heavy industrial engineering. He had joined Tenneco in 1972 and had been in charge of Newport News Shipbuilding before becoming President of Tenneco in 1979. Of all the five Tenneco Chairmen of A&W, he was the most remote, perhaps because of his lack of background in chemicals, perhaps through preoccupation with the problems in the rest of Tenneco, where his responsibilities included Case as well as A&W and Packaging Corporation of America. He retired from A&W and Tenneco at the end of 1988, leaving behind few people in A&W with any recollection of his presence.

In May 1983 Tony Ward retired after a distinguished career of 30 years with A&W, the last 14 as Finance Director and then Deputy Managing Director. He was succeeded by Hugh Podger, General Manager Finance since 1978 who had previously held financial and planning posts with a spell of 7 years in BBA, of which 4 were spent as Managing Director of BBA Australia. Also appointed to the Board of A&W was George James as Technical Director, the first technical director of A&W since the retirement of John Hughes in 1974. With a degree in chemistry and engineering, he had come into A&W with the acquisition of Gardinol by A&W (Australia) in 1966 and had successively become managing director of Australia, Detergents and Phosphates Divisions between 1976 and 1980.

At the same time, there were significant changes in organisation. The operating divisions, including the Resins & Organics Division formed from Tenneco Chemicals Europe at the beginning of 1983, became responsible to executive directors, who also had territorial and functional responsibilities. The Managing Director's Office was replaced by an Executive Committee of the executive directors. That meant that there was an orthodox devolved organisation in place of the previous structure wholly centred on David Livingstone. That organisation continued until the end of 1986 and accommodated the addition of Albright &

---

[3] George Meason had been a Director of A&W since 1976 and Chairman since 1978. A chemical engineer, he had joined Tenneco in 1956 and had been concerned with the oil operations throughout his time with Tenneco. He was critical of the Long Harbour and F5 projects, which preceded his chairmanship, and of the general standard of engineering in A&W. Although his background had some affinity with chemicals, his short time with A&W made it difficult for him to make much impact. He regretted approving the BBA onion project on the basis of insufficient time for consideration of it.

Wilson Inc. in 1985. At the beginning of 1986 Bill Adair, until then heading Phosphates, joined the Board as Development Director with responsibility for planning, information, patents and the Technical Resource Group as well as the Resins & Organics Division. A chemistry graduate, he joined Marchon as an assistant chemist in 1963 and had roles in exports and South Africa before joining Phosphates. Replacing Bill Adair in Phosphates was Ian Black, a chartered accountant who joined Marchon in 1967. Ian moved from accountancy to marketing for Detergents in 1979 and to Phosphates in 1983.

In October 1986 David Livingstone was informed by Jack Diesel that he was to be replaced as Deputy Chairman and Managing Director at the end of the month. The abruptness of the news shocked and angered him. He had had no warning of this, except for Jack Diesel's comment at the Board meeting a month before that A&W had to rise above the plateau of profitability that had prevailed for 3 years. By then, the decision to replace David had already been taken. Tenneco had hired an executive search company which approached possible candidates in June 1986. David's eventual successor, Robin Paul, was interviewed by Jack Diesel in August and offered the job in September. Jim Ketelsen (Chairman of Tenneco) took the view that it would be inadvisable to have a long period when David was in a 'lame duck' situation.

Tenneco had been dissatisfied for some time that A&W's results were not improving and were concerned that there had been very little infusion of new staff in positions of responsibility. They also believed that the Company needed to have a chief executive with a technical background who would give greater priority to technical regeneration and development and they could see no possible internal candidate. Although David had proved to be a good leader in hard times and had steered A&W through its Long Harbour crisis, Tenneco believed a chief executive of a different kind was then needed. In retrospect, Tenneco's senior management believed that they should have acted earlier. The fact that they did not was attributed to a number of reasons: David's determination combined with his eloquence and disarming politeness, the lack of any pressure for change from within A&W, Tenneco's preoccupation with other problems, and reluctance to take the drastic step of sacking a chief executive. David's retirement was only 15 months before his normal retirement age of 62. At that time, there was still a tradition in A&W of long service through to normal retirement age; later, retirement beyond the age of 60 became much less common.

At a retirement presentation on his last day in office, Ray Naish spoke of David's contribution to Albright & Wilson, including the following words: "...a remarkable man, a penetrating if at times paradoxical mind, urbane, witty, quietly spoken, but as hard as steel when occasion requires ... humour was never far away. A man of the highest integrity, of rigorous standards but, on a personal basis, a very kindly man. His influence in Albright & Wilson has been great for 35 years and decisive for 15".

Chapter 7

THE FINAL YEARS OF
TENNECO OWNERSHIP

1986-1995

*"Tenneco has been proud of its association with the fine people of Albright &
Wilson for 17 years. It makes sense for solid, strategic reasons to resume its status
as a privately owned corporation"*
(Dana Mead, Chairman of Tenneco, March 1995)

Overview

In the final years of Tenneco ownership, leading up to the re-flotation of Albright & Wilson as a publicly-owned company in February 1995, there were major disposals imposed on A&W by Tenneco, which was passing through a period of crisis. A&W nevertheless was able to show rising profits after the disposals, as its remaining operations improved margins through better efficiency, some new developments and the effect of exchange rates favourable to the UK. Tenneco's sale of A&W was part of a rationalisation process which improved its cash position but the price it obtained was disappointing.

Political and economic background

- Mikhail Gorbachev became President of the USSR in September 1988 but was forced to resign in December 1991 by Boris Yeltsin, who had become President of Russia

- the Communist regimes of Eastern Europe were replaced and Germany was reunified but the Communist party retained power in China after the Tiananmen Square massacre in June 1989

- F W de Klerk became President of South Africa in September 1989 and was succeeded by Nelson Mandela in July 1991

- George Bush succeeded Ronald Reagan as President of the USA in January 1989 and was defeated by Bill Clinton in November 1992

- Iraq-Iran ceasefire took place in August 1988, Iraq invaded Kuwait in August 1990, the Desert Storm ground campaign against Iraq was launched in January 1991 and there was a ceasefire in February 1991

- Conflict in the Balkans began with an insurrection in Croatia in August 1990, followed by UN sanctions against Yugoslavia in November 1991, fighting in Bosnia-Herzegovina in February 1992 and eventually the Dayton, Ohio peace agreement in November 1995

- after the Delors Plan of January 1989 for a single currency and European Central Bank, the Maastricht Treaty of European Union was signed in December 1991, with opt-out clauses for the UK, and ratified by Parliament in November 1992; the Single European Market was established in January 1993 and the European Union in November 1993; Jacques Santer became the EU President in July 1994 and Austria, Finland and Sweden joined the EU in January 1995

- the Conservatives won the June 1987 election with a 101 majority; Margaret Thatcher resigned in November 1990 and was succeeded by John Major, who won the April 1992 election

- The Channel Tunnel was opened in May 1994 and the National Lottery started in November 1994.

- weakness of the USD led to a collapse in stock markets in October 1987; that led to action by the Group of Seven in 1987/8, resulting in a growth of 4.3% in world economy in 1988 and 3.5% in 1989, followed by a deep and widespread recession in 1990-92

- during this period the USA ran a current account deficit of over $1.1bn while Japan ran a surplus of $0.9 bn.

- the boom in the UK economy in 1987 (election year) was stimulated by tax cuts in 1988, leading to overheating, inflation of 7% in 1989, high interest rates (a Treasury Bill rate of 13% in 1988 and an average of 15% in 1989-90) and an exchange rate of over DEM 3 in 1988-89

- in October 1990 the UK joined the ERM (Exchange Rate Mechanism) at a rate of DEM 2.95 with permitted variation of +/- 6%; the £ declined in the next 2 years until 15th September 1992, "Black Wednesday", when the UK was forced out of the ERM and the £ dropped 16%

- from September 1992 to the end of 1995 the £ fell to around DEM 2.2, improving competitiveness and stimulating exports - chemical exports rose from 36% of sales in 1979 to 51% in 1994

- from mid 1988 to mid 1990 the UK suffered from rapid inflation, reaching nearly 7% in the first 6 months of 1990; with high interest rates and recession in 1991-2, there was greatly reduced inflation in 1992-6.

The movement in the UK retail price index in this period was (1986 = 100):-

1987: 104;
1988: 109;
1989: 118;
1990: 129;
1991: 137;
1992: 142;
1993: 144;
1994: 147.

A&W Progress 1986 - 1994

(£ million)	1986	1987	1988	1989	1990	1991	1992	1993	1994
Sales: Total	**652**	**650**	**655**	**695**	**663**	**589**	**583**	**609**	**642**
of which: continuing	528	521	539	554	555	520	542	609	642
Paper Chemicals	39	41	50	56	30				
Pulp & Paper:	39	38	47	85	78	69	41		
incl. systems	*6*	*n.a.*	*7*	*27*	*21*	*n.a.*	*n.a.*		
Ireland	46	50	19						
Operating profit: Total	**45.6**	**46.6**	**49.2**	**56.8**	**45.0**	**24.2**	**51.2**	**57.0**	**62.7**
of which: continuing	36.6	38.0	38.1	38.0	24.6	11.1	48.5	57.0	62.7
Paper Chemicals	3.9	2.8	1.8	2.2	2.1				
Pulp & Paper:	3.2	4.2	8.6	16.4	18.3	13.1	2.7		
incl. systems	*2.4*	*2.3*	*2.5*	*4.9*	*5.3*	*n.a.*	*n.a.*		
Ireland	1.9	1.6	0.7						
by origin: UK	13.9	14.8	22.1	18.8	11.3	1.4	17.0	27.4	22.2
other	31.7	31.8	27.1	38.0	33.7	22.8	34.2	29.6	40.5
Net interest payable	-12.7	-7.1	-6.0	-11.3	-12.9	-12.9	-8.4	-1.2	-1.7
Exceptional/extraordinary			-33.7	+7.0	+24.0	-45.6	-6.8	+3.7	-20.2
Pretax profit	**32.9**	**39.5**	**9.5**	**52.5**	**56.1**	**-34.3**	**36.0**	**59.5**	**28.3**
Dividends to Tenneco	10.0	15.0	18.0	10.0	6.4	-	-	4.0	90.1
Capital expenditure	32.6	33.9	51.6	55.5	85.3	64.0	38.0	38.8	42.4
Net cap. emp. end of year	**289**	**259**	**256**	**327**	**338**	**350**	**294**	**317**	**261**

A reorganisation of Albright & Wilson (Australia) in 1991, reducing A&W's holding from a majority to 50%, eliminated its sales from the group total; in 1990 they had contributed £34.3m. to the total. Operating profit was also reduced by about £0.8m. through including 50% instead of the whole of its profit, as a subsidiary.

The results in this period reflected the economic background and the disposals dictated by Tenneco. In real terms (i.e. if adjusted for the UK retail price index), operating profit for the continuing businesses was higher in 1994 than in 1986 but the loss of the paper chemicals, pulp & paper and Irish operations meant that in real terms the total operating profit was lower. (Divestments are described fully in a later section of this chapter.) The margins on sales of the continuing businesses were improved, from less than 7% in 1986 to nearly 10% in 1994, through restructuring, better efficiency and product development, but the exceptional and extraordinary charges involved in restructuring were heavy.

The closure of Long Harbour in 1989 led to a provision in 1988 of £38.6m. to cover write-offs and closure costs (partly offset by profits of £4.9m. on the sale of Albright & Wilson Ireland and Butler Oil). In 1991 there were further provisions of £45.6m.. The main item was £26 million of additional costs arising from the cessation of phosphorus operations, at Long Harbour, Varennes (closed in 1992) and Portishead, including estimated costs of cleaning up the sites to meet environmental standards. There were also costs associated with the planned 1992 closure of the F5 phosphoric acid plant and environmental improvements at Whitehaven and with a reduction in the number of employees in the UK and continental European sites. In 1994 a review of the plans for dealing with environmental conditions at Long Harbour and Varennes led to the provision of another £9.8 million for remedial work, bringing the total provided for closure and clean-up of the phosphorus sites to nearly £75 million. Remediation plans were approved in 1996 and work at Varennes was completed in 1998, while the programme for Long Harbour was continuing in 1999, ten years after operations ceased. The Long Harbour venture cast a long shadow over the 30 years since the opening of the plant. It remains a matter of speculation how the history of Albright & Wilson would have differed if the heavy costs and managerial efforts incurred by Long Harbour had never happened.

The other exceptional or extraordinary items included profits and losses on divestments. Chief of these were the profit of £24 million in 1990 on the sale of the paper chemicals business and the loss of £7 million in 1992 on the sale of the pulp & paper chemicals operations. In 1994, prior to the flotation in 1995, there were rationalisation charges of £6.8 million relating to the surfactants operations at Whitehaven and in Spain and £3.7 million provided for foreign currency losses incurred on US dollar denominated borrowings as a result of the devaluation of the Mexican peso. The tale of exceptional charges was, however, to continue after flotation as year by year there were further rationalisations and environmental costs. There seemed to be a sort of inevitability about such costs, associated perhaps with membership of the chemical industry - characterised by the impact of growing concern with the environment and the consequences of advances in technology and market demands. Albright & Wilson was perhaps also paying for slowness to acknowledge change in some of its fundamental businesses.

Tenneco

The influence of Tenneco on A&W in this period was greater than in the preceding fifteen years, in the divestments forced upon A&W, the changes in management attitudes and techniques, and finally in the flotation. The years from 1986 to 1994 were for Tenneco a time of turmoil, with divestments, losses and changes of management. The results are shown in the tables below.

Tenneco Results: 1986 - 1994

($ million)	1986	1987	1988	1989	1990	1991	1992	1993	1994
Sales	**14,529**	**14,790**	**15,707**	**14,083**	**14,511**	**13,662**	**13,139**	**13,255**	**13,171**
Income before									
interest & tax	1,010	664	903	1,314	1,373	-93	-80	1,169	1,379
Interest payable	908	907	888	-489	-516	-585	-527	-460	-407
Pretax profit	**102**	**-243**	**15**	**825**	**857**	**-678**	**-607**	**709**	**972**
Net for Common shares	-105	-243	-70	566	543	-748	-1,339	412	396
Earnings per share ($)	-0.70	-1.80	-0.70	4.50	4.40	-6.10	-9.30	2.40	2.20
Equity	4,412	3,773	3,161	3,277	3,367	2,774	1,330	2,601	2,900
Debt	11,023	11,919	7,519	8,468	9,792	9,289	8,096	6,073	4,115
Total capital employed	**16,139**	**16,127**	**10,914**	**11,955**	**13,360**	**12,439**	**9,782**	**8,990**	**7,482**
Debt as % of total cap.	68	74	69	71	73	75	83	68	55

The 1988 figures exclude $892m. profit on disposal of the oil & gas businesses. From 1988 finance subsidiaries were consolidated, which had the effect of increasing debt and assets by around $3.7bn; the 1986 and 1987 figures above have been restated onto the same basis. In 1992 changes in the accounting treatment of employee benefits and deferred taxes gave rise to a charge of $0.7bn, equivalent to $4.86 per share.

Tenneco results: Analysis by business

($ million)	1986	1987	1988	1989	1990	1991	1992	1993	1994
Sales:									
Oil & Gas	2,773	3,117	2,473						
(productn & marktng)									
Gas pipelines	3,139	2,535	3,003	2,638	2,459	2,183	2,183	2,862	2,378
Case	3,358	3,664	4,306	5,066	5,390	4,449	3,829	3,748	3,881
Shipbuilding	1,641	1,659	1,671	1,949	2,113	2,216	2,265	1,861	1,753
Automotive	1,254	1,484	1,665	1,879	1,731	1,701	1,808	1,839	1,989
Packaging	944	1,144	1,298	1,336	1,469	1,934	2,078	2,042	2,184
Chemicals	952	1,068	1,217	1,224	1,298	1,160	951	914	986
Other	468	119	74	91	51	19	25	11	-
	14,529	14,790	15,707	14,083	14,511	13,662	13,139	13,255	13,171
Income before interest & tax:									
Oil & Gas	153	233	125						
(productn & marktng)									
Gas pipelines	394	92	114	325	340	561	360	411	415
Case	-1	-259	-59	228	186	-1,079	-1,180	82	326
Shipbuilding	246	175	175	200	225	225	249	225	200
Automotive	179	195	203	218	213	175	230	215	223
Packaging	110	166	215	200	190	139	221	139	209
Chemicals	71	77	18	113	160	-21	72	78	52
Other	-142	-15	112	30	59	-98	-32	19	6
	1,010	664	903	1,314	1,373	-98	-80	1,169	1,431

Chemicals includes Tenneco Minerals in 1986-90. 1988 chemicals figure is after $58m. rationalisation provisions. Case losses in 1991 & 1992 are after restructuring provisions of $920m. and $552m..

Reference has already been made (p.244) to the sale of the Tenneco oil and gas business, at a time when the prices of oil and gas were depressed and profits from those operations greatly reduced. The sale bought a respite from the acute financial problems. As the table shows, debt was reduced but because some of the proceeds were applied to the purchase of the company's shares the debt ratio remained high.

Debt rose again in the following two years and Case's losses and restructuring costs in 1991 and 1992 almost extinguished the equity. The effect of Case was more serious than indicated by its results at the level of income before interest and tax. The assets employed in Case were around half of Tenneco's total assets; thus a large part of the heavy interest bill was attributable to Case. Moreover, Tenneco and some of its officers were sued in 1991 for misrepresentation of the results of Case, through treating as profit the anticipated and unrealised margins on the very large inventories in the hands of dealers. Since the products were often sold later at a discount, involving an adjustment to profit, the valuations at the time of shipment to the dealers were overstated. The suits were settled out of court. (The auditors were Arthur Andersen.)

Tenneco's disposals, primarily to improve its financial position, were not confined to the oil and gas businesses. As already described (p.243), the precious metals operations and the life insurance subsidiaries were sold in 1986 and the Tenneco West agricultural operations in 1987, resulting in a combined loss of $274 million after tax, on net proceeds of $913 million.

In 1990, A&W's paper chemicals operations were sold (see further on p.287). In the Tenneco annual report, the disposal was described as "part of our continuing, Tenneco-wide review of underperforming assets...The proceeds are being used to speed our development in several other areas". The sale realised $100 million and produced a pre-tax gain of $43 million. Within A&W, paper chemicals was regarded as a growth area, with an above-average return on assets in Europe and South Africa but substantial losses in the USA, where it was proving difficult to carve out a viable share of the market. Tenneco's cash requirements, however, continued to be heavy. In 1990 the increase in its net debt was $1.3 billion, as a result of rising working-capital and capital outlays and the share repurchase programme. The main increase in working-capital was in Case, which also acquired an 11% stake in Cummins Engine Co., supplier of engines to Tenneco's joint venture with Cummins. There was a "dramatic expansion" in packaging, through acquisitions of paper mills and box plants. And the dividend was increased.

In the three months from the end of July 1990 the Tenneco share price fell from just under $70 to $40. There was a brief recovery to $52 in February 1991 but then the fall continued, to a low of $27 in December 1991. The company was haemorrhaging through the Case operations. Case's sales fell in 1991 by $940 million. Higher sales incentives and production cutbacks reduced inventories by $750 million (though still to more than 6 months' sales) but contributed to a loss by Case of $618 million before restructuring charges.

Eventually in September 1991 Tenneco brought in a new Chief Executive to succeed Jim Ketelsen, who remained as Chairman until May 1992. Mike Walsh, who was 49, came from Union Pacific railroad. He came with a portfolio of management techniques and - more importantly - the ability wherever he went to inspire a new spirit of determination and confidence. His early meetings with senior and middle management were memorable experiences. His message was that targets had to be attained, by Plan B if Plan A did not produce the result; as he put it, "We had to focus on results, not excuses". His message to stockholders in the annual report for 1992 described his approach. He wrote: "we energized the entire company. Almost everyone was involved in one way or another. We operated differently. We set some very public stakes in the ground and then moved heaven and earth to do what we said we would do".

His first task was crisis prevention. He introduced a restructuring plan with a target of raising $2 billion to reduce debt. First he halved the dividend, bringing an annual saving of $200 million and giving a clear message that the priority of rising dividends regardless of earnings was no more. $500 million was raised through the issue of new equity. Capital expenditure was cut by $50 million in 1991 and by $250 million in the budget for 1992. A restructuring programme was implemented, consisting of plant closures, product rationalisation, inventory write-downs and reducing employee numbers by 8,000, to produce annual savings of $250 million, involving a charge of $550 million in 1991, mostly in respect of Case.

There were also divestments. In 1991 the natural gas liquids business was sold for $632 million and three railroads for $54 million. In 1992 Tenneco Minerals was sold for $500 million, some timberlands for $79 million and the Albright & Wilson pulp chemicals business for $202 million. Whereas the Tenneco Minerals sale showed a net profit of $96 million, the pulp chemicals business was sold at a loss of $25 million against its book value. There were some good business reasons for selling: the narrowness of its product range and geographical base, growing competition, its capital expenditure requirements and the lack of connection with the rest of A&W's operations (other than the shared site at Buckingham, Ont.). Because, however, the sale was announced in 1991 as part of a programme to raise cash, the 'fire sale' price eventually obtained in 1992 was deeply disappointing.

Mike Walsh described the results in 1992 as "an extraordinary turnaround and the beginning of a fundamental transformation of Tenneco". A start had been made in introducing new management processes, profits from continuing operations had improved and there was a different atmosphere at headquarters in Houston and farther afield. Mike Walsh brought in General Systems Company, which he had used when he was at Union Pacific, to help in introducing a quality management programme, aimed at enhancing operating profits by $600 million by 1996 (later increased to $680 million by 1994). That included measuring 'costs of quality', particularly failure costs, 'matrix management', 'employee empowerment', a 'bolted together' organisation and 'operating cost leadership'. Reporting achievements from the programme became a priority.

Some progress had already been made in turning round Case but major structural problems remained: it had too much production capacity, too many products, poor marketing and distribution and a history of seeking market share by price cutting. A restructuring charge of $920 million was taken in 1992, on top of the $460 million for Case in 1991.

The steps taken at Case succeeded in producing an operating profit of $82 million in 1993, which was increased to $326 million in 1994. In that year, Case Corporation became an independent quoted company, after Tenneco had divested 56% of its holding through public offerings of stock, raising $750 million - a remarkable transformation from the time when the oil and gas interests were disposed of and Case was unsaleable. Tenneco's divestment of Case was completed in 1995, raising a further $1.4 billion. Taking into account also the transfer of debt and tax benefits, the total benefit to Tenneco from the divestment of Case was nearly $4.4 billion. Ironically, the performance of the Case shares after divestment was substantially better than that of the Tenneco shares.

In January 1993 Mike Walsh was found to be suffering from a brain tumour. He undertook a course of treatment and in November 1993 announced that his doctors had concluded that the tumour was declining and that he could expect a normal life-span. He made a video describing his struggle with his illness, which was shown throughout the company. In February 1994, however, he had to relinquish the position of Chief Executive Officer because of the deterioration in his condition. He died three months later, aged 51. There was an extraordinary sense of loss and sorrow amongst the employees. Mike Walsh had succeeded in bringing Tenneco through a crisis and the chronic problem of Case had been solved. How Tenneco would have fared if he had lived longer in good health is a matter of speculation.

Mike was succeeded as Chairman and CEO by Dana Mead, whom he had brought in as President in 1992. Dana continued the programme begun by Mike and for a while it seemed that progress was continuous, with increased earnings and reduced debt. In the end, however, Tenneco shrank to virtual extinction, through a succession of divestments. The heyday of the conglomerates was over. The new business philosophy favoured concentration rather than diversity, which might mean distributing to the shareholders shares in the separate businesses or selling them and investing the proceeds in the remaining parts of the company. Mike Walsh, however, in his brief term at the head of Tenneco, concentrated initially on overcoming a cash crisis and reforming Case. His longer-term aim was to make each of Tenneco's businesses a leader and to bolt them together through consistent enlightened management practices. He did not advocate divestment; the emphasis was rather on corrective action where goals were not reached. In the 1993 Tenneco Annual Report Dana Mead reported that the change in leadership through Mike Walsh's withdrawal "only intensifies Tenneco's commitment to our goal of becoming a world-class global industrial company in every essential element of our businesses". He went on to say that the strategy was to add new business opportunities for consistent growth, including acquisitions and redeployments.

There was a change of emphasis in the 1994 Annual Report. The stated intention was to generate more stable and less cyclical earnings. The value of Tenneco stock was affected by investors' perception of Tenneco as a cyclical company. Therefore steps were taken to divest Case and Albright & Wilson (see the last section of this chapter) - "among the most cyclical businesses we had in Tenneco". That left four businesses: packaging, automotive, gas transmission and shipbuilding. It was said that there was a "conglomerate bonus" in spreading best practices from one business to another, opportunities for improvement arising from the diversity of Tenneco's businesses.

Two years later, in 1996, Tenneco disposed of the gas transmission and shipbuilding operations. Tenneco's shareholders received shares in El Paso, which had acquired the gas transmission operations, and in Newport News Shipbuilding. The remainder of Tenneco benefited from transferring liabilities to El Paso and Newport News. Tenneco moved from its historic headquarters in Houston to Greenwich, Connecticut. The transactions were described as in line with the "continuing strategy to invest in less cyclical, higher margin, and faster growing business opportunities". The report, however, went on to record that the profits from packaging were less in 1996 than in the previous year because in 1995 the containerboard pricing cycle was at its peak.

In the first quarter of 1999 the linerboard business was moved into a joint venture, in which Tenneco held 45% (involving a loss of $178 million after tax relief); the 45% interest was later sold. The folding carton business was also sold. Then shares in the speciality packaging remainder were distributed to Tenneco shareholders. The company bearing the Tenneco name was thus reduced to the automotive business, with annual sales in 1998 of $3.2 billion and profit (before interest and tax) of $300 million. The company was renamed Tenneco Automotive Inc., based in Illinois, and the short-lived Connecticut headquarters was closed.

The market value of the shares of Tenneco Automotive after the split was around $1.3 billion, about one-seventh of the value of Tenneco at its peak (and in real terms of course much less). Tenneco's shareholders had, of course, acquired shares in El Paso, Newport News and Pactiv (as the speciality packaging was called). Nevertheless, a shareholder who retained all the shares distributed would have ended 1999 with a much lower dollar value of his holdings than before the splits started. The proxy document for the Annual General Meeting of Tenneco Automotive in May 2000 showed that between the end of 1994 and November 1999, when the final split occurred, an investment of $100 in Tenneco (with dividends reinvested) would have shrunk to $52. During that period, an investment in the leading US stock index. the Standard & Poor 500, would have grown to $351. The corresponding document for May 2001 showed a further deterioration, to only 38% of the November 1999 figure, i.e. that the original $100 would have shrunk to about $20, while the Standard & Poor 500 investment would have declined slightly, to $344. There remains the question of whether a shareholder would have done even worse if there had not been the divestments of Albright & Wilson and the others.

A&W's Management Developments

The combination of changes in the top management of Albright & Wilson and the philosophy and techniques introduced by the new management in Tenneco resulted in a considerable, though not radical, shift in attitudes and practices away from A&W's traditional ways.

Reorganisations

It was hardly surprising that the advent of Robin Paul as Managing Director in November 1986 led to changes in organisation and management. He began by consulting senior managers and Charles Suckling, a non-executive Director. When Charles had been deputy Chairman of the Mond division of ICI, he had been responsible for Robin's appointment as works manager of the Castner Kellner works. Robin decided that the first priority was a reform of the organisation. The three divisions in the UK had separate headquarters and acted independently. Even at Board level, there was too much sectionalism. Other priorities were forming a strategic approach and strengthening the technical function.

At the meeting of the Company Council in April 1987, Robin Paul compared A&W unfavourably with three other leading UK chemical companies (ICI, Fisons and Laporte): 'They have changed the shape of their portfolios to concentrate on their best market and technical opportunities, and they have cut their costs to make themselves more competitive in their commodity chemical areas...we need to show that we can improve our profitability'.

Within two months, radical changes in organisation were announced. The heads of the operating divisions were to report directly to the Managing Director and the three UK divisions were all to be headquartered at Warley (Birmingham), which became the centre of European operations. The general managers of the three new business groups were Ian Black (Detergents), Michael Winstanley (Phosphates) and Bob Chalmers (Resins & Organics). The two Directors previously responsible for operations, Ray Naish and John Wills, took early retirement after service of 32 and 25 years. The remaining executive Directors had Company-wide functional roles: Bill Adair commercial, George James technical and Hugh Podger financial. The next stage, announced in April 1987, was for the UK divisions to become business groups, supported by common service departments, further integrating them and reducing their independence. While the Phosphates team, on their 'home ground', were largely unchanged, several of the senior staff at Whitehaven left and almost all the Resins & Organics senior managers declined to move to Warley.

Another significant move was for the merging of the US and Canadian operations under the title Albright & Wilson Americas, with its headquarters in

Toronto, recognising the preponderance of interests in Canada. The President of A&W Americas was Claude Hollands, previously in charge of Erco. In 1990, the headquarters was moved to Richmond, Virginia, in recognition of the greater importance of the US market, the potential for growth and the increasing importance to A&W of the US operations (as described later).

The third main area of operations for A&W, the Asia-Pacific region, was also reorganised, to a limited extent. Singapore became the centre for A&W's interests in Asia, excluding India, covering manufacturing and sales in Singapore, Malaysia, the Philippines and Thailand, and sales offices in Hong Kong and China. A&W (Australia) remained a separate division.

In November of the following year, 1988, the Phosphates and Resins & Organics business groups were merged to form the Phosphates & Organics group, under Michael Winstanley. Bob Chalmers became Company Quality Manager.

The next turn of the wheel came in March 1990, when the Executive Directors were given line responsibility for operational activities: Bill Adair for Europe, Hugh Podger for Asia and Australasia, Michael Winstanley (newly appointed to the Board) for the Americas and John Adsetts for speciality businesses world-wide. John Adsetts had joined the Board as Technical Director in October 1987, when George James retired from that position. He remained Technical Director, while Bill Adair continued as Commercial Director and Hugh Podger as Financial Director.

That structure lasted only until September 1991, when there was another major change. The Executive Committee was abolished, Board meetings became only formalities and a 5-level structure was introduced throughout the Company, i.e. from Robin Paul to first-line supervisors. That involved wider spans of responsibility, more delegation and less management by committee. The monthly meetings of senior managers (entitled 'Level 2' meetings) were for communications and not decisions. A&W joined the growing number of companies engaging in 'downsizing', stimulated to streamlining their operations by the recession in that year. The driving force for the reorganisation was, however, declared to be the creation of successful business teams. In the latest reshuffle of positions, Bill Adair retired since his position represented a redundant layer in the organisation and the heads of the European operations reported directly to Robin Paul.

The existence of a global headquarters in London had for some years been looking increasingly anomalous, with Warley the centre for the businesses. The departments at Knightsbridge had one by one moved to Warley until there remained only the Directors and a small number of staff in financial, legal and company secretarial functions. The possibility of moving into the Tenneco London office had been considered, as well as finding a new office in Birmingham. Logic finally prevailed and the Knightsbridge office was closed in October 1991, with most of the staff moving to Warley, where downsizing had ensured that there was ample space available.

Thereafter, in the rest of the period covered by this chapter, there were no further significant changes in organisation. There were several changes in non-executive Directors. Jack Diesel ceased to be Chairman at the end of 1988, on his retirement from Tenneco, and was succeeded by Allen McInnes, a Director and Executive Vice-President of Tenneco. In turn, Allen McInnes was succeeded on his departure from Tenneco in September 1992 by Dana Mead, President and later Chairman of Tenneco. Charles Suckling resigned in April 1989. Hans Lottig, formerly General Manager of Deutsche Shell Chemie, became a non-executive Director in January 1990. In 1993, Hugh Podger retired and was succeeded as Financial Director by Michael Winstanley, who was replaced as head of A&W Americas by Paul Rocheleau (who was to succeed Robin Paul as Chief Executive in August 1997).

Management practices

The period from the arrival of Robin Paul to the end of 1994 saw the introduction of more new management techniques than at any other time in A&W's history. Some were A&W's initiatives, others were introduced by Tenneco.

One of Robin Paul's concerns was with what he called "feather-edged forecasting". Five-year plans had been produced since Tenneco acquired full ownership in 1978 which always showed profits five years ahead doubling or trebling, while from 1983 to 1986 the actual profits remained on a plateau. To improve that record, Robin Paul introduced a greater emphasis on return on sales, aiming for an average 10% on commodity chemicals and 15% on specialities, against the 7% prevailing for the whole company in 1983-6. For that to be translated into a better return on capital, attention had to be paid to the utilisation of capital; a more critical appraisal of capital expenditure proposals and the elimination of bottlenecks in production were other areas for action.

Robin Paul was dissatisfied with the financial information regularly provided: results were being reported several weeks after the period to which they related. The first move was for 'quickshot' figures to be reported a week after the period; that was followed by rolling 3-month forecasts, which allowed corrective action to be taken where shortfalls were foreseen.

Another initiative was "King John management", robbing the poor to give to the rich, expressed particularly in backing speciality products and services and reducing capital expenditure on commodity products. An example of the latter was the rejection of a proposal to spend £5 million on building new sulphuric acid units at Whitehaven, which was the start of a move away from manufacturing sulphuric acid and then green (unpurified) phosphoric acid.

With the objective of improving strategic planning, in June 1988 consultants

(Bracken Kellner Associates) were hired. That led to a large-scale information-gathering process, on markets served, the strength of competition and A&W's relative position, etc.. Like so many consultant-led management moves, however, it is hard to say that there was any enduring benefit from the considerable effort.

There were also initiatives in the area of human resources (the new term for personnel), apart from the change involved in the 5-level reorganisation. At Whitehaven, a flexible working programme, under the title "Towards 2000", for multiskilling by craftsmen, was launched in March 1987 and agreed by the Unions two and a half years later, so ending 40 years of demarcation. The move came against the background of reduced Union powers under the administration of Margaret Thatcher and the perceived need to improve the economics of Whitehaven. The process workers on the site made a similar agreement in March 1988. Similar changes were negotiated at the other UK sites during this period. Reductions in employee numbers were reflected in substantial charges against profits for the cost of redundancies, which were still largely (but not wholly) voluntary. Redundancies extended to office employees.

Several steps were taken to improve human resource management. Performance appraisals, which had lapsed, were resumed. Salaries were geared more to assessed performance. The concept of 'forced ranking' was introduced: within a defined group, there was ranking by performance used for the allocation of a total of salary increases. There were also 'upward assessment' questionnaires, for managers to be assessed by those reporting to them.

The most important of the techniques employed in this period was Total Quality Management. One aspect of this was the national quality assurance programme under the title 'BS5750', for works and offices, which consisted of formal written procedures on which suppliers and customers in particular would be able to rely. The programme was adopted by A&W in the UK in 1988, under the direction of Bob Chalmers, appointed Company Quality Manager when the Resins & Organics group was merged with Phosphates. Later, the British Standards were superseded by similar qualifications under the International Standards Organisation (ISO9000, etc.).

Of more significance for profit performance was the Total Quality Management process introduced into A&W in the following year. The Crosby process was adopted in the UK, Asia and Australia; the Americas had earlier adopted the Conway system. Quality was defined as conformance to requirements. The price of non-conformance was measured, there was an emphasis on zero defects (right first time) and prevention rather than cure and the aim was for continuous improvement. Quality Improvement Teams and Corrective Action Teams were formed and training was extensive. Targets were set for cost reductions and progress reports were issued to senior management monthly. A Quality Council was formed, chaired by Robin Paul. A Quality Partnership was formed with ICI at the beginning of 1991, to use shared techniques for enhancing profitability by improved efficiency in dealings between the two companies. Similar partnerships with other companies followed.

As already mentioned (p.279), when Mike Walsh took over at Tenneco, he brought with him management techniques that he had been practising at Union Pacific with the assistance of a consultancy firm, General Systems Company. They too placed emphasis on quality management. In December 1991 representatives from A&W and the other Tenneco divisions were called to Chicago for the launch of the Tenneco Quality Cost Measurement and Control System (TQCMS). That was a more precise system than A&W's previous TQM system and required measurement of internal failure (scrap, rework, etc.), external failure (lost sales, rejected products, etc.) and the costs of control and prevention. There were targets and monthly reporting of 'quality cost takeouts'. A&W budgeted to save $11 million in 1992.

Further General Systems techniques followed towards the end of 1992 - GSC IV (a management information system applied to strategic planning, innovation, human resource management, asset management, etc.), Matrix 2 (for 'bolting together' functions), Matrix 1 (a comprehensive matrix type management system), EVA (Economic Value Added, another measurement tool), operating cost leadership, and empowerment. Forecast shortfalls against budgets were required to be overcome by alternative actions - the 'Plan B' approach. In 1993, Tenneco assessed A&W's Quality programme as having reached 43% of potential, with the expectation of rising to 70% within two years.

A&W's profit in 1992 was ahead of budget for the first time for many years and in the years 1993 and 1994 there were further advances. Tenneco calculated that its Cost of Quality programmes saved $450 million in 1992 and $560 million in 1993, i.e. that in 1993 without the COQ programmes its profit would have been half of the $1.2 billion declared. It is fair to say that the management techniques led to improvements in profits, although they did absorb a lot of management time.

Divestments & Acquisitions

This was a period of significant divestments, mainly required by Tenneco. The most important were of the paper chemicals and pulp chemicals operations.

Paper Chemicals

As already recorded (p.253), Tenneco transferred the paper chemicals operations of Tenneco Chemicals Europe to Albright & Wilson in 1983, as part of the reorganisation of its chemicals interests. The paper chemicals business was regarded by A&W as a growth point, being a speciality chemical area, with well-based technology and a good competitive position in Europe, Canada and South Africa. In addition to the traditional rosin sizes, there were developments in synthetic sizes, chemicals for deinking paper, coatings and adhesives: a key to success was the provision of a comprehensive service to paper mills. With factories at Avonmouth, Blackburn and Aberdeen in the UK, Maastricht in Holland, Bordeaux in France, Kristinehamn and Landskrona in Sweden and Toronto in Canada, there was a solid basis for expansion.

A stronger position in the USA was essential and so in the first half of 1986 A&W bid for the Monsanto paper chemicals interests but A&W's offer was not sufficient. In the autumn of 1986 it was decided to build a large plant at Charleston (the Mobil Chemicals site acquired in that year) to make paper size chemicals, both the traditional rosin sizes and the newer alkyl ketene dimer synthetic sizes. That was the first step in a five-year programme to sell paper chemicals throughout the USA, including deinking and coating chemicals. The plant was opened in the second Quarter of 1988 but sales were very disappointing and for the next two years the US operation made a loss of around £1.7 million per annum, substantially more than the value of sales.

Towards the end of 1988 Colas Bewoid, a family-owned Spanish producer of paper chemicals founded in 1932, was acquired. Colas Bewoid had a small but profitable factory in Barcelona producing chemicals, some under licence from A&W, for whom it was its sales agent in Spain.

Another expansionary move was made at the beginning of 1989, when Pine Chemicals New Zealand (PCNZ) was acquired from Elders Resources NZFP, owner of forestry operations and paper mills in New Zealand and a producer of tall oil and turpentine. PCNZ supplied paper size materials to a plant built near Melbourne by Albright & Wilson Chemicals, a company formed to develop the Australian market in paper sizes. A part of PCNZ's operations, concerned with crude sulphate turpentine, was not relevant to A&W and was disposed of after months of negotiation, at a disappointing price. The then Chairman of A&W, Allen McInnes, had consented with reluctance to the acquisition of PCNZ; his reluctance was proved to have been well-founded as the company failed to meet expectations of sales and profits.

Early in 1990, Tenneco informed A&W that the paper chemicals business was to be sold, as part of its programme for raising cash. The links between that business and the rest of A&W were not so strong that A&W's other operations would be directly affected and the business was potentially attractive to at least four potential buyers. There followed intensive negotiations, led by Peter Salmon, which resulted in a sale at the end of June 1990 to Eka Nobel, part of the Swedish Nobel Industries group. The sale excluded the Avonmouth and Charleston sites (with provision for A&W to manufacture for Eka Nobel for a limited period). The price was $100 million (£55.3 million), which resulted in a profit of $43 million

(£24 million) over book value, despite write-offs necessary in the USA and only a nominal value being attached to PCNZ.

Although not initiated by A&W, the timing of the sale was good and in the general cash situation further development of the business might have proved difficult. In the announcement of the sale, it was said: "This divestment of operations that are not closely bound up with our other activities will free resources for the faster achievement of our strategic objectives". It was pointed out that paper chemicals accounted for only 7% of A&W's total sales; attention was not drawn to the profit contribution, which would have been greater than 7% if it had not been for the losses incurred in the USA.

Pulp Chemicals

When the sale of the paper chemicals business was announced, A&W's core businesses were defined as "surfactants, phosphates and other phosphorus compounds and pulp chemicals". It was not surprising that pulp chemicals were regarded as a core business. A&W had been producing sodium chlorate since the beginning of the century and more capital had been invested in its production than in any other sector of A&W. Tenneco had seen A&W's pulp chemicals as a world-class business and had encouraged capital expenditure on projects that were almost always very large, in the context of A&W.

Major expansions in sodium chlorate capacity were approved in 1989. They followed the Buckingham Phase II project, which replaced graphite cells with metal, at a cost of more than CAD40 million and came on stream at the end of 1988, the installation earlier that year at Vancouver of the plant transferred from Monroe and uprating electrical capacity at Buckingham and Thunder Bay. In January 1989 approval was given for spending over CAD40 million on increasing the capacity at Buckingham from 77,000 to 122,000 tonnes and in May the replacement of the rest of the graphite cells at Vancouver was authorised at a cost of CAD62 million. In November 1989 the Buckingham project was modified to add a further 10,000 tonnes capacity.

Also during 1989 it was decided to build a sodium chlorate plant at a new location, at Grande Prairie in Alberta, with a capacity of 45,000 tonnes pa, at a cost of CAD52 million. The Chairman, Allen McInnes, expressed doubts about the return to be expected from a project with a strong defensive element, i.e. to prevent a competitor from supplying a new mill being built by Procter & Gamble. A further defensive move was the announcement early in 1990 that a plant was to be built in southern USA with a capacity of 50,000 tonnes pa, to bring A&W's total capacity up to 407,000 tonnes pa. There was, however, no definite proposal and nothing came of it. The relationship between supply and demand was critical for the price of sodium chlorate; although demand was rising because of the conversion of pulp bleaching to the environmentally friendly chlorate processes, expansion by many of the producers was causing the price to remain weak.

Another move designed to broaden A&W's position in chlorine dioxide bleaching was the acquisition in 1989 of a majority stake in the Rio Linda Chemical Company, of Sacramento, California. Rio Linda's business was in selling patented small generators of chlorine dioxide as a bactericide, serving food processing, oilfield drilling, municipal water treatment and agricultural markets and supplying sodium chlorite for the generators. The Buckingham Phase II expansion included a plant to make sodium chlorite, whose commissioning turned out to be outstandingly difficult.

A&W had a strong position in pulp bleaching: its plants were large and had been modernised and it had the leading position in the technology of pulp bleaching through the R processes. Up to the end of 1991, 101 Erco chlorine dioxide generators had been installed worldwide, four times the number installed by the competition. The latest generators, the R9 and R10, had succeeded in almost eliminating chlorine discharges and had cut the usage of sodium sulphate by 40%. Through royalties, profits on the supply of generators and engineering services, and the benefit to sales of chlorate from the relationship with customers, the ESG (Engineering Services Group) activities were especially valuable. The weaknesses of A&W's position were the capital demands - $140 million in 4 years - and the lack of production facilities in the USA. Shares in installed capacities in North America at the beginning of 1992 were: Eka Nobel 30%, Oxychem 20%, A&W 17%, Kerr-McGee 8%, captive plants 13%, others 12%.

In mid-1991 at an Executive Committee strategic discussion, Michael Winstanley, then President of Albright & Wilson Americas, voiced the opinion that A&W should divest its pulp chemicals business at the appropriate time, which he believed was about 5 years ahead, as part of the strategy of moving from an asset-based company to a people-based company, from commodity businesses to specialities. Unfortunately, A&W was not allowed to choose the moment for disposal.

As already mentioned, when Mike Walsh became Chief Executive of Tenneco in September 1991 his first action was to produce a plan to overcome Tenneco's financial crisis, by raising $2 billion. Divestments were an important feature of the plan and the intention to sell A&W's pulp chemicals business was made public in October 1991. The result was that the price obtained was deeply disappointing. The purchaser was Sterling Chemicals, a US petrochemicals producer. The price initially agreed was USD240 million, which was subsequently reduced to USD202 million because Sterling identified potential liabilities for which they wanted cover. The price was below the net book value of the assets sold, which included nothing for the intangible assets underlying the ESG operations. Rio Linda was not included in the sale, which was concluded in August 1992. The only published comment by A&W on the sale was in the 1991 Annual Report: "This business is outside the mainstream of Albright & Wilson's global development of phosphates, surfactants and specialities".

Other divestments

In 1986 a team from Tenneco visited A&W for the purpose of investigating opportunities for raising cash through disposals. **Albright & Wilson Ireland** was identified as a candidate. Although an agent for A&W's sales in Eire, its main business had become the distribution of consumer products to supermarkets, in which it had a leading position in the country. It was thus outside A&W's main interests and eminently saleable. Negotiations were opened in 1987 with three interested parties, which ended in March 1988 with the sale of the company to a syndicate arranged by Allied Irish Bank. The company, renamed Allegro, was to continue as an entity under its existing management, with the intention that it would be floated in about five years. In the event, that did not happen; the company was heavily dependent upon the willingness of the principals, particularly Procter & Gamble, for which it acted as distributor, to continue that relationship and when they took over their own distribution Allegro ceased to be viable. The Irish market was too small for alternative trading to be successful. When the sale by A&W was announced, it was explained in these words: "The transfer of ownership results from a review by A&W of its strategic objectives, leading to the conclusion that A&WI, though a strong, successful and highly reputable company, is not in the mainstream of A&W's business". Although the sale was prompted by Tenneco, there is little doubt that it would have happened sooner or later.

Another divestment required by Tenneco was of A&W's interests in **South Africa**. Tenneco was under pressure from its institutional shareholders, particularly some university funds, to dispose of all its investments in South Africa, because of the apartheid regime then still in existence. When the subject was first raised in March 1987, Jack Diesel was reluctant to sell because A&W's paper chemicals and surfactants operations in South Africa were very profitable: in 1987, Sapcco (South African Paper Chemicals Company) made a pretax profit of over £1 million, while A&W's share of Akulu Marchon's profit was over £0.5 million. Sapcco's return on assets was 70%. An attempt was made to negotiate with Chemserve, A&W's partner in both companies, a 5-year option to sell at an agreed price but when Chemserve indicated in November 1988 that the price would be only five times earnings negotiations were discontinued. In March 1989, however, Tenneco set a limit of six months for divestment to be completed, which not surprisingly resulted in an even lower disposal price.

Oldbury site, before Ted Lowe's rationalisation moves; entrance & research laboratories centre left, phosphoric acid towers centre, M5 motorway across the top.
[photo: Aerial Surveys Ltd]

Yarraville (Melbourne) works of Albright & Wilson (Australia) alongside Yarra river.

Wetherill Park (Sydney) works of Albright & Wilson (Australia); sulphonation plant opened 1978.

The A&W Board in 1990; l. to r. Bill Adair, Allen McInnes (Chairman), Michael Winstanley, Hugh Podger, Robin Paul (Managing Director), John Adsetts, Hans Lottig.

There were other divestments in this period that were decided on by the A&W management in line with the strategy of disposing of peripheral operations. In September 1988 the Company's interest in **Butler** (1843), a distributor of oil products, and **Nubex**, marketing timber treatment materials and services (parts of the original Avonmouth business acquired by A&W ten years before) were sold for nearly £3 million, realising a profit of more than £2 million over book value.

Acquisitions

This was also a period of considerable activity in acquisitions, including several that did not come to fruition.

At the end of 1986 **Chemrich** Inc., of Westwego, Louisiana, was acquired for around £1 million. Its business was the supply of chemicals and services to oilfields, particularly for the Gulf Coast producers. At that time, Tenneco still had substantial interests in offshore oil production and so the acquisition fitted in with both A&W's aim to develop speciality chemicals and Tenneco's position as a customer. Oilfield production was also a target for A&W's surfactants and biocides, in the North Sea and elsewhere. One of the main factors favouring the purchase of Chemrich was, however, removed when Tenneco disposed of its oil interests and Chemrich never attained the level of profitability expected. The company was sold in February 1997 at a small loss.

In February 1988 15% of the equity in **Surfachem** Ltd, the leading independent distributor for surfactants in the UK, was acquired. Since 1982 it had been distributing A&W's surfactants to its smaller customers, which constituted about half of its business, and had added the distribution of phosphates and specialities. In August 1992 Surfachem International was formed to handle A&W's smaller export orders. It was contemplated that in due course Surfachem would be floated as a public company and in that event A&W would increase its investment. That did not happen and in April 1994 Ellis & Everard was appointed as the Company's main UK distributor and the connection with Surfachem was terminated, resulting in an immediate profit on disposal but the loss of ongoing returns from A&W's equity investment.

There were many proposals for acquisitions that were not brought to fruition. One of the first decisions taken after Robin Paul became Managing Director was that long-running discussions for the acquisition of **Camille Simon**, a manufacturer of private-label detergents, should be terminated. While Camille Simon was an efficient producer and a competitor, it was decided that the price required (£8.5 million) was too high.

Of potentially much greater significance was the proposal to acquire some of the operations of **Stauffer**, a significant US chemical producer. Stauffer had been founded in 1886 and initially manufactured sulphur compounds, inorganic acids and superphosphates. It went on to acquire the phosphorus derivatives business of Victor Chemicals and hydraulic fluids from Celanese. Stauffer was acquired by Chesebrough Ponds and in February 1985 the A&W Board agreed to approach Chesebrough Ponds to see if it was willing to dispose of the phosphorus and derivatives side of Stauffer. At that time the approach came to nothing but two years later Chesebrough Ponds was acquired by Unilever and ICI bought the chemical operations from Unilever. ICI put up for sale Stauffer's Basic Chemicals Division, which included the Specialty Division, making organophosphorus compounds for crop protection and other applications.

A&W was prepared to pay $100 million for the Specialty Division and joined a consortium put together by the US investment house Kidder Peabody. The consortium bid $480 million for the Basic Chemicals Division, which allowed for having to spend $50 million to clean up the phosphorus production sites closed by Stauffer, but was outbid by Rhone Poulenc with a bid of $520 million. In itself, the failure to acquire Stauffer's specialities was probably not of great significance but Rhone Poulenc's presence in North America was much enhanced. Shortly after, Rhone Poulenc approached A&W to see if there was scope for cooperation in purified wet acid (PWA) in the USA but was rejected.

In the following year there were several abortive proposals for acquisitions. In March, the Board approved $5 million for the acquisition of Valchem, an Australian company manufacturing paper sizes and acrylics but the company fell to ICI Australia. In the UK, proposals to add to the service chemicals range for water treatment, etc. by acquiring two small companies, Applied Chemicals and Oakite, were not pursued because of doubts about their commercial potential for A&W. There was also an attempt to buy Bozetto, an Italian company engaged in speciality surfactants and phosphonates, especially with industrial applications, but the family owners refused to sell at that time - they sold the company not long after.

Another attempted acquisition was of **Manro**, a UK company engaged in surfactants in direct competition with A&W. There was scope for rationalisation between Whitehaven and Manro's site at Staly Bridge (Cheshire), as well as a broadening of A&W's product range and an important strengthening of position in relation to major customers. The Company's bid of £16 million in cash was, however, trumped by Hickson, which offered £18 million, including £16.5 million in shares of Hickson. An element of the deal was that Manro's chief executive became Managing Director of Hickson. The share price of Hickson, however, languished because of problems with earlier acquisitions and Manro was disposed of through a management buy-out, for £10 million more than the price of acquisition.

In June 1988 Jack Diesel, then Chairman of Albright & Wilson and President of Tenneco, told the Board that Tenneco's disposal of its oil interests would mean that there would be money available for acquisitions. A team was therefore set up to develop a strategy for acquisitions. By March 1989 a list of 120 possible targets was produced, which was then reduced to 21, mainly in paper chemicals and surfactants. The then Chairman of Albright & Wilson, Allen McInnes, said that the strategic plan for the next five years should include $50 million per annum for acquisitions. In the event, Tenneco's financial position did not improve and there was a general recession, which made expenditure on acquisitions subject to more critical scrutiny. Although capital expenditure peaked in 1990 there were no acquisitions after Colas Bewoid, Rio Linda and Pine Chemicals New Zealand in 1988/9 (already referred to). The lack of acquisitions was also due to commercial doubts about the candidates chosen.

In 1990 the possibility arose of making a bid for De Soto, a US company in surfactants that was up for sale at the time. Sites were inspected but enthusiasm was limited and it was decided to put in a low bid, which not unexpectedly was rejected. There was also some interest in acquiring the European surfactants intermediates business of Rohm & Haas, which did not progress beyond an early possibility. A number of possible targets in Eastern Europe, two in Czechoslovakia and one each in East Germany and Hungary, were examined following the collapse of the Communist regimes in 1989-1990. As the Annual Report for 1992 stated, "In the longer term, Eastern Europe promises significant economic growth and we shall continue to develop links with this region".

In East Germany, there was an opportunity to acquire some or all of a chemical complex at **Bitterfeld**, near Leipzig, which included phosphorus derivatives and chloralkali operations. It would have provided a base for selling into the rest of Germany and Eastern Europe and a second source of phosphorus chlorides, the key to organophosphorus compounds. There was also the possibility that Bitterfeld, using cheap phosphorus from Kazakhstan, could provide damaging competition. The Treuhandstalt, the government agency charged with the reorganisation of industry in the former East Germany, was prepared to give A&W exclusive negotiating rights and indemnity from environmental liabilities. By November 1991 the point had been reached when A&W had signed a letter of intent for the acquisition of the phosphorus derivatives and chloralkali operations and was investigating the viability and investment needs of the plants concerned. It was recognised that significant expenditure would be required to regenerate the manufacturing operation, including the demolition of buildings, clean-up of the site, improving the plants and broadening the product range. Like many plants in the former East Germany, there were severe problems of pollution. Eventually it was decided that the problems and the demands on A&W's management time were too great to proceed.

Much time was spent on evaluating and negotiating the purchase of an interest in a sulphonation plant of **Caola**, a Hungarian state-owned company producing retail detergents and toiletries, with factories in Budapest and in the south of Hungary. Under consideration in June 1990, eventually a proposal was submitted to Houston in May 1991; it would have involved the expenditure of $0.5 million plus a value of $4.5 million placed on know-how and engineering services provided as part of the input by A&W. The proposal was not supported by Allen McInnes, who wished a way to be found to avoid any cash outlay. Don Beck (then heading A&W's surfactants operations) approached Oleanne, an investment group, which was interested in having an entry into Eastern Europe, and would provide the cash wanted by Caola. Negotiations were protracted and then in 1993 Caola was bought by Benko, a Hungarian financier. Don Beck left A&W in November 1993 and his successor, John Markham, did not have the same interest in pursuing the Caola project, which was dropped.

Don Beck was also interested in expanding in private label detergents and toiletries, i.e. finished products for supply to supermarkets, in which A&W had been engaged for many years in various ways in the UK, Italy, France and Spain. The first project was for the acquisition of **Lorhebor**, a Spanish producer. In November 1990 a proposal was put to the A&W Board for the expenditure of 1.1 billion pesetas ($6 million). It was not approved by the Board because of doubts about the management and financial condition of the company. Lorhebor remained independent but in 1995 went bankrupt.

In 1992 a joint venture was established in Spain, initially under the name Promotora Quimicentro and then as Detergentes y Productos de Higiene (**DPH**), with Centra Industria (CIN), a subsidiary of Centra S. Coop, a major retail cooperative. CIN contributed a spray tower producing detergent powders at a site north of Madrid, while Albright & Wilson Espana contributed its blending and bottling lines at Alcover (Tarragona). A&W was the sales agent for the company, while Centra was to provide a baseload of demand for the products. A&W held 43% of the equity. The value placed on the Albright & Wilson Espana assets put into the joint venture made a useful contribution to A&W's profits in 1992. From then on, however, DPH made losses and at the end of 1994 A&W acquired CIN's shares and renamed the company Albright & Wilson Iberica. The spray tower was closed and in 1995 the Alcover bottling business was sold. Substantial write-offs and termination costs were charged against profits in 1994.

In May 1991 consideration was given to the possibility of buying the Ciba-Geigy operations at Trafford Park, Manchester. Since A&W's sale of its phosphate plasticisers business to Ciba-Geigy in 1983, the main customer for the phosphorus oxychloride produced at Oldbury had been Trafford Park. The move would therefore have been partly defensive but it would also have expanded A&W's position in phosphorus derivatives. The price demanded by Ciba-Geigy, however, was beyond the resources of Tenneco and A&W. The operations were acquired by

FMC, the leading world producer of phosphorus and derivatives. While FMC continued to buy oxychloride from Oldbury, its entry into the UK, added to its ownership of Foret in Spain and its dominant position in the USA, put pressure on sales and prices.

Developments

Although there was no success in acquisitions, there was much activity throughout A&W in this period.

Research & Development

At his first Board meeting, in November 1986, Robin Paul asked for a review to be made of the Company's technical strength. Albright & Wilson was lacking in technical strength at Board level: Dr Suckling was an external Director and George James, the other Director with technical qualifications, was due to retire in June 1987 after 41 years' service in Australia and the UK. In October 1987 Dr John Adsetts (aged 43) was appointed Technical Director. John Adsetts was a Director of MTM (Marlborough Teeside Management, the specialist chemical company that in 1983 had bought A&W's West Bank operations.) and Chairman of Marlborough Bipolymers, a subsidiary of ICI.

In November 1987 Charles Suckling presented a report to the Board. A&W, he said, possessed a basis for profitable organic growth, with a strong market position in several businesses, a number of well-motivated competent people and a few very good ones. There was a good production base and no shortage of ideas for process development. The existing technical strength was enough to maintain existing operations but not enough for the growth to which the Company was committed. There was a shortage of bright young scientists and a failure to make the best of them through career development. Some promising ideas for product development were not being pursued because of a lack of technical resources; some technical advantages were not fully exploited because of a lack of equipment for testing, etc. and insufficient market knowledge. Charles proposed an increase of 20% in R & D spending over the next two years, concentrated on projects likely to give an early return.

At the same meeting, John Adsetts proposed that an International Technical Centre (ITC) be set up at Oldbury. As stated in the 1988 Annual Report, "This represents an entirely additional research effort dedicated to accelerating the discovery and development of new products and processes in strategic business areas". Teams of specialists were formed, staffed partly from within the Company but also through an intensified programme of recruitment. By 1989 there were 50 researchers, rising to 70 in 1990, with a target of 90 by 1992. The Centre was initially headed by David Connor, previously technical manager of the Detergents Group, with the scientific effort led by Jerry Strong, recruited from A&W Americas. The main research laboratories at Oldbury were modernised in a 3-year programme, at a cost of over £3 million. In order to house Phosphates technical and managerial staff displaced from the main laboratories, a new building costing £1.4 million was built (see p.307).

Initial areas of research were structured liquids (developing from the successful work done at Whitehaven on heavy-duty liquid detergents), phosphine chemistry (as a foundation for organophosphorus chemicals) and new products for flame retardants, water treatment and paper sizing. Corporate R & D costs rose rapidly, from less than £0.5 million in 1988 to nearly £2.5 million in 1989, over £4 million in 1990 and over £5 million in 1991.

The 1990 Annual Report stated: "The first fruits of the activities of the International Technical Centre were realized....The ITC undertook several projects to exploit short-term, as well as medium-term, opportunities". Significantly, the success reported was for a new process for the production of dimethylhydrogen phosphite at Charleston, leading to savings of several hundred thousand dollars a year. The emphasis of the work of ITC was changing towards projects bringing early benefits to profits. In 1991, in the context of very difficult trading conditions, there was a further shift of emphasis away from exploratory research. While several new products reached the point of commercialisation - in surfactants, flame retardants, water treatment chemicals, high-value pharmaceutical intermediates and environmentally-friendly reformulations - more effort was put into direct technical support for the businesses, including seconding ITC staff to help solve day-to-day problems.

In real terms, corporate R & D expenditure declined after 1991. In 1994, the recruitment of technical graduates was scaled down. There continued to be successes as in the invention of 'ITC 288' (an environmentally-friendly corrosion inhibitor) and in the development of THPS as a highly effective biocide, also environmentally-friendly (see p.312). The original concept of the ITC, however, as contributing to exploratory research (albeit clearly related to A&W's existing businesses) was not realised. Circumstances placed a higher priority on immediate profits. There was not enough time for the Suckling theory (see p.258) of the period needed for recovery after years of underspending on R & D to be tested.

Phosphates

For the mainstream phosphates business of A&W this was a period of high profitability and expansion, particularly in phosphonates and food phosphates, and of significant advances in production facilities, although capital expenditure was kept on a tight rein because of Tenneco's difficulties. Much of the prosperity was, however, due to the weakness of sterling against other currencies, particularly those of Continental Europe, which was to be reversed in the next period.

There were five main strands of development in phosphates in this period:-

- *Cessation of phosphorus production*
- *Purified wet acid in America*
- *Phosphoric acid in the UK*
- *Mexico*
- *STPP and other phosphates*

Cessation of phosphorus production

Extensive reference has already been made to the problems at Long Harbour, leading to the decision to cease production, which was also prompted by the developments in PWA as a preferred route to most phosphates. The decision had been taken within A&W well in advance of the formal resolution by the Board of Albright & Wilson in December 1988 to accept the recommendation of Albright & Wilson Americas to cease production not later than mid-1989. Closure would involve a substantial provision for the costs associated with closure - write-offs, termination payments and the anticipated costs of clean-up for the site - and the surplus arising from Tenneco's disposal of its oil and gas interests made it possible to take the hit involved in 1988. The charge against the 1988 accounts was £39 million ($70 million). The Press release in February 1989 announcing the closure emphasised the reduction in demand for elemental phosphorus as a result of the development of PWA technology. Phosphorus would no longer be shipped in bulk to the UK and the two ships were sold by the end of 1989. Varennes was to be retained in production, primarily to satisfy A&W's North American requirement, and A&W's requirements elsewhere would be met by purchases from Hoechst in the Netherlands and from China.

In January 1992 the cessation of phosphorus production at Varennes, because of the reduction in demand for phosphorus, was announced. Further substantial provisions were made for the costs of closure of Varennes as well as additional costs relating to Long Harbour and Portishead. Remediation work at the former phosphorus-producing sites was to take many years: it was complete at Varennes by September 1998 and at Portishead three years later, with work still to do at Long Harbour.

Albright & Wilson's exit from phosphorus manufacture after 140 years was dictated primarily by economics, not only the lower costs of PWA but also the high costs of production relative to other phosphorus producers. There was also the continuing burden of dealing with pollution created by the processes, which compared unfavourably with the much cleaner Hoechst-UHDE design. By ceasing its own manufacture of phosphorus, however, A&W obviously became vulnerable to pressure from producers that were also competitors in products derived from phosphorus. In due course, prices for phosphorus increased as producers passed on their environmental costs. In Australia, where a wet acid plant (producing 'green', not purified, phosphoric acid) had been closed, in favour of importing and burning phosphorus, there was a move back to wet acid. There was, however, no thought of building a phosphorus plant. The only new phosphorus capacity built during this period was in China. The availability and price of Chinese phosphorus fluctuated, while capacity for derivatives was developed, introducing further competition.

Purified wet acid in America

In America there had not been the move to purified wet acid that had occurred in the UK, Israel and Germany. Elemental phosphorus was the starting-point for phosphates as well as organophosphorus compounds. Mobil, however, which had ceased to manufacture phosphorus, had been interested in PWA for some years and there had been discussions between Frank Kuhn (head of the Mobil chemicals operation) and Dave Edmiston of Texasgulf, who was keen to upgrade his company's output of fertiliser-grade phosphoric acid. In 1983 Mobil had acquired PWA know-how from Budenheim and had considered building a plant with Olin (see below) as a customer. The idea, however, was not pursued and phosphorus continued to be purchased from Monsanto (one of the two main US producers, the other being FMC).

After A&W's acquisition of Mobil Chemicals in 1985, a study group was formed to decide on strategy for the supply of phosphoric acid; the fact that A&W's phosphorus was more expensive than Monsanto's provided an added stimulus. David Livingstone agreed that the possibility of building a PWA plant, probably in conjunction with a producer of phosphate rock, and closing Long Harbour should be investigated, a course supported by Robin Paul. A&W had talked with Texasgulf in 1980 about wet acid and there was a further meeting in 1983, before serious discussions began in 1986, by which time A&W's know-how had reached the stage of food-grade acid.

When an outline proposal for a 50-50 joint venture with Texasgulf was presented to the Board of Albright & Wilson in March 1987, the Chairman (Jack Diesel) asked for an alternative to be considered since his experience of joint ventures by Tenneco had not been good. Nevertheless the project went ahead and was announced in November 1987.

Texasgulf, a subsidiary of the French company Elf Aquitaine, had a phosphate rock mine and fertiliser complex at Lee Creek, near Aurora in North Carolina. That provided a low-cost source of wet phosphoric acid. A&W would provide the technology and plant design, based on its development of PWA processes at Whitehaven, and Texasgulf would construct and operate the plant. The raffinate (impure stream from the solvent extraction process) would be returned to the fertiliser plant. The plant design differed from Whitehaven because of the outlet for raffinate and because it used columns for extraction rather than the mixer-settlers used at Whitehaven - an improvement in technology resulting in a more compact and controllable plant with much reduced losses of solvent.

The capacity of the plant initially was to be 75,000 tons pa. The partners were, however, approached by Olin, a major diversified US company which was one of the main producers of STPP in the USA, to take a share in the venture. Mobil had had some discussions with Olin in 1983. Olin was buying green acid from Texasgulf but wanted a purer raw material for its phosphates, produced at Joliet, Illinois. It aimed to take 50,000 tons pa of PWA. The design was therefore revised to provide a total capacity of 120,000 tons pa (which proved capable of 135,000 tonnes pa, 10% more), produced in two streams. Olin contributed $16 million towards the cost of the enlarged plant but did not have a share of the equity in Albright & Wilson Company, the name given to the company formed at the beginning of 1989. Texasgulf contributed $25 million, while Albright & Wilson provided the know-how and market position and about $1 million. The agreement with Olin provided for the partners to purchase Olin's share in the output of the plant and its Joliet phosphates plant after 5 years, or to reform the joint venture as a 3-way partnership. In the event, Olin terminated its connection with Aurora in April 1991 and closed its Joliet plant; its US phosphates business was taken over by Albright & Wilson Company.

It had originally been expected that the Aurora plant would be completed by mid-1989 but the change in scope delayed commissioning and the official opening until March 1990. The plant performed well and 72,000 tonnes of acid were produced in 1990, rising to over 110,000 tonnes in 1992. It was the first of its kind in North America, with highly competitive economics and superior product quality.

A&W increased its market share of phosphoric acid and phosphates in the USA from 5% in 1990 to 19% in 1993 (including the former Olin share). Sodium and calcium phosphates were supplied from the two Canadian plants, at Port Maitland and Buckingham, which remained in A&W's sole ownership outside the joint venture and used most of the PWA previously supplied to Olin. The Cincinnati (Ohio) plant, originally part of Mobil and then transferred to the joint venture, produced potassium phosphates and phosphoric acid derivatives and distributed phosphoric acid. Over 200 railcars were used to move the acid from Aurora to

Canada, Cincinnati and external customers. Distribution depots were set up in the USA and Canada and A&W's share of the merchant acid market grew to a dominant 35%. The exit of Olin meant that the output from Buckingham was doubled and Port Maitland's output, operating at full capacity, was two and a half times what it had been in 1990. At Port Maitland the main product became granular STPP for dishwashers and industrial and institutional markets; STPP powder declined as domestic laundry detergents increasingly were reformulated to exclude phosphates. Buckingham produced mainly blends of food phosphates. The capacity of Aurora was extended in 1994 to 135,000 tonnes pa and modifications to the plant enabled a higher proportion of the output to be used in food-grade materials, while improving the economics of the process.

Coincidentally, on the day in 1991 that it was announced that Olin had disposed of its phosphates operations, Occidental announced closure of its phosphorus plant at Columbia, Tennessee, and sale of its phosphates business to FMC, thus reducing the industry to four producers: FMC, Monsanto, Albright & Wilson and Rhone Poulenc. FMC had approached A&W in March 1990 to see if there could be a joint venture in phosphates but it would have involved phosphorus manufacture as well as STPP production, in the shrinking US market for detergent phosphates. Later that year consideration was also given to a deal with FMC involving swapping Port Maitland for Foret, FMC's Spanish company making wet phosphoric acid and phosphates, but there was no clear advantage to A&W in such a move. Rhone Poulenc closed its phosphorus plant at Mount Pleasant, Tennessee and opened a PWA plant in Louisiana in 1992, but with economics and product quality inferior to those of Aurora. The rationalisation of the industry had a beneficial effect on prices. The Americas phosphates business became highly profitable: in 1994 the operating profits from it, including A&W's share of the profit of the joint venture, amounted to £13 million out of a group total (before exceptional items) of £55 million.

Phosphoric acid in the UK

The Whitehaven site, A&W's largest, had important strengths and weaknesses. It was the home of A&W's PWA technology. The final step in purification at Whitehaven was the MOS (Marchon Oldbury Sodium) plant to produce food-grade acid, which was authorised towards the end of 1986 and completed a year later at a cost of over £5 million. Initially the capacity for food-grade acid was about 35,000 tpa out of the total PWA capacity of 142,000 tpa; subsequent modifications increased the food-grade proportion to 55,000 tpa to meet the trend towards food phosphates and away from detergent phosphates. Other phosphates manufacturers were showing interest in the Whitehaven developments. In September 1988 Hoechst and Budenheim were seeking to buy PWA, which would have required the

Whitehaven MMO plant to be extended, but they then pursued other plans. In November 1990 Rhone Poulenc suggested moves to rationalise the European phosphates situation, including the closure of the Whitehaven green acid production, but at that time A&W did not wish to give up its basic position in manufacture. There were further discussions with Rhone Poulenc in April 1991 on merging the companies' European phosphates operations if the market for STPP contracted severely but they again came to nothing.

The basic economics of the Whitehaven manufacture of phosphoric acid had several disadvantages and there were also environmental problems. Large volumes of phosphate rock had to be shipped from Morocco and then transhipped to allow access to Whitehaven. Sulphur was imported via Workington and burnt in ageing sulphuric acid plants. The F5 plant producing green phosphoric acid from the action of sulphuric acid on phosphate rock had a history of unreliability linked with a lack of computerised controls. The processes produced unacceptable effluents, discharged from the site into the sea and air. One of the capital expenditure projects facing Robin Paul was a proposal to spend £5.5 million on refurbishing nos 1 & 2 streams on the sulphuric acid plant, which was put forward towards the end of 1988 (nos 4 & 5 streams were continuing). Consideration was given to buying by-product sulphuric acid from Imperial Smelting, a subsidiary of Rio Tinto but the quality made that unattractive despite the relatively low price. A lesser sum (under £2 million) was spent on keeping the plant open while alternatives were being investigated, including purchasing green phosphoric acid, or PWA or STPP.

Merely buying sulphuric acid, however, would not overcome the main production problems at Whitehaven - the limitation on output caused by the unreliable F5 plant, the high costs of production and the pollution problems. It was therefore decided to close F5 from mid-1992 and with it two out of the three sulphuric acid plants (the remaining plant was needed for the PWA process and for the sulphonation plants). The Press announcement in December 1991 stated: "The advent of world-scale phosphoric acid production close to phosphate rock deposits has long threatened to make European production uneconomic. The Whitehaven phosphoric acid plant is currently the last operational plant in the British Isles". The announcement also stated that acid could be imported as cheaply as it could be made on site and that cessation of manufacture would avoid high capital expenditure as well as eliminating most of the discharges to the sea and gaseous emissions.

It was, of course, essential to secure a supply of acid of adequate quality and at the right price. That was achieved through a contract with OCP, the Moroccan government operation which had been the supplier of phosphate rock for Whitehaven. Technical assistance was given to OCP to ensure that the acid was of the required quality. The price of acid was based on a formula related to world prices. One of the perceived advantages of the arrangement with OCP was that it would (it was hoped) prevent OCP from developing downstream further, to PWA and industrial phosphates. As will be seen in the next chapter, that was not the case.

Whitehaven and the environment

The 1990 and 1991 annual reports described some of the environmental problems at Whitehaven and the actions being taken to remedy them. There were significant problems at Whitehaven, which over many years had led to complaints from the public. In March 1988 the BBC Wildlife named A&W as recipient of its Eyesore Award for alleged pollution of the Whitehaven coast. In October 1989 the Daily Mail published an article stating that the Company was exceeding the permitted concentrations of trace metals in its discharges to the sea at Whitehaven. The Company's response, in a Press release, was that although the total quantity of metals discharged had not increased, the concentration had because the Company had been saving water.

In October 1990 Greenpeace announced its intention to bring a private prosecution for the same reason. The Whitehaven magistrates decided that the consent level of concentration had been exceeded, although the Company argued that the sample taken by Greenpeace was unrepresentative. The Company was fined £2,000 with £20,000 costs. The Company indicated that it was considering an appeal, while Greenpeace threatened further prosecutions. A few days after the magistrates' decision, members of Greenpeace blocked the sea end of the main outfall pipe from the factory, in what was believed to be an attempt to close the factory. 23 people were arrested. A&W obtained an injunction to restrain Greenpeace from trespassing or interfering with the discharge pipelines and commenced proceedings against Greenpeace to recover the cost of damage and lost production. Two months later, the Company agreed with Greenpeace to drop proceedings in return for an undertaking by Greenpeace to take no further action. In September 1992 the Company issued a strangely-worded Press release under the heading "Albright & Wilson disappointed with Greenpeace", complaining that Greenpeace had not recognised A&W's commitment to environmental improvement.

The main problems giving rise to local complaints were exhaust gases from the sulphuric acid plants, odours from the spray driers and amine plant and foam slicks on the sea below the hill on which the factory stood. The first two problems were dealt with by scrubbers. The third was caused by the run-off of spills and washings from the detergent plants which were draining through a geological feature known as the Byerstead Fault into the sea. While the foam was harmless to marine life and human health, it was unsightly. In 1991 a prosecution was brought by the National

Rivers Authority because of an accidental spillage of a copper chromite solution. Eventually the problem of washings and spillages was solved through a closed circuit system of drains and through using the former phosphate rock store (known as 'Paddy's Wigwam' because of its shape) as a lagoon where effluents from the detergent plants could be neutralised.

The problem with which Greenpeace was concerned was of a different order of magnitude. Discharges to the sea through the main outfall pipe consisted of millions of gallons of water, thousands of tonnes of gypsum from F5 and raffinate from the PWA processes containing contaminants occurring in the phosphate rock, of which the most important was cadmium. While the closure of F5 in mid-1992 ended the discharge of some 750,000 tpa of gypsum, the raffinate remained a problem. In 1990 the third North Sea Conference proposed a reduction of discharges of heavy metals from all sources, calling for a 70% reduction in the levels of 'Red List' substances, which included cadmium. The limit for Whitehaven was 40 tpa in 1990, reduced to 14 tpa in 1991; the actual quantity discharged in 1990 was 20 tonnes, which was reduced to 8 tonnes in 1991. Although it had been possible to cut the discharges substantially, through the choice of phosphate rock, it was not expected that they could be cut further to the 1995 target level of 6 tpa. There were also other potential problems as long as there was any effluent from the site; 80,000 tonnes of raffinate were produced annually, containing other potentially toxic substances.

In September 1989 a team was set up to find a solution. Since the heavy metals in phosphate rock had shown no tendency to leach, a material was sought in which the contents in the raffinate could be permanently locked. Quicklime, a common and inexpensive material, was found to achieve that. 1.2 tonnes of solidified 'Landfill' material resulted from each tonne of raffinate. The raffinate treatment plant, which cost £2.6 million, came into use in June 1992. A grant was obtained from the European Commission on condition that the plant would serve as a demonstration unit for anyone interested in applying the technology. The Landfill material was spread on a part of the factory site, which was estimated to have a capacity of 1 million cubic metres, equivalent to ten years' accumulation. The process was patented. Perhaps surprisingly, there do not appear to have been applications from other possible users for use of the technology. The one drawback of the process was its annual cost, in excess of £1.5 million.

During 1990-2 some £20 million was spent at Whitehaven on environmentally-driven projects, which included a new boiler-house and equipment for dust collection and to reduce fume emissions. Several commendations and awards were received for the Landfill project. In a relatively short time, the company had progressed from a target for Greenpeace, Friends of the Earth and others to an example of good practice in the chemical industry. In 1993 a programme was instituted to measure discharges - gaseous, liquid and solid - for all sites under the company's control, with a target to reduce emissions by 5% pa and within two years was ahead of target.

Mexico

The earliest commercial-scale PWA plant was in Mexico, at Coatzacoalcos, on the southern shore of the Gulf of Mexico, within Mexico's largest petrochemical complex. The technology used was from Israel Mining Industries, assisted by A&W's expert in PWA, Alan Williams. The plant was built in 1969 as part of the Fertimex fertiliser factory, acquired by a government-controlled monopoly from Texasgulf. It was able to produce a technical grade of phosphoric acid but the plant was inefficient and unreliable. In 1992 Troy Industrias, owned by a group of Mexican investors, bought the PWA plant, which was sold as part of the government's privatisation programme. In 1993-4 $20 million was spent on plant expansions, to bring the technical grade PWA capacity up to 150,000 tonnes pa, add to the capacity for ammonium phosphates and improve the fertiliser and animal feed (dicalcium phosphate) facilities.

Paul Rocheleau, then President of Albright & Wilson Americas, wished to obtain control of Troy. One reason was the strategy of expanding sales in Central and South America, seen as one of the most promising growth points, after the abatement of inflation and currency depreciation. It would also strengthen A&W's position as the world's largest producer of PWA and one of the main producers of phosphates and obtain a second source of supply for the North American market, while preventing the facility from falling into the hands of one of A&W's main competitors. He also attempted to buy Occidental's holding in Polyfos but was outbid by the main Mexican phosphates producer, Resistol, which was Troy's largest customer. The Mexican shareholders in Resistol also bought out Monsanto, which had been a partner in that company.

In December 1994 A&W acquired 50% of the shares in Troy, which was renamed Albright & Wilson Troy de Mexico. The cost of the acquisition was $58 million. For that, A&W acquired a half-share in a company with annual sales of $100 million, assets with a replacement cost of $250-300 million and potentially high profitability . Troy provided the lowest cost source of PWA within A&W, with scope to reduce costs further and raise capacity. A&W was able to apply its know-how in PWA and phosphates to upgrade the quality of the acid produced to food grade from the technical grade previously produced and help in marketing the acid and industrial phosphates. In 1994, Troy's exports amounted to $2.2 million, which were expected to rise to nearly $10 million in 1995 and to over $22 million in 1996.

STPP and other phosphates

By the 1990s sodium tripolyphosphate was no longer the most important contributor to profits. In North America STPP had virtually ceased to be used as a builder for domestic detergents. In the face of the claim that detergent phosphates were the cause of eutrophication, particularly in the Great Lakes, the soapers (Procter & Gamble and Unilever) reformulated using zeolites (silicates). There were similar pressures in Continental Europe, where Henkel launched zeolites in its detergents (including Persil) in 1986 and promoted the argument against phosphates on the grounds of eutrophication.

The **eutrophication** argument arose from the growth of algae in shallow and slow-moving fresh water, particularly in the Great Lakes. Phosphates are a nutrient and when combined with nitrogen can promote algal bloom. The phenomenon is rare where, as with the UK, the run-off of water is mainly into streams and rivers. Detergent phosphates on average accounted for only a quarter of phosphate in run-off, the rest being from fertilisers and human sewage. Water has to contain some phosphate to promote life. Any excess should be removed through sewage treatment. The UK had the highest level of sewage treatment anywhere except Scandinavia. When the problems with the Great Lakes were first identified, there was almost no sewage treatment for the water entering them. In 1991 the European Municipal Wastewater Directive required sewage treatment of water entering the most environmentally sensitive waterways - which would make the purchase of phosphate-free washing powder irrelevant.

Detergent phosphates were still used in formulations in Britain, but because of the decline in the usage of STPP on the Continent the producers there were looking to market their output in Britain. Thus in June 1986 Unilever placed half of its UK purchases of STPP with Hoechst: in November it reverted to purchasing all its requirements from A&W, but at the Continental price. At the beginning of 1986 the price of STPP to the soapers in Britain was £415 per tonne; in 1995 the price was £410, after inflation of about 50%. In North America, where STPP continued to be used in detergent formulations for dishwashers and institutional use, and in some private label detergents, the price had stabilised at a higher level. The tonnage of STPP sold from Whitehaven had peaked at 200,000 tonnes in 1983, of which 150,000 tonnes were sold in the home market. In March 1991 Unilever stated that its new formulations would exclude phosphates. By 1995 sales in the home market had declined to 80,000 tonnes. Exports were maintained to countries that had not accepted the argument against phosphates.

A report entitled "Pollutants in Cleaning Agents" published by the Department of the Environment in 1991 concluded that "no individual substitute builder has been found to equal the performance of sodium tripolyphosphate in isolation".

STPP performs several functions in detergents: it softens water, maintains the right balance of alkalinity for good cleaning, helps break up dirt and stains and keeps dirt suspended in the wash water. The most common substitute, zeolite (aluminosilicate), was shown to fail to prevent redeposition of dirt, leading to progressive build-up of dirt and unhygienic conditions. For adequate performance it required the addition of an agent, initially polycarboxylates and later phosphonates (themselves, of course, containing the phosphorus atom). With non-phosphates, greater quantities of cleaning materials were needed. In 1988 an investigation in Switzerland (which had banned phosphates from detergents in 1986) reported significant increases in the consumption of detergents, stain removers and decalcifiers as a result.

In the USA, Procter & Gamble had a short-lived experiment using citrates instead of phosphates in dishwashing detergents, which failed on performance grounds. Another substitute tried was sodium nitrilotriacetate (SNTA), which was more effective than zeolites but created a problem of toxic heavy metals and was therefore banned in most countries. In April 1990 a survey by the journal 'Which?' in the UK of 22 detergents stated that powder and liquid detergents formulated with phosphate performed significantly better than their phosphate-free counterparts, which also cost on average 50% more per wash than the phosphate-containing powders. The survey also noted that environmental experts stated that phosphate-free products would not solve the problems they were supposed to address. A French court had recently prohibited advertising claims that such products would benefit or protect the environment.

In January 1994 a report published by Landbank Environmental Research and Consulting, written by an ex-director of Greenpeace and a senior lecturer in statistics, concluded that zeolites had an environmental impact at least as damaging as had been alleged for phosphates. Being insoluble, they tended to produce sludge that could clog sewage treatment plants and gave rise to problems of disposal, whereas phosphates were recyclable. A&W produced samples of detergents containing recycled phosphates (under the name 'Encore') but failed to interest sewage works in adopting the recycling process as an alternative to incineration.

There was some recovery in the UK usage of phosphates in detergents in 1994, through their use in private-label standard and compact powders and heavy-duty liquid detergents (HDLs, see p.260) and through their use also by Unilever in HDLs but after 1995 the decline in STPP was resumed. Despite consumers' preference for the performance of phosphate-based detergents, the international power of the soapers was such that the substitutes prevailed in developed countries. In countries where phosphates were still used their prices fell, as producers competed for the shrinking total market. There was also competition from new plants in China. So after nearly 50 years STPP no longer had a leading position in the profits of Albright & Wilson.

The **other phosphates**, excluding the phosphorus derivatives that were in the Specialities group, were important contributors to profit in this period. Included in the Phosphates group were long-standing products such as the sodium and calcium phosphates used in baking and dicalcium phosphate used in toothpastes. More recent products (but of several years' standing) were the Kalipol range of sodium, potassium and ammonium polyphosphate solutions used in liquid detergents and hard surface cleaners, other polyphosphates with applications in foods, sodium monofluorophosphate providing fluoride in toothpastes and ammonium phosphates used in flame retardants. The most important relatively new products were the Briquest phosphonates, which had properties similar to those possessed by STPP, leading to use in detergents, water treatment, textile bleaching, oil recovery and ore flotation.

Many phosphorus derivatives were used as intermediates for plastics additives, agrochemicals, flame retardants, lubricant additives and pharmaceutical chemicals. They included phosphorus trichloride and oxychloride, phosphorus pentasulphide, phosphorous acid (with a major application in the manufacture of glyphosates for herbicides sold as RoundUp, etc.) and organic phosphates and phosphites. The main centres of production were Oldbury and Widnes in the UK, Charleston and Buckingham in North America and Yarraville in Australia.

During this period capacity for several products was extended, through plant additions or improved operation, and there were major improvements in the Oldbury and Widnes sites. The developments in PWA enabled the Widnes thermal phosphoric acid plant to be closed and the Oldbury one to be reduced to the production of phosphorus pentoxide as an intermediate. Rationalisation of production between Oldbury and Widnes was based on a new sodium phosphates plant at Widnes, completed in 1985, and a monocalcium phosphate plant at Oldbury, commissioned towards the end of 1986. By the end of 1988 the oldest plant on the Widnes site was less than ten years old.

At Oldbury many of the older buildings were demolished, new roadways and vehicle routing were created, the works entrance was transformed and the distribution of materials radically improved by building new overhead pipe runs to replace pipes previously attached to the old buildings, including the pumping of molten phosphorus through small-bore heated pipes. At the beginning of 1990 a building providing new offices and a technical department for Phosphates was completed at Oldbury, making possible the demolition of the very old office block and the relocation of technical work from the ITC laboratories. The new building, completed in 8 months at a cost of only £1.4 million, was dubbed "Ted's Shed", after Ted Lowe, then the General Manager, Phosphates. The new building at the entrance to Oldbury Works was called "Ted's Tug", because of its resemblance to a small and somewhat tubby ship.

The nicknames reflected the unique contribution made by Ted Lowe to the development of Oldbury works and to the technology of the products made there, over many years. Ted joined Albright & Wilson in 1946 at the age of 16, as a junior assistant in the research department. He studied at night school for an external degree in chemistry, which he obtained in 1952. He went on to be a section head in the research department, becoming responsible for phosphates. From 1965 to 1967 he was personal assistant to Alf Loveless, then the Phosphates Technical Director, before becoming head of the inorganic group in the research department and then technical service and product development manager, which gave him contact with customers. From 1974 he was Phosphates technical manager and a member of the Long Harbour technical committee and in the late 1980s became responsible for both production and technical development. In 1990 he was appointed General Manager, Phosphates, the position he held until his retirement in June 1991.

Ted was an essentially practical man with a particular interest in process development. He was critical of the over-theoretical character of the research department and of the separation of most of the technical effort from production. He believed that if Albright & Wilson had had good processes, especially in phosphorus production, the company could have led the world. It fell behind in its key technology and for a long time, there were barriers to communication between Whitehaven and Oldbury.

Ted had 30 inventions patented, including several important processes installed by A&W. These included the manufacture of phosphine, sodium monofluorophosphate, ADPA (acetodiphosphonic acid) and pyrophosphorous acid and the distillation of phosphorus mud . He was also involved in the development of the MOS process for food-grade PWA, especially the defluorination of PWA (which he was particularly pleased with), in the dearsenication of thermal phosphoric acid, the production of phosphorus oxychloride by direct oxidation of trichloride, the use of large calciners in the production of sodium, calcium and potassium phosphates, low-temperature calcination of phosphate rock for PWA (adopted in Morocco) and effluent treatment processes. Other achievements for which Ted was responsible were the production of polyphosphoric acid from WPA, sodium phosphate prills (as an alternative to crystals), phosphorous acid, the Kalipol tetrapotassium pyrophosphate process, and the solution of the problem of caking in dicalcium phosphate (which saved the business with Colgate). Capacity of the DCP plant was doubled without major capital expenditure by some debottlenecking and general improvements in operation; that was true of other plants, notably the Briquest plant.

One of Ted's developments not adopted by A&W was a new route for the production of red amorphous phosphorus (RAP), a form of phosphorus originally used in safety matches and later as an intermediate for flame retardants and other organic phosphorus chemicals. The amorphous phosphorus plant at Oldbury was one of the oldest on the site, using a primitive and labour intensive process in unpleasant working conditions. Ted wished to follow the route used in the manufacture of phosphine from the reaction of RAP with phosphoric acid and constructed a pilot plant. The RAP converters used for phosphine produced 800 tpa of RAP. What was wanted was 2,000 tpa, to replace plants at Oldbury and Buckingham. In April 1986 David Livingstone, in addressing the Company Council, referred to "an exciting red amorphous development at Oldbury".

There was, however, concern that a larger unit could experience a runaway exothermic reaction. Ted argued that there could be more than one smaller unit but the process was rejected in favour of a modification of the Canadian mud furnaces.

The Canadian plant (for which government grants were available) was authorised in 1988 and commissioned in 1989. In 1990 a 5-year Memorandum of Understanding between A&W Americas and the governmental Industry, Science and Technology department was signed, to develop flame retardants for plastics starting with red phosphorus. The RAP process won a Certificate of Merit from the Canadian Ministry of Regional Industrial Expansion for 'Invention'. The process was described as safe, environmentally acceptable, producing a better quality of product and "a radical departure from existing technology…and can be produced at a much lower cost than is possible by any other method". Very soon, however, severe problems were experienced on the plant because of the scaling-up and 'improvements' on the original simple mud furnace design. The plant operated at only half the intended capacity in 1990, when the Annual Report stated "Technical start-up problems had to be resolved so ensuring that the full capabilities of this plant are realised in 1991". The plant, however, never operated satisfactorily and was closed in 1995.

A conspicuously successful project at Oldbury was the change in the method of transporting chlorine to the site. For many years transport had been by rail, which it had been thought was less hazardous than movement by road. The receipt of trainloads of chlorine, however, involved the presence on site, in storage and in the rail tankcars, of a quantity of chlorine that had come to be designated as a major accident hazard, despite a 100% safety record during the 70 years of dealing with chlorine. That meant that there was a zone of 2 kilometres radius around the site within which there were restrictions on schools, hotels and businesses. The project put forward under Ted Lowe's direction was for chlorine to be moved in road tankers, with improved facilities for reception and distribution and a 90% reduction in the quantity on site, costing altogether £2.8 million in 1992/3. The zone of restriction was as a result reduced to 750 metres, thus releasing from planning restrictions 47,600 people and 27 schools and allowing new businesses that were expected to create 1,000 new jobs. The project, supported with loan finance by the Black Country Development Corporation, attracted three awards, from the Royal

Town Planning Institute, the British Urban Regeneration Association and Business Committed to the Environment.

Specialities

Historically, the specialities activities of Albright & Wilson in the UK had been centred on three businesses: flame retardancy, water treatment and surface technologies, all based on chemicals derived from phosphorus. Additional strands were added with the inclusion of first Avonmouth and then Charleston, where the emphasis was also on phosphorus derivatives but for additional applications, as intermediates for pharmaceuticals, agricultural chemicals and metal extractants. In the reorganisation of 1991 the Specialities business group also encompassed acrylics (made at Box Hill, Melbourne) and petroleum additives made at Whitehaven, neither being derived from phosphorus. The expectation was that the company should and would develop in specialities rather than in commodity chemicals. That was on the agenda of all chemical companies in the 1990s. The appointment of Dr John Adsetts, the Technical Director, to head the Specialities businesses was a recognition of the necessary orientation of specialities towards expertise requiring technical support.

The most important sector of Specialities was **Flame Retardants**, accounting for about a quarter of sales and a higher share of profits. Sales of Proban, world leader in fire retarding cotton textiles, continued to grow. Early in 1988 agreement was reached for a test centre for Proban to be set up in China, where there were two licensees. In 1990 an additional reactor for Proban was commissioned. In 1991 a £2 million fabric applications development plant was installed at Oldbury, to provide a commercial scale textile finishing facility, primarily for trials and demonstration of the application of Proban to fabrics for workwear, protective clothing, children's sleepwear, curtains and hospital bedding. The plant was also used for applying Amgard products (see next paragraph) to domestic furnishing and industrial fabrics. This investment at a time of recession and continuing decline in the British textile industry seems uncharacteristically bold.

Towards the end of 1987 the UK government banned the use of foams other than 'combustion modified foams' in domestic upholstered furniture. The move was welcomed by A&W, as the major European supplier of the key flame retardant used, in a Press release listing the applications for the Company's flame retardants - for upholstery and bedding foams and textiles, fabrics for furnishing and clothing, intumescent coatings for buildings, bromine-free fire resistant plastics and rubber belting, paper for packaging and in construction, and timber. Most of the flame retardants for foam materials were made at A&W's Avonmouth works, where the key chemical was Amgard V6. In 1989 plant improvements and additions were completed at Avonmouth which provided facilities for ethoxylation and introduced computer controls. It then became possible for all stages in the manufacture of Amgard V6 to be carried out at Avonmouth. The UK-based flame retardants business was consistently profitable, producing around £5 million annual operating profits from around £30 million sales in this period.

At Charleston flame retardants similar to those at Avonmouth, including Amgard V6, were made under the trade name Antiblaze. The phosphorus trichloride plant there was expanded in 1989. The laboratories at Richmond, in the new building occupied in 1987, were second only to ITC at Oldbury. The Charleston factory was fortunate in surviving hurricane Hugo in September 1989 with only minor damage. Early in 1991 Olin decided to pull out of flame retardant phosphorus chemicals and sell its business (but not any plants) to Albright & Wilson, thereby greatly increasing A&W's sales and profits from fire retardants.

Then on 17th June 1991 there was an explosion at Charleston, which was the worst accident in the history of Albright & Wilson. The explosion occurred in the Special Products Unit, which was producing Antiblaze 19, a phosphorus-based flame retardant not made elsewhere in A&W. The plant operator and eight contract workers working in another part of the plant were killed and many others were injured in the blast. Within hours, teams went out into the local community to monitor the impact; tests showed that no hazardous substances had been released. Soon after, expert staff were sent from the UK and Canada to determine the cause of the explosion, assess the extent of the damage, tackle customer supply problems, work with regulatory bodies and help with the emotional problems of employees and the local community. A Community Advisory Board was set up, including the local Senator, representatives of the community and union, and A&W staff, and the local Congressman and Mayor were also involved. Within ten days, all but one of the plant units at the site were restarted. The lost production was largely covered by shipments from Avonmouth and tolling within the USA but there was an unavoidable hiatus in the development of the business affected, comprising agricultural and pharmaceutical intermediates and oil additives as well as flame retardants for textiles and polyurethane foams. Operating practices within the site were reviewed in depth and a 'Zero Incidents Program' was instituted at Charleston and later elsewhere within A&W. The US Environmental Protection Agency (EPA) used the Charleston operation as a demonstration facility for safety precautions.

The plant was rebuilt, incorporating many improvements in safety, process control, quality and efficiency, and recommissioning of the new Organic Specialities Unit began in August 1992. Although the capital and additional operating costs involved while the plant was not operating were covered by insurance to a considerable extent, it then took a long time for profits to recover and overtake the level before the explosion.

The long-established interests of Albright & Wilson in **Water Treatment** were based on the use of alkali phosphates in water softening and descaling, encompassing boiler water treatment for industry, branded consumer products (Calgon, Micromet) and scale inhibition in desalination plants. Typical of the last-named business was a 3-year contract in 1993 for the supply of Albrivap DSB scale inhibitor to the Saline Water Conversion Corporation of Saudi Arabia, to which over 2,000 tonnes pa of the product were being supplied, for the world's largest desalination complex, at Al Jubail, supplying water to Riyadh. Another application of phosphorus-based chemicals was in the control of plumbo-solvency to prevent the intake of lead from water pipes. In 1993 a product developed in the ITC, initially known as ITC288 and later given the name Bricorr, was launched; it was an all-organic, environmentally friendly, corrosion inhibitor for industrial water treatment and the most important product created by ITC to satisfy a defined market need.

In this period the water treatment operations - or, as they became known, Water Management and Service Chemicals - were broadened to include biocides. From Avonmouth came MBT (methylbisthiocyanate), which gained approval by the US Environmental Protection Authority in 1986 and TCMTB, introduced in 1987. The most important biocide developed by A&W was THPS (tetrakis hydroxymethyl phosphonium sulphate), a serendipitous development from the THPC flame retardant forming the basis of Proban (p.30). Its outstanding biocidal power and environmental benefits made it potentially a world beater. Clearance by the US EPA, which was essential for many of the markets for the product, proved to be a lengthy process which was eventually successful in 1995. Meanwhile it was sold in limited applications, as for oil well drilling under the name Tolcide and for boiler water treatment as Albricide.

During this period the water management/service chemicals business excluding biocides achieved a moderate growth in volume and an improvement in profit, to a level of around £800,000 in 1994 from sales of £4 million. The biocides side was growing more rapidly and moved into profit in 1993 as the sales of THPS grew, to nearly £6 million in 1994. The ingredients for significant growth were present but required substantial investment in people, technical effort and capital for this sector to become as important for A&W as flame retardants.

Another sector of the water management/service chemicals operations was the Rio Linda business in small chlorine dioxide generators for the treatment of waste water, especially from food processing plants, sterilisation and bleaching. Before the acquisition of Rio Linda in 1989, Service Chemicals had looked at the potential for chlorine dioxide in industrial water treatment. Rio Linda provided the patented know-how that was needed. They had sold generators for municipal water treatment, tomato processing plants and oil refineries in the western American states. Jobs done by Rio Linda also included detoxification of gold mining waste and cleaning of sulphur contaminated ponds at a tyre factory. From 1991 some units were also sold in the UK. Rio Linda was profitable from the latter part of 1990 but moved into loss in 1994. The sale of the pulp chemicals operations removed one of the original reasons for its acquisition - the chlorine dioxide technology and the supply of the sodium chlorite used in the generators. A&W's holding in the company was sold in May 1995.

The third of the original components of Specialities was **Surface Technologies**, which was concerned principally with the treatment of metals and was known under the title of Metal Treatment until the reorganisation of the Specialities group in 1990. The traditional products were used in chemical polishing and anodising aluminium (Phosbrites), trivalent chromium plating (Alecra) and pretreatment of steel coil (Accomet). To those were added the production of coloured finishes on metals (Albrifin), other pretreatment processes (Albritect) and protective coatings for concrete and other building materials (AlbriShield). Despite the addition of new products and increased export efforts, however, the sales and profits of the UK-originated Surface Technologies business showed little growth in this period, remaining a little below £1 million profit on sales of around £9 million.

In the reorganisation of 1990, acrylics were added to the remit of Surface Technologies. Acrylic solutions and emulsions, principally for the treatment of concrete roofing tiles and masonry and for use in printing inks, textile printing and industrial paints, had been made at Box Hill, Melbourne, for many years. Up to 1990, the business had been operating at a loss, despite the plant's operating at close to capacity. At the end of 1990, A&W's Australian interests were reorganised (see below) and acrylics were transferred into a new wholly-owned subsidiary, Albright & Wilson Specialities. The introduction of computer controls on the plant from the beginning of 1992 increased its effective capacity, improved product quality and reduced operating costs. It then became a profitable operation. Product was exported to several countries, including Malaysia, Singapore, Indonesia and - most importantly - Thailand. So in 1991 it was decided to set up manufacture in Thailand as a joint venture between Albright & Wilson and its sales agent in Thailand, using the existing company AWAT Thai, in which A&W held 49.9%. The plant, located on the partner's site south of Bangkok, was commissioned in 1993.

Also brought into the Specialities group in 1990 was the **Petroleum Additives** sector, based on plants at Whitehaven making methacrylates (not connected with the Australian acrylics operation). Raw materials for these products were purchased acrylics and natural alcohol - which was the main reason for the long-standing Whitehaven operation. In the mid-1950s Castrol (later Burmah Castrol) invited A&W to make polyalkylmethacrylates for its engine oils, to ensure good lubrication across a wider temperature range. Uses for the products, marketed under the name

Empicryl, broadened over the next 30 years to include not only viscosity index improvers for vehicle engine lubricating oils but also pour point depressants and dispersants for oils used in engineering, including fluids for hydraulics, transmissions and shock absorbers. Up to 1988 customers were serviced through Ethyl Corporation, the US company that took over Edwin Cooper, Castrol's specialist additive company. In 1988 A&W began servicing its customers directly. 75% of the output was exported.

In the late 1980s, however, the business was making losses. The two plants, producing monomers and from them polymers, were old and in poor condition and working conditions on them were unsatisfactory. Serious consideration was given to abandoning the business. The products, however, were selling well, with good prospects in Asia. So it was decided to invest, first in improvements to the polymers plant and then in a £3 million new plant for monomers, with computer controls throughout. Commissioning of the new monomer plant began at the end of 1989 but took longer than expected, sales were affected by the delay, raw material costs were higher and there were write-offs of spoiled materials. With the change in organisation in March 1990 and success in selling speciality monomers into new markets - for paint, adhesives and other acrylic resin systems - profits began to be made from late 1991 and in 1994 were approaching £1.5 million pa. from sales of over £11 million, five times the level in 1988.

At the time of its acquisition by A&W in 1985, sales of the specialities produced by Mobil Chemicals at the **Charleston** plant amounted to $30 million pa. They comprised organophosphorus compounds used in agricultural chemical intermediates, extractants for metals in mining, flame retardants and a number of minor products manufactured to meet the specific requirements of customers. Sales were greatly expanded in succeeding years, reaching nearly $150 million in 1994. Some of the expansion resulted from A&W products introduced from the UK but the main engine for expansion was the technical effort by the teams working in the laboratories in the new headquarters of A&W Americas at Richmond, Virginia.

The objective was not to invent new chemicals. Rather, it was to manufacture chemicals, for example intermediates for pharmaceuticals, that the customer was unwilling or unable to make. The quantities might be small but prices were often very high. Success required well-directed laboratory work, good process technology, multipurpose plant and basic raw materials. At the beginning of 1989 the capacity of the plant at Charleston making phosphorus trichloride, the basic material for the specialities, was increased by 50%, making it the largest producer in North America. In 1990 a plant to produce Briquest phosphonates was added, to replace imports from Oldbury, supplying customers in water treatment and oilfield drilling, some of whom had come in 1988 as a result of the purchase of Olin's 'Wayplex' organophosphorus business.

Then in June 1991 came the explosion at Charleston, as already recorded. Profits were sustained in 1991 and 1992, because of business interruption insurance cover, but fell in 1993/4 as the new and restored plant was worked up to full operation. At the same time, new products were introduced, particularly intermediates for pharmaceuticals used in glaucoma, osteoporosis, dental care, antiviral drugs and reagents for pharmaceutical syntheses. There were also new chemicals for water treatment, lube additives and metal extractants. The products tended to be known by abbreviations of their chemical names - for example, DEHPA (di(2 ethyl hexyl) phosphoric acid).

Surfactants

A&W's strategic plan for 1987-92, produced a few months after Robin Paul's appointment, included in the section dealing with surfactants the statement "we are convertors caught between the major suppliers of our raw materials and the major consuming groups such as P & G, Unilever, and Beecham. Meanwhile, we compete with small companies with low overhead structures, less demanding corporate standards, and faster responses. This all leads to a low return on sales profile and thus leaves the business sensitive to changes in sales volume and value and to raw material costs. This is an uncomfortable position to be in....". Several actions were proposed to deal with the situation: reducing costs and strengthening the raw material position, developing proprietary products, withdrawing from lower margin activities and seeking industry rationalisation through alliances.

In 1986 European surfactants produced a record operating profit of a little less than £10 million, compared with £3 million in 1985. The increase occurred in the UK, where favourable raw material prices turned round what had been a loss-making situation for most of the time since 1979. Nevertheless, the 1986 profit represented a return of not much more than 5% on sales of £180 million. In the next few years profits fluctuated but at the end of this period, in 1994, the operating profit was a little less than £9 million on sales of more than £250 million, a return of only 3.5%. The actions during this period therefore did not succeed in consistently improving the return despite progress in several of the planned directions.

The Annual Report for 1993 recorded that the surfactants sector "fell well short of target and expectations, representing a poor reward for all the effort and technical input expended on it. Overcapacity and depressed European markets resulted in severe downward pressure on volumes and erosion of prices. The Company's policy is to differentiate its business in terms of product quality and customer service. Although progress was made in both these areas it is clear that further rationalisation of manufacturing capacity and reduction in costs will be necessary to restore this business to an acceptable level of performance. We believe, however, that it can be done, and we retain our commitment to a business sector in which Albright & Wilson has both the technical expertise and the international market position to be a leading supplier". This gloomy picture followed a statement by Robin Paul at the beginning of 1994: "The need to improve the structure of our manufacturing facilities across Europe should have been seen early in 1993, so that decisive action could have been taken sooner".

The Annual Report for 1994 then recorded another difficult year's trading with operating margins continuing to be squeezed; in that year £6.75 million was charged for restructuring European Surfactants. The major part of the charge was in respect of redundancy payments and plant write-offs at Whitehaven, under the leadership of John Markham, who had been brought in from ICI in 1989 to manage the Whitehaven site and became General Manager of Surfactants in October 1993.

Preceding the restructuring in 1994 was a reform of working practices at Whitehaven. Although since 1980 the number of employees at Whitehaven (for Phosphates and Surfactants operations) had been reduced from 2,250 to 1,800, labour costs remained a high percentage on sales. The initiative launched early in 1987, under the title "Towards 2000...a Challenge", was to achieve flexible working agreements, in place of the rigid demarcations among engineering and process workers that then prevailed. A year later the Union covering process workers on the site signed an agreement to remove demarcation between its members, who were to engage in a 3-year training programme for multiskilling. The mechanical craft Unions on the site signed a similar agreement in mid-1989. These changes enabled the workforce at Whitehaven to be substantially reduced over the next ten years, to fewer than 1,000.

Some of the Whitehaven surfactant operations were closed; in 1991 one of the smallest and oldest plants, making Eltesols (industrial surfactants used mainly in the manufacture of moulds for castings) was closed and in 1994 plants making SLS (sodium lauryl sulphate) powders and needles were also closed. Production was transferred to the factories in continental Europe, where there was considerable capacity and growing sales of industrial surfactants. There was also a general rationalisation of the product portfolio to eliminate 'small load' business, which reduced the number of product lines from nearly 5,000 in 1991 to 1,350 by the end of March 1993. Products were classified: in the top category were those that were profitable and demanded by major customers, in the next those expected to be future high earners, then those that were speculative and finally products at the research and development stage.

The remainder of the restructuring charge made in 1994 was £1.2 million to write down the investment in Detergentes y Productos de Higiene SA (p.294), which had been a disaster from the time of its acquisition in 1992.

The most important raw materials for the surfactant operations were fatty alcohols, which were then converted to detergent and toiletry materials by two basic processes: sulphation and sulphonation (employing sulphur trioxide, from burning sulphur) and ethoxylation (using ethylene oxide, from oil).

Surfactants

Surfactants are surface active agents that break down the barriers between water and grease and so allow grease to dissolve in water. The organic part of the surfactant molecule can be made from petrochemicals or from natural oils such as palm oil. A water-seeking portion is then attached to the organic (water-hating) molecule by sulphation or sulphonation and/or ethoxylation. Marchon's toiletries had always been based on the reaction of sulphur trioxide with fatty alcohols (sulphation), while detergents and industrial surfactants were generally produced through the reaction of sulphur trioxide with alkyl benzene (sulphonation). Sulphates are compounds where sulphur is always connected to an oxygen atom, while sulphonates have only one sulphur/carbon bond.

The **alcohol** plant at Whitehaven, which made detergent alcohols from imported fatty acid derived from natural oils, mainly palm oil, was a key element in the profitability of the site's operations. (Marchon had always preferred natural alcohols to alcohols derived from mineral oil, particularly for toiletries.) Although the plant's capacity had been doubled over a long period to 30,000 tonnes pa, that satisfied less than half the total requirements of Whitehaven and the continental European plants. There were also severe problems in operating the plant in 1989-90. In 1990 there were discussions with Henkel, Procter & Gamble and Unichema concerning purchases of alcohol and a possible joint venture with Unichema. There were also discussions with the Salim Group in 1991 on collaboration in surfactants including supplies of natural alcohol; Salim had substantial interests in palm oil in Indonesia. A&W, however, was not prepared to invest in plantations. Supplies of natural alcohols were becoming more plentiful and prices more stable and so there was insufficient reason to enter into special arrangements for supply.

In this period there was substantial further investment in **sulphonation** (this term is used hereafter also to include sulphation). In 1984, when sulphonation capacity at Whitehaven was doubled, the Annual Report claimed that the combined capacity at Whitehaven and in Italy, France and Spain was the largest installed in Europe. In April 1990, a further investment of £2.6 million was announced, to increase the capacity at Whitehaven and produce higher-quality products, from Ballestra falling-film reactors. The original reactors at Whitehaven had been Baker-Perkins batch reactors; the expansion in 1984 added a loop reactor and a

Mazzoni reactor (similar to the Ballestra), both for continuous output. The obsolescent Baker-Perkins and the loop reactor were suitable for the production of the commodity sulphonic acid but not for more specialised products. An improvement in technology was needed particularly because in the late 1980s there were demands for products, particularly toiletries, low in 1,4-dioxane, which was suspected of being carcinogenic. The sulphonation plants in Italy and France were originally Baker-Perkins but increasingly production was on falling-film units there and in Spain, as capacity was expanded and updated in 1990-1991. The same trend applied in Asia and Australia. There was further expenditure on sulphonation at Whitehaven in 1994-5. Costs were also improved through the installation of sulphur burners in France and Spain. Altogether, there was major investment in sulphonation over a decade, on which the demonstrable return was low because in part it represented a catch-up in technology and because of weakness in the prices of bulk surfactants. The impact of investment in **ethoxylation** was even more significant.

Ethoxylation

Ethoxylation is the application of ethylene oxide to organic feedstocks (alcohols or alkyl amines) to produce mainly nonionic surfactants. The largest group of surfactants is the anionics, which bear a negative charge on the hydrophilic end of the molecule. The second largest group is the nonionics, which bear no charge but are soluble in water. Ethoxylates with 2 or 3 molecules of ethylene oxide are used principally in toiletries whereas with 7 molecules or more the application is primarily in detergents and emulsifiers.

There were ethoxylation plants at Whitehaven, Castiglione, Frosinone and Barcelona and in July 1987 a plant was commissioned at St Mihiel. The St Mihiel plant operated to capacity in 1988. All those plants, however, were at a cost disadvantage because of their size and were dependent upon transportation by road tanker of ethylene oxide, a hazardous material. Discussions began in March 1988 with BP, one of the producers of ethylene oxide in its petrochemical operations, on the possibility of cooperation in ethoxylation.

The discussions on ethoxylation led to an agreement in September 1989 for A&W to build an ethoxylation plant at Lavera, near Marseilles, adjacent to the large petrochemical plants of BP and Atochem (the French petrochemical company jointly owned by Total and Elf), on land leased from BP Chemicals. The project was for ethylene oxide to be supplied by pipeline from Naphthachemie, a company jointly owned by BP and Atochem, to an ethoxylation plant with a capacity of 70,000 tonnes pa, the largest in Europe. The plant, estimated to cost £6 million, was to come on stream in early 1991. The existing A&W ethoxylation plants would continue in operation, for smaller tonnage toiletries and specialities with a lower ethylene oxide content. It was hoped that smaller European producers would withdraw from production and buy ethoxylates from Lavera.

The Lavera plant was eventually commissioned in September 1991, after a series of difficulties and setbacks, which were attributed in part to the fact that the plant was engineered by Italians, with Italian management but under the administration of St Mihiel. The cost was nearly £2 million more than the original estimate. There were only 16 employees, making it the most capital-intensive plant in A&W but not exceptional by the standards of petrochemical operations. The economics of the Lavera plant were highly dependent upon the price at which ethylene oxide was supplied, which was linked to the cost to Naphthachemie, under a long-term contract; that cost, including processing costs, proved to be higher than expected, while the market price of ethylene oxide remained low, because of plentiful supplies. Also, a potential partner in the Lavera project, DAC of Italy, decided to build its own ethoxylation plant (which was later bought by Condea, a leading German surfactants company). Margins therefore were very low and the venture was unprofitable.

There was considerable success in this period in developing **speciality surfactants**. Chief among these were the heavy duty liquid detergents (HDLs) (p.260). The initial plant built at Whitehaven, with a capacity of 5,000 tonnes pa, which came into operation in 1987, was quickly sold out and was expanded in 1987 and again in 1988. Plants were built in France and Italy and sales, mainly to supermarkets, were made in other Continental European countries. The formulation was improved in 1988 and at the beginning of 1992 a double strength HDL was introduced. The patent position was strong and a cross-licensing agreement with Unilever (with a payment to A&W) removed a possible cause of dispute. A&W's sales to supermarkets were made through Robert McBride (an offshoot of BP), which packaged and distributed the products made at Whitehaven. In 1993 A&W signed an agreement with BP and McBride requiring the expenditure of £1 million at Whitehaven for the supply of HDLs to McBride and detergent materials to BP, which then reduced its capacity for sulphonation.

A&W, however, did not succeed in selling products to the major detergent manufacturers and the advent of compact powder detergents from 1990 halted the growth of HDLs, despite the development of concentrated HDLs. Sales fell sharply in 1991. Meanwhile considerable technical resources were applied to developing industrial uses of HDLs, in drilling muds, cutting oils, general lubricants and pesticides, as well as applications in cosmetics and personal care products. Providing an alternative to solvent-based formulations, they had advantages for health, safety and the environment.

The second speciality surfactants area that grew in this period was mild surfactants, increasingly employed in frequently-used toiletries and products for babies. These were based on amines (organic nitrogen compounds), for which capacity had been doubled in 1987. The amines were used in the manufacture of ampho(di)acetates (toiletry imidazolines) and coco amido propyl betaines (CAPBs), for which capacity was more than doubled in 1992 at a cost of £900,000.

A third area of speciality surfactants were the naphthalene sulphonates, with industrial applications, for which a plant was built at Alcover, Spain in 1990. Also ranking as a move away from commodity products was the development of high-active surfactants, with 70% of active matter, against about 30% for surfactants generally, which reduced transport costs and extended markets.

While these developments went some way to achieving the objective of moving from commodity to speciality surfactants, there was an adverse trend in another of the consumer-directed sectors. The bottling business, which had been very important in Italy and of some significance in France and Spain, began to decline. Italy's profits peaked in 1988-9, at over £3 million pa, but in 1990, Italy's profit fell below budget because of the loss of bottling for customers that had been acquired by major marketers of detergents and toiletries with their own bottling facilities. Early in 1991 a proposal for increased bottling capacity in Italy was rejected by the A&W Board. The decline continued and in 1995 the Castiglione bottling operation was hived off into a joint company, Sintesi Srl, with the Italian company Pizzalotto. Later that year, the loss-making bottling operation at Alcover was sold to a Spanish company, Roval SA. The operations at Frosinone, whose main activity was the supply of bottled liquid detergents and toiletries, were run down in the late 1990s to essentially a care-and-maintenance basis.

There was some geographical extension for surfactants in this period. In December 1992 a sales company was formed in Portugal jointly with A&W's agent there. Of more significance was the extension into the United States, initially by starting a marketing organisation at the beginning of 1992 and then establishing a base for manufacture through an arrangement with Pilot Chemical Company, an independent speciality surfactant supplier with plants in New Jersey, Texas, California and Ohio. Pilot built a plant at Middletown, Cincinnati,to make high active alcohol and ether sulphates, which came on stream in March 1995. In August 1994, A&W formed a joint company in China, Hunan Resun - Albright & Wilson Industrial Company, with equal shares for A&W and Hunan Resun Industrial General Corporation, to acquire and operate the Ballestra falling-film sulphonation plant owned by Hunan Resun and producing sodium lauryl ether sulphate, at Changsha, the capital of Hunan province. The investment involved was a little under $5 million. Dr S.L. Tan, from A&W Singapore, was appointed general manager. There was an unsuccessful attempt to form a joint venture in Japan to market HDLs.

Asia and Australia

A&W's interests in Asia, the region in the world with fastest growing gdp in this period, were significantly expanded from 1986 to 1994 and contributed an increasing share of profits. Most of A&W's interests were in jointly-owned companies, generally not majority-owned, for one or both of two reasons: the importance of having local partners and in some instances the difficulty of setting up majority- or wholly-owned companies; and/or the shortage of finance, leading to contributing know-how in exchange for equity and financing through borrowing (not consolidated in the accounts of A&W and Tenneco).

In April 1985 Albright & Wilson Asia Trading (AWAT), based in Singapore, was formed to bring together A&W's direct interests in the factories and sales offices in Singapore and Kuala Lumpur, offices in Hong Kong, Tokyo and Osaka and newly-opened offices in South Korea and Thailand and its participation in the manufacturing companies in Thailand (TPC) and the Philippines (PPL). The President of AWAT, Don Beck, had served in posts in Ireland and South Africa (p.256); he reported to George Pekarek, the General Manager Commercial, who was based in Whitehaven and responsible also for the network of sales agents and offices in other parts of the world. George Pekarek was on the Board of AWAT, together with John Wills, the Commercial Director of A&W, particularly concerned with Asia, and Ray Naish, the Director responsible for Europe and America. In 1987 an office was opened in Taiwan and the name of the headquarters company was changed to Albright & Wilson Asia, recognising that its operations were not confined to trading but included the manufacturing companies. In the following year, on 8.8.88 (recognising the Chinese belief in 8 as a lucky number) a new office and laboratory were opened at Jurong, Singapore, the factory making surfactants built originally by UIC. Singapore then became the technical centre for the region.

In 1991, after six years of great activity (described below), Don Beck moved from Singapore to become General Manager of Surfactants for A&W and was succeeded by Lyall Work, who had been in charge of the Industrial Chemicals division of A&W Americas. In 1993, after Hugh Podger's retirement, Lyall became directly responsible to Robin Paul and his responsibilities were widened to include Australia. Reflecting that, the name of the Singapore headquarters company was changed to Albright & Wilson Asia Pacific in December 1993. In 1994, out of A&W's total trading profit of £56 million, Asia Pacific accounted for £9 million, which was almost double the profit in 1991. A&W's share of the associated (i.e. not majority-owned) companies accounted for nearly 75% of the total profit of Asia Pacific in 1994. In terms of both growth and structure, Asia Pacific was rather different from the rest of A&W.

The main development in **Singapore** was a joint venture with P T Prima Inti Perkasa of Indonesia set up in 1987 to build an ethoxylation plant on Pulau Ayer Merbau, an island off Singapore. The company, Ethoxylates Manufacturing Private Ltd (EMPL), was equally owned by the two partners. The plant, which was commissioned in November 1987 with a capacity of 18,000 tpa and at a cost of £3 million, took its ethylene oxide by pipeline from the adjacent Ethylene Glycols, part of the complex of the Petrochemical Corporation of Singapore. Highly automated, it employed only 18 people. The plant was intended primarily to supply the ASEAN region, where the use of fatty alcohol ethoxylates for liquid detergents and textile auxiliaries was expected to expand from the current 10,000 tpa. Key to its economics was the contract for the supply of ethylene oxide, the price of which was linked to international prices. Unfortunately, the under-utilisation of the plant and the price basis meant that the company made losses for many years. Eventually, under threat of closure, the terms were renegotiated and the plant became marginally profitable.

Albright & Wilson **Malaysia** was consistently profitable, through its main product, phosphoric acid, which was supplied to the palm oil refineries in the peninsula and exported. Thanks to tariff and licence protection, the ability to deliver in bulk by tanker and the need for a food-grade acid, the plant was not subject to competition from imports. In 1988 a joint venture, Speciality Phosphates Malaysia, was formed with Omichi Seiyaku (49%), of Japan, to manufacture sodium hexametaphosphates for food phosphates, all to be exported to Japan. Other activities on the site were the manufacture of small quantities of metal finishing products based on phosphoric acid and contract packing. For many years, it had been the intention of the Malaysian Government that A&W's holding in A&W Malaysia should be reduced from 100%, initially to 60% and later to a minority. Although there were discussions in this period with possible Malaysian partners, A&W was able to preserve its holding at 100% because of the contribution made to the Malaysian trading balance.

In June 1996 A&W applied for a licence for a sulphonation plant in **Indonesia**, to be operated as a joint venture with local interests. A licence was granted in 1987 and it then took a further year for a proposal to be put together for a plant costing £4.8 million. In February 1990 a joint venture was formed: A&W took a 50% shareholding in a company at Gresik, Surabaya, which was making surfactants for the Indonesian market, with partners among its customers and the adjacent supplier of sulphur trioxide, a key raw material. The company was renamed P.T. Albright & Wilson Manyar. A Ballestra sulphonation plant was built and commissioned towards the end of 1990, to expand capacity from 7,000 to 21,000 tpa. The factory became a showpiece in its efficiency and cleanliness and within 16 months was operating to capacity. In 1991 the product range was extended by the addition of a plant to make amine derivatives. One consequence of the success of the Indonesian

Roha, India, showing the surfactants plant taken over from Dharamsi Morarji 1998; inset Ishwar Khandelwal, the Managing Director of Albright, Morarji & Pandit.

Albright, Morarji & Pandit's 25th anniversary celebration 1991; the AMP Board.

LABS (linear alkyl benzene sulphonate) plant at Roha (1991), with Peter Salmon & Robin Paul.

Polyphosphates Inc. (Philippines) sodium tripolyphosphate plant packing area.

LII

Tony Baldry at the opening of the raffinate plant.

LIII

company was the decline in the operations at Jurong (Singapore) whose old sulphonation plant was not competitive. For a time the plant made sulphonic acid, surfactant blends and heavy duty liquid detergents but within ten years manufacturing ceased.

In the **Philippines**, where A&W had been engaged in the manufacture of polyphosphates since 1980, through Polyphosphates Inc., its joint venture with Chemphil Corporation, there was a move into surfactants through a second joint venture with Chemphil. In 1990 A&W paid $1.8 million for a 40% equity holding in Chemphil Specialty Chemical Corporation (CSCC), which had been formed in 1989 to build a 14,000 tpa Ballestra sulphonation plant at San Pascual Batangas, 75 miles south of Manila. The plant came on stream in early 1991 but commissioning was prolonged until August 1991, when commercial production started, to make initially sodium coconut fatty alcohol sulphate (which the Philippine government required detergent producers to use to replace 60% of the sulphonic acids hitherto used, mainly in detergent bars), alkylbenzene sulphonate and sodium lauryl sulphate. An unusual investment for A&W was the shareholding taken by A&W Australia in 1993 in a fast-track power generation project at Batangas, one of the steps being taken by the government to overcome the chronic power shortage; the investment promised to be highly profitable but did not live up to its promise and was disposed of some years later.

A&W's largest interest in **Thailand**, its 30% holding in Thai Polyphosphates & Chemicals, continued to be profitable in this period, despite growing competition from imports, and extended its range of phosphates into food and other specialities. The extension of the operations of A&W's other investment in Thailand, AWAT Thai, into acrylics has already been described (p.256). Also added to AWAT Thai's activities was the production of heavy duty liquid detergents, with an initial small plant in 1991 and a larger plant in 1993.

This was a period of development and growing prosperity for Albright, Morarji & Pandit (AMP) in **India**. Hitherto, manufacturing had been confined to phosphates, mainly STPP, produced at the factory at Ambarnath, north of Bombay, using sulphuric acid produced at Roha, to the south of Bombay. At the beginning of 1991, the first step in surfactants was taken with the commissioning of a plant at Roha to make linear alkylbenzene sulphonate for supply to Hindustan Lever and other detergent manufacturers. In November 1991 AMP celebrated its 25th anniversary. In 1993, AMP acquired from Dharamsi Morarji, A&W's main partner in AMP, its surfactant operation at Roha, based on a Chemithon sulphonation unit, together with a spray dryer enabling powder products to be produced. The plant had been operating at a very low level and required considerable refurbishment, under the direction of AMP's Managing Director, Ishwar Khandelwal, the driving force behind the creation in AMP of an environment of clean and efficient operation well above the average.

In 1990, A&W's partner in **Australia**, ICI Australia, decided that it wished to dispose of its interest. The price at which ICI offered its shareholding to A&W was not accepted and so the shares were then put up for auction, i.e. bids were invited, without success. Meanwhile A&W had discussions with the Salim Group of Indonesia, one of the shareholders in both EMPL and Chemphil, to see if it would like to take the place of ICI Australia. In December 1990 a deal was done, for A&W to acquire ICI Australia's holding and for Salim to acquire 50% of A&W Australia excluding the speciality operations based on Box Hill, principally the acrylics business. Those operations, which accounted for 10% of A&W Australia's £35 million sales, were hived off into a wholly-owned subsidiary of A&W, Albright & Wilson Specialities. For the Salim group, with chemical interests extending from palm plantations through fatty alcohol production and alkylbenzene production to surfactants, as well as phosphoric acid and phosphates, the deal fitted well into its strategy of downstream development. Peter Hoxley remained Managing Director of the joint company and when he retired in 1993 he was succeeded by Geoff Frank, transferred from the Phosphates business group in Warley. Management of the Specialities company was also unchanged, under Bruce Henshaw. After installation of computer controls on the acrylics plant, the company became profitable, after many years of poor profitability.

Prior to that reorganisation the surfactant operations at Box Hill were transferred to Wetherill Park, whose capacity had been expanded, in two stages in 1988 and 1989. The Wetherill Park sulphonation, however, was still based on batch production from Baker Perkins units, which proved to be insufficient. Sulphonic acid was therefore purchased from Lever Rexona's site at Minto, also on the outskirts of Sydney. Early in 1993 Lever decided to close the Minto site and in 1994 A&W Australia bought the Ballestra plant, transferred it to Wetherill Park and closed the Baker Perkins units. That trebled capacity and enabled higher quality products to be produced. It also meant increased sales to Lever in Australia and New Zealand, previously supplied from Minto.

There were significant changes in the phosphates sector of A&W Australia. During 1993 the production of wet phosphoric acid from the Nissan plant (purchased from ICI Australia) ceased because the availability of very competitively-priced Chinese phosphorus made the Nissan acid uneconomic. It was also unsuitable for food phosphates, for which thermal acid was being used, and for which a new plant was being built at Yarraville. Although for some years the change proved advantageous, in the late 1990s the rise in the price of phosphorus led to a restart in wet acid production.

For many years, A&W had been exploring the possibility of investing in **China**, potentially the largest market and most significant producer for chemicals in the region. There were discussions with phosphorus and STPP producers in the early 1980s which came to nothing. A&W did not have any significant technology to contribute: Chinese producers of phosphorus already had Uhde-designed furnaces and efficient STPP plants and there was no interest in purified wet acid since there were plans for major expansion in phosphorus using local deposits of phosphate rock. Reference has already been made (p.320) to the joint venture in 1994 with Hunan Resun Industrial General Corporation for the manufacture of surfactants.

The Environment

One of Robin Paul's declared priorities when he became the chief executive in 1986 was to improve A&W's impact on the environment. He was also active in environmental initiatives outside the Company. In 1989, as Chairman of the Confederation of British Industry's Environmental Committee, he announced the setting up of a CBI unit to help companies implement an action plan for a cleaner environment. In that year A&W became a founder member in the UK of the Responsible Care programme set up by the Chemical Industries Association (CIA). The Responsible Care initiative originated in Canada in 1987; its aim was to improve the chemical industry's performance in all areas of health, safety and the environment. A&W joined the programme in Canada, the USA and Australia.

In November 1990 A&W was one of twelve UK companies that contributed to "Business in the Community" (later renamed "Business in the Environment"), an initiative aimed at increasing environmental awareness throughout business and the community. In accordance with the initiative, the companies agreed to publish a policy statement in their annual reports. A&W's 1990 annual report stated: "Albright & Wilson attaches the highest priority to the protection of the health and safety of its employees, customers, neighbours and others who may come in contact with, or be affected by, its operations or products. It recognises equally its duty to protect the environment both in the vicinity of its operations and elsewhere by the responsible management of its waste materials".

The UK chemical industry also adopted the concept of 'BATNEEC' - Best Available Technique Not Entailing Excessive Cost - based on standards prescribed by Her Majesty's Inspectorate of Pollution. In 1991 Robin Paul was one of 25 representatives of British industry appointed to an Advisory Committee on Business and the Environment set up by the Environment and Industry Secretaries (Michael Heseltine and Peter Lilley); he was also appointed to its sub-committee on Global Warming. A&W's Technical Director, John Adsetts, was a member of the National Advisory Group on Eco-labels.

There was thus in this period something approaching a ferment of concern for the environment, particularly in the chemical industry. In June 1993 the CIA published statistics for 1990-2 showing expenditure of over £1 billion on environmental protection and made it clear that companies could not be members of CIA without signing up to implement Responsible Care.

The steps taken by A&W in this period were well up to the requirements defined. There were several in addition to those already described. In 1989 a programme was started of rolling audits of health, safety and environmental controls and performance. A Health, Safety and Environment Committee and Department and a Public & Regulatory Affairs Department were set up in 1990 and programmes for reduction of waste and emissions instituted, with regular reviews. In 1991 the Widnes site piloted the British Standards Institute standard of environmental performance. The BATNEEC criteria were applied to all new plants and a target was set for existing plants to be brought up to that standard within 5 years. Where that was not practicable, as with the Eltesol plant at Whitehaven, the plant was closed.

Early in his time with A&W, Robin Paul had spoken of his "town hall door" policy, i.e. being open with the facts on the environment. In 1993 A&W began to measure all sites' emissions to air, water and land and in the annual report charts were published showing tonnages for the main items. The target was to reduce emissions (weighted according to hazard rating) by 5% per annum. In 1994, the reduction was 3.5%, which was followed by a sharp drop in 1995, to a plateau of 80-85% of the 1993 levels in the next few years.

The 1989 annual report stated: "Half of the Company's forward capital expenditure is now environmentally driven". That covered not only remedial work on plants to reduce emissions but also new and expanded plants for products that were environmentally-friendly. Those included sodium chlorate (leading to reductions in dioxins in pulp bleaching through substitution for chlorine), low-dioxane sulphonation, chromium plating products (displacing carcinogenic hexavalent compounds), water-soluble agricultural chemicals, phosphorus compounds for the control of plumbosolvency (lead in drinking water), biocides with an improved environmental profile and oil-free drilling fluids. The importance of environmentally-friendly products was demonstrated by taking the example of detergents: with 99% efficiency in materials utilisation, 1,000 out of every 100,000 tonnes made are discharged as effluent at the factory but the remaining 99,000 tonnes enter into domestic effluents after use.

The environmental problems at Whitehaven and the steps taken to overcome them have already been described (p.302-304). The other main problems were associated with the cessation of phosphorus production at Long Harbour, Varennes and Portishead. Although production at Portishead had ceased finally in 1969, the site was contaminated with phosphorus and clean-up proved to be a very slow process, not completed until 2001. The problems at Long Harbour and Varennes were more severe and the remedial action was different. For each, it was necessary to obtain agreement by the provincial authorities to the plan for decommissioning and rehabilitation. The plans for the two sites were similar: that phosphorus and other waste materials should be contained within the site by the use of the slag heaps to cover the deposits in ponds, mud holes, etc.. Consultants were engaged in 1994 to assess the plans and reported that they represented "the most secure approaches". From towards the end of 1994 the Quebec and Newfoundland authorities began issuing certificates for the implementation of the plans.

The estimated costs of closure and remediation of the phosphorus sites had risen since provisions were made in 1988 (£39m.) and in 1991 (£26m.) and so in 1994 an additional provision of £10 million was made. While A&W's costs for site clean-up were undoubtedly much higher than they would have been with more efficient production at the three sites, the problems associated with chemical plant closures generally were a factor not well appreciated earlier. Capital expenditure evaluations had tended not to take into account costs of cessation. 'Terotechnology', the evaluation of the total life-time costs of production including termination, was not a commonly-used tool.

The improvements to chlorine handling and the site rationalisation at Oldbury have already been described (p.309). Another contribution to environmental improvement at Oldbury was the installation of a Combined Heat & Power (CHP) unit in 1992. The £3 million plant, owned by National Power, was capable of producing the factory's requirements for heat and energy at twice the efficiency of conventional power plants. A much larger unit was installed at Whitehaven in 1994 at a cost of £6 million.

At many of A&W's sites steps were taken in this period to reduce liquid and gaseous emissions. When John Markham was appointed as site director at Whitehaven in 1990 he produced a 'Strategy for Environmental Improvement', dealing with airborne emissions and liquid effluents. The former included: powder and fume from spray driers, fishy smells from the amines plant, sooty acidic particles from the boiler chimney, sulphur dioxide and sulphuric acid mist emissions from the sulphuric acid plant and fluorine from the STPP plant. Actions taken included the installation of scrubbers and the closure of inefficient plants, including two of the three sulphuric acid units. The liquids consisted mainly of phosphogypsum containing cadmium and uranium (dealt with by the raffinate plant) and surfactants from plant washings and other discharges, which caused foam in the sea. The surfactant liquids were first contained within the site and then neutralised in a biological treatment unit.

There were several biological treatment plants at other locations, the design of which was based on the unit at EMPL (Singapore). In 1990 plants were installed at Frosinone (Italy) and Alcover (Spain), to be followed by Castiglione. In 1993 a £2 million plant came into operation at St Mihiel. $15 million (£8 million) was spent in 1990-2 on waste water treatment plants at Charleston and Varennes. Other projects in this period to reduce aerial and ground emissions were completed at Widnes, Cincinnati, Jurong and Surabaya. At Vancouver, the replacement of the graphite cells with metal removed the problem of toxic graphite mud. At all sites, there was a new awareness of the priority to be given to environmental improvements.

Health & Safety

There was also growing attention to safety in the workplace, although not involving major capital expenditure. Many years before, A&W's Canadian management had declared safety to be their first priority. The wearing of protective clothing (especially safety spectacles and helmets) was slow to catch on but by the beginning of this period it was almost universal. A&W's 1992 Annual Report included the sentence: "A company's safety performance is an excellent indicator of the general well-being of that company".

As with the environment, several general rules and procedures developed during these years. The 'Hazop' (hazard operability) process, originating from ICI, was adopted by A&W in 1984, for application initially to proposed new plants and later to existing plants. Hazards were classified as low, medium or high according to the flammability and toxicity of the chemicals used and a risk assessment made. In 1987 the Americas embarked on a programme to evaluate existing plants, over a period of five years. Four years later, in June 1991, the accident at Charleston (p.311) occurred because of a combination of circumstances that were deemed unforeseeable. That led to the development of the ZIP (Zero Incident Process), in the Americas and elsewhere.

Also in 1984 the CIMAH (Control of Industrial Major Accident Hazards) regulations were introduced. They required risk analyses and safety reports, in particular the reporting of specific quantities of hazardous substances. Oldbury was required to register for chlorine and phosphine and issued leaflets to 15,000 local residents giving information on what to do in the event of leakages; the changes in the transportation and storage of chlorine, the main hazard, have already been described (p.309). Avonmouth was required to register for propylene oxide, a highly flammable liquid used in the production of flame-retardants.

In October 1989 the Control of Substances Hazardous to Health Regulations (COSHH) came into force. They placed on employers specific duties to ensure that employees and other persons were protected from health risks due to hazardous substances. Risk assessments had to be carried out for each area of potential exposure. A&W appointed a hygienist and a toxicologist and ran occupational health and hygiene courses for UK staff with the assistance of the Institute of

Occupational Health, a department of Birmingham University opened in 1981.

In March 1991 an EC Directive imposed requirements on all manufacturers, importers, distributors and suppliers of dangerous substances or preparations. Safety Data Sheets (SDS) covering all aspects of safety at work were to be in force by June 1993. The UK produced Chemicals (Hazard Information and Packaging) Regulations (CHIP), including an approved code of practice for preparing SDS. Also, the Chemical Industries Association in 1991 introduced 'Chemsafe', a scheme for members to respond to incidents involving chemicals at factories or in transit, to which A&W Oldbury responded by acquiring a vehicle equipped for call-outs. In the USA a Process Safety Management Law was introduced in 1992, covering the management and control of highly hazardous chemicals. In 1993 Tenneco carried out a Risk Management Review, led by Tenneco's General Counsel (chief lawyer), which was aimed at reducing the risk of legal action on health and safety issues.

A&W willingly accepted these manifold regulations, which were paralleled by the Company's own moves. In 1985 a Health and Safety Improvement Plan was produced for the period 1985-7. The Martin Rowe (named after a former Whitehaven site manager) Safety Award was introduced, for the site showing the most improvement in its safety record each year. Some sites had incentives for good safety performance, even including the award of a car. A Health, Safety and Environment Department was created, with a Health and Safety Advisory Committee.

One of the main measurements of success in improving safety at work was the frequency of Lost Time Accidents (LTAs), i.e. accidents preventing the person from returning to work at the next shift. In 1985 the frequency was 1.23 per 100,000 hours worked. That was reduced year by year to below 1.0 in 1988 but then increased in the next three years to between 1.3 and 1.4. It fell below 1.0 in 1993 and in 1994 reached 0.32. In that year, A&W recorded only 39 LTAs world-wide, against 76 in 1993. An example of the progress in this period was Whitehaven, which had 43 LTAs in 1989, falling year by year to 6 in 1993. Port Maitland maintained its record of avoiding LTAs, reaching 23 years free of LTAs in 1994. There were several awards by the Royal Society for the Prevention of Accidents (RoSPA).

Nevertheless it was still admitted that A&W was not among the leading chemical companies in its accident record. Although LTAs had fallen, there were still serious incidents. Dr John Adsetts, the Technical Director, wrote in 1993: "in the past five years we have had a series of incidents - fatalities, serious injuries, explosions, fires and emissions at Avonmouth, Oldbury, Portishead, Whitehaven, Barcelona, Charleston, Buckingham, Yarraville, Varennes, Ambarnath, Surabaya, Manila, Monroe…". He urged that every incident should be reported, especially any fires. In 1990 there were two fires caused by phosphorus at Oldbury and Portishead, which fortunately were dramatic rather than damaging, and of course there was the very serious accident at Charleston in 1991. It is arguable that such incidents were not preventible. What is undisputed is that the general level of plant control and good housekeeping was immensely better than twenty years before.

The Flotation

The financial pressures on Tenneco and the general move away from diversified or conglomerate businesses eventually brought to pass the divestment of Albright & Wilson, for which flotation rather than a trade sale was chosen.

Earlier attempts

On several occasions, as has been recorded in earlier chapters, Tenneco contemplated disposing of Albright & Wilson. In 1988, when Tenneco's cash crisis led to the sale of Tenneco Oil, there were advocates of disposing of the non-energy businesses, including A&W, but it was thought that they would not raise enough cash to achieve the improvement desired. Some three years later, when Mike Walsh and Dana Mead were embarking on major changes in Tenneco, their view of the six businesses then constituting the conglomerate whole was that each business, despite many competitive strengths, had serious flaws or looming troubles. Disposal of the whole of A&W at that time would, however, have been very difficult. The easier course, disposing of the pulp chemicals operations, was chosen as part of the initial rescue plan and announced within a month of Mike Walsh's becoming Chief Executive.

Nevertheless, Mike and Dana were still looking to shed A&W, which was a small unit, not linked to Tenneco's main businesses, headquartered outside the USA, not a platform for significant growth and never well understood. Early in 1992 the process of disposal was started, with a team from Lazards in London. Lazards had had dealings with Mike Walsh when he was in Union Pacific and earlier. The plan was to sell the shares through an Initial Public Offering (IPO) since the prospects of finding a buyer on satisfactory terms were not good (and that route had failed on earlier occasions). The project was assigned the code word 'Tempest' and intensive work proceeded with merchant bankers, lawyers and accountants. In the next few months, however, two obstacles to a flotation became clear. The lesser one was the estimated $300 million tax liability that would be incurred, which would reduce the proceeds and adversely affect Tenneco's published profits. The liability arose from the difference between the price paid by Tenneco for the first half of the A&W shares (acquired under the 1971 terms) and the possible realization. The greater problem was the potential liability for dealing with environmental issues, notably the clean-up of the three phosphorus manufacturing sites.

Lazards advised that a public flotation would not be possible with a large overhanging liability. Dames & Moore (prominent international environmental consultants) were commissioned to survey the sites and advise on the 'environmental impact statement' that would be required for the prospectus. Their report made it clear that a flotation would not be feasible unless the liabilities were defined after agreement with the authorities concerned or Tenneco was prepared to give an open-ended commitment in circumstances over which they would not have control. The attempt to float was then abandoned in July 1992, after the expenditure of nearly £1 million in fees and expenses.

Successful flotation

Early in 1994 Lazards was asked by Bob Blakely, Tenneco's senior financial officer, to consider again the possibility of an IPO, in the light of the progress made by A&W towards solving its main environmental problems. In June 1994 Lazards and BZW (Barclays de Zoete Wedd) were selected to advise on and manage a possible flotation in the first Quarter of 1995. It was still possible that a buyer for the whole company would emerge and it was thought that the existence of an IPO as an alternative would ensure that a bid would not result in a 'fire sale', as had occurred with the pulp chemicals sale, even if Tenneco's wish to dispose of A&W was well known. In an interview with The Financial Times when the flotation was announced, however, Dana Mead said that there had been talks with several companies about buying A&W but they had failed because the potential buyers "wanted to cream off what they regarded as the better parts".

A lot of preparatory work was required to disentangle A&W from the rest of Tenneco. For tax reasons, A&W's operations in Canada and Spain had been merged with Case and other units of Tenneco. Also, A&W Americas was directly owned by Tenneco Inc. and the company chosen for flotation (whose name was changed from Tenneco International Holdings Ltd to Albright & Wilson plc) was the immediate parent company of Albright & Wilson Ltd (renamed Albright & Wilson UK Ltd), and had other subsidiaries that had to be stripped out. A&W also had loans with Tenneco, which were settled after the flotation. And it was necessary for A&W to make separate arrangements for insurance, treasury and other operations, estimated to cost £3.5 million per annum.

Dames & Moore were hired again to make a worldwide environmental assessment. Their report included the statements: "The environmental practices of the Group and its associated companies were generally observed to be proactive in terms of compliance with regulation...No significant issues were identified by us that were previously unknown to Albright & Wilson's management, and all the significant compliance and remediation issues identified are in the process of being addressed....The Group's remediation plans; including those prepared for Long Harbour and Varennes, represent the most secure approaches to the decommissioning and remediation of the sites in terms of safety for health and protection of the environment and are based upon the use of economical and proven technological methods". Furthermore, Tenneco agreed to indemnify A&W against any costs of decommissioning Long Harbour in excess of the provisions in the accounts at the end of 1994.

Tenneco's intention to float A&W was announced in December 1994. Dana Mead stated: "Tenneco is planning the flotation of Albright & Wilson as part of our programme to refocus on our stated core businesses of packaging, automotive parts and natural gas operations". The 1994 Annual Report of Tenneco defined one of its strategies as being "to reduce Tenneco's overall cyclicality, which means reducing our exposure as a corporation to markets with sharp fluctuations in demand and pricing...Case and Albright & Wilson were among the most cyclical businesses we had in Tenneco". The report went on to record: "The company (A&W)...has strengthening worldwide demand, respected senior management, and prospects for continued gains in operating income". Tenneco's 1995 Annual Report, referring to the flotation of A&W, said "we only offer strong companies with enhanced growth prospects to the market: not cripples stripped of cash, assets, and potential by short-term or expedient tactics". It is tempting to question how far events and actions by Tenneco before and after the flotation supported these statements.

When the forthcoming flotation was announced in mid-December 1994, the general expectation was that Tenneco would raise about £600 million, which was based on a price of 180-185p. per share for about 325 million shares. Press comment was generally favourable, based on an upward trend of results in 1991-3 but a warning note was sounded by The Financial Times: "investors' enthusiasm should be tempered. For a start, they should ask why Tenneco has chosen to float Albright instead of selling to a trade buyer - an option it has sought for at least a decade. The main reason is that the US conglomerate thinks it will receive a better price from a float. But potential investors will wonder why they should pay more than trade buyers are willing to put up".

In the next few weeks, Robin Paul and the Financial Director, Michael Winstanley, made the rounds of over 100 institutions. The climate for a flotation worsened, with a slump in the new issues market and a belief that the chemicals sector was in for a tough time, through rising input prices and pressure on sales. There were also specific factors for A&W. The indicated pre-tax profit for 1994 was reduced by £20 million, which included £10m. for environmental costs and £3.6m. for a currency exchange loss on the recent purchase of a holding in Troy Mexico, as the peso lost 40% of its value because of a severe political and economic crisis in Mexico. Institutions also believed that Tenneco had no alternative but to sell. It was true that if the issue had been pulled a subsequent flotation would probably have been more difficult. In those circumstances, Dana Mead agreed to cut the price to

150p. per share, which represented a price/earnings ratio for 1995 of 10 against 14 for the chemicals sector. The stock was fully booked with institutions within 2 hours.

The gross proceeds of the sale of 313,500,000 shares amounted to £470.25m.. The net received by Tenneco was $700 million (about £452 million, including a final dividend of £50 million). Tenneco recorded a loss on the sale of $170 million including tax charges of $115 million.

Out of the total of 313,500,000 shares, 15% (47,025,000) were reserved for the public. There were applications for 216,546,000 shares, i.e. 4.6 times the number available. 1,540,000 shares were allocated in priority to employees, who had been offered 1 free share for each subscribed for, up to 225 shares. Applications by the general public were allotted in full up to 400 shares and then scaled down, with no allotment for 150,000 and over. The shares went to a premium when dealings opened, being in the range 162-165 up to the beginning of April, and then in the range 170-175. Later, the price rose briefly to over 200p.

Soon after the flotation, Dana Mead issued a message to all A&W employees. In it he said: "Tenneco has been proud of its association with the fine people of Albright & Wilson for 17 years. It makes sense for solid, strategic reasons for A&W to resume its status as a privately owned corporation. A&W can once again focus all of its resources on strengthening its businesses and regaining recognition as a distinct company with its own proud history. But it's difficult for friends to separate. We offer our sincere thanks to the A&W employees around the world who have been a part of Tenneco's colourful history during almost two decades. You have been full contributors to Tenneco's turnaround and transformation. You were a vital part of our success, and we all - at corporate headquarters and in your partner operating divisions - appreciate your hard work and the results you have achieved. I have the highest respect for Robin Paul and his leadership team. They have helped Tenneco become a global competitor and have managed the flotation superbly. A&W could not be in better hands".

Robin Paul's response included these words: "It is a rare event for a company to be taken over by an overseas group and re-emerge many years later as a restructured and repositioned international business able to attract a whole new set of investors. We are grateful to Tenneco for the exciting opportunity we have been given, and we look forward to maintaining the many personal friendships built up over the years spent in the Tenneco family".

*****

So ended 24 years of Tenneco involvement with A&W. It had been preceded by 23 years of full independence. The next and final stage was to be very much shorter, less than 5 years.

Chapter 8

THE CONCLUDING YEARS

1995 - 2000

"The Board of Albright & Wilson plc has for some time been seeking to pursue a strategy of participation in the consolidation of our industry which could create long term value for our shareholders. It has become increasingly apparent that our options to achieve this are limited as an independent public company in current market conditions"
(Sir Christopher Benson, March 1999)

Overview

For Albright & Wilson the period started with optimism but trading deteriorated and from a weakened position it was not possible to avoid submergence.

Political and economic background

1995:
- Austria, Sweden and Finland joined the European Union
- USA & IMF $53bn credit for Mexico, following 40% fall in peso in December 1994
- Collapse of Barings Bank
- Dayton, Ohio, agreement re Bosnia

1996:
- Introduction of landfill tax
- Taliban captured Kabul
- Clinton re-elected President

1997:
- Death of Deng Xaioping
- General Election: Labour 419 seats, Conservative 165. Tony Blair Prime Minister.
- Bank of England to control interest rates.
- William Hague leader of the Conservative party
- Hong Kong handed over to China. East Asia financial crisis started.
- Tax credits on UK dividends abolished
- Death of Diana, Princess of Wales
- FTSE 100 index fell 615 points (October)

1998:
- Good Friday peace agreement in Northern Ireland
- FTSE 100 index reached record 6,515 points (July)
- Second largest fall in Dow Jones index (August)

1999:
- Brazilian devaluation caused world fall in share prices
- Euro in operation for trading
- Dow Jones index over 10,000 (March)
- UK basic income tax rate 22%; minimum wage £3.60 per hour
- Elections for Scottish parliament and Welsh assembly
- Antitrust suit launched against Microsoft

- Debt relief for poorest countries
- Serbian army left Kosovo
- Putin Prime Minister of Russia

2000
- Opening of Millennium Dome (January)
- Y2K computer problems minimal.

In most respects, the five years after 1994 were a period of favourable economics. In the United States and Western Europe there was uninterrupted growth in domestic product, inflation was falling and in the UK there was also a substantial fall in unemployment. There were, however, some adverse factors in the UK, particularly affecting A&W: the weakness of continental European currencies, a sharp downturn in the Far East and a shrinkage of the manufacturing base.

From the beginning of 1995 up to the first Quarter of 2000, the £ was stable against the US dollar, with quarterly values in the range 1.52-1.66. The Japanese yen weakened from mid-1995 up to the third Quarter of 1998, reaching over 230 yen:£, against 135 in mid-1995, but then strengthened to around 160 in mid-2000. Most importantly for the UK, the continental European currencies declined during the whole of this period. When the timetable for the introduction of the Euro was set in mid-1995, the Euro was worth about 85p. By the beginning of 1999, when it came into operation commercially, it was worth 70p and in the next two years fell to around 60p. The equivalent rate for the deutschemark moved from about 2.25 in 1995 to 3.20 at the beginning of 2000.

From the middle of 1997 there was a severe general downturn in the Asian economies. Booms in investment were followed by large current deficits and heavy borrowings, leading to a flight of capital. The Thai baht was devalued in July 1997 by over 40%. That was followed by a fall of 75% in the value of the Indonesian rupiah and over the 6 months to February 1998 there was an average fall of 43% in the value of Asian currencies. The downturn and movement in the currencies caused a sharp fall in exports from the UK.

Other features of the economic scene in this period were:

- the UK retail price index rose by less than 3% pa
- UK gdp at constant prices rose by an average of 2.5% pa but the rise in manufacturing was less than 1% pa
- UK producer input prices, after rising by nearly 10% in 1995, fell by one-sixth in the next four years
- UK producer output prices rose by 4% in 1995 and then by only 5% over the next four years

- the net rate of return for UK manufacturing rose from around 8% at the end of 1994 to over 13 % at the beginning of 1998 but then fell to less than 6% at the end of 1999
- UK unemployment fell from 8.9% of the employable population in 1995 to 6.2% in 1999
- the UK balance of payments improved from a £3.9bn deficit in 1995 to a surplus of £6.6bn in 1997 but then deteriorated to a deficit of nearly £10bn in 1999
- UK bank base rate, 6.25% at the beginning of 1995, rose to 7.5% in June 1998, falling to 5% in 1999
- the FT industrial Ordinary index rose from 2,328 at the end of 1994 to 4,021 at the end of 1999 almost uninterruptedly except for a fall from August to December 1998.

Albright & Wilson as a public company

Albright & Wilson managed the transition from the wholly-owned subsidiary of an American company to an independent quoted company without a hiccup but was to find that outside the Tenneco umbrella survival as a medium-size industrial company was a hard struggle.

Albright & Wilson's results

Because of the takeover of the Company in 1999, the latest period for which results were published was the year 1998. In broad terms, total sales and operating profits moved within a fairly narrow range from 1994 to 1998 but downturns became apparent during the first half of 1996, affecting particularly the UK. The three tables below outline the results.

A&W progress 1994 - 1998

(£ million)

	1994	1995	1996	1997	1998
Sales: subsidiaries	641.6	703.2	703.4	665.2#	730.3#
Share of associated companies	101.8	141.0	154.2	119.7#	84.6#
	743.4	**844.2**	**857.6**	**784.9#**	**814.9#**
Operating profit	62.6	64.1	70.5	68.4	59.7
Exceptional items	-6.7*	-5.0	-3.5	-28.9	-7.9
Interest (net)	-11.5	-4.1	-4.5	-7.8	-3.5
Pretax profit	**44.4**	**55.0**	**62.5**	**31.7**	**48.3**
Tax	12.4	16.5	18.9	16.3	14.0
Profit after tax	32.0	38.5	43.6	15.4	34.3
Earnings per share (pence)	10.2	12.3	13.9	4.8	10.8
Dividends (pence)	*	6.5	6.9	7.15	7.15
Capital expenditure	42.4	42.1	39.8	60.2	51.1
Acquisitions & investments	1.3	0.8	3.4	25.0	22.0
Net capital employed (incl. borrowings)	**273.8**	**404.7**	**409.5**	**459.7**	**494.6**
Borrowings	9.0	53.4	56.2	124.6	161.1
Gearing (%) (net debt : net capital employed)	3.3	13.2	13.7	27.1	32.6

* 1994 adjusted to comprise post-flotation group; £3.7 million charges for Troy exchange loss excluded; dividends in 1994 to Tenneco exceptional as part of flotation terms. # presentation changed to exclude freight costs recharged to customers, reducing 1997 total by £56.6m.

A&W results analysed by business 1994 - 1998

(£ million)	1994	1995	1996	1997	1998
Sales: Phosphates	236.9	263.7	289.4	300.3	318.6
Surfactants	263.1	296.6	288.5	284.5	308.6
Phosphorus Derivatives & Acrylics	200.8	230.3	224.7	200.1	187.7
	700.8	**790.6**	**802.6**	**784.9**	**814.9**
Operating Profit before exceptional items:					
Phosphates	36.9	40.9	39.9	32.0	31.2
Surfactants	8.6	7.7	13.7	17.6	18.0
Phosphorus Derivatives & Acrylics	18.5	19.6	20.9	22.7	15.5
Corporate costs	-1.4	-4.1	-4.0	-3.9	-5.0
	62.6	**64.1**	**70.5**	**68.4**	**59.7**

[1] See table note A opposite.

A&W results analysed by geographical area 1994 - 1998

(£ million)	1994	1995	1996	1997	1998
Sales by origin: UK	269.2	286.8	290.8	253.8	241.3
Continental Europe	183.7	208.3	205.3	180.6	199.7
Americas	196.4	241.7	243.7	232.4	270.1
Asia Pacific	94.1	107.4	117.8	118.1	103.8
	743.4	**844.2**	**857.6**	**784.9**	**814.9**
Op. Profit by origin: UK	27.8	30.6	30.6	24.6	10.7
Continental Europe	8.8	5.1	9.8	12.5	14.4
Americas	17.0	20.0	23.2	21.4	26.1
Asia Pacific	9.0	8.4	6.9	9.9	8.5
	62.6	**64.1**	**70.5**	**68.4**	**59.7**
Sales by destination: UK	172.2	179.4	186.8	168.3	160.6
Continental Europe	221.2	255.2	247.8	213.5	228.9
Americas	203.0	249.2	251.6	238.5	272.5
Asia Pacific	121.4	134.7	148.0	144.4	127.3
Rest of World	25.6	25.7	23.4	20.2	25.6
	743.4	**844.2**	**857.6**	**784.9**	**814.9**

[2] See table note B opposite.

(Table note A) In 1997 phosphorus halides and phosphonates were transferred from Phosphates to the Specialities group, which was renamed Phosphorus Derivatives & Acrylics. The figures for 1994-6 have been restated to follow that definition. They also exclude freight etc. in all years.

(Table note B) In the absence of figures for sales by destination for the associated companies it has been assumed that their sales were within the region of origin.

Organisation & Management

The Board of Albright & Wilson plc **at flotation** comprised:

• Sir Christopher Benson (Chairman): non-executive, aged 61, Chairman of Sun Alliance (insurance) and Costain (engineering) and previously Boots (retail chemists, etc.) and MEPC (property); also a member of the Panel on Takeovers & Mergers; he became a Director of A&W in January 1995

• Dr Robert (Robin) Paul (Chief Executive): aged 59, a chemical engineer, joined A&W in 1986 as Managing Director after 27 years in ICI, finally as Deputy Chairman of Mond Division

• Michael Winstanley (Financial Director): aged 58, with a degree in law, joined A&W in 1959 and became a Director in 1990, when President of Albright & Wilson Americas, before becoming Financial Director in 1993

• Dr John Adsetts (Technical Director): aged 50, with a PhD in chemistry, serving in ICI from 1968 to 1983, when he joined MTM (speciality chemicals) and became a Director, before joining A&W as Technical Director in 1987

• Hans Lottig: non-executive, aged 63, a lawyer who joined Shell in 1967 and was a member of the Board of Deutsche Shell from 1979 and Chief Executive of Deutsche Shell Chemie; he became a non-executive Director of A&W in 1990

• Nicholas Barber: non-executive, aged 54, Chief Executive of Ocean Group 1986-94, Deputy Chairman of Royal Insurance, a non-executive Director of Barings and Bristol & West Building Society and a governor of the London Business School; he became a Director of A&W in January 1995

• Michael Garner: non-executive, aged 57, a non-executive Director of Clyde Petroleum, acting Chairman of Taunton Cider, a member of the Accounting Standards Board and a former Finance Director of TI Group (engineering).

The five Business Groups were headed by:

• *Phosphates*: Ian Black, aged 54, a chartered accountant who joined A&W in 1967 and became Sales Director of Surfactants in 1979, becoming General Manager of Phosphates in 1986 and of Surfactants in 1987, returning to Phosphates in 1991

• *Surfactants*: John Markham, aged 48, a chemical engineer, serving in ICI from 1969 until he joined A&W in 1989 as manager of the Whitehaven site, becoming General Manager of Surfactants in 1993

• *Speciality Chemicals*: John Ullmer, aged 50, with a degree in chemistry, serving in ICI and then May & Baker from 1965 until he joined A&W in 1971, holding positions in Phosphates until becoming manager of Paper Chemicals in 1988; he became General Manager of Speciality Chemicals in 1991, after the sale of Paper Chemicals

• *Americas*: Paul Rocheleau, aged 40, a chemical engineer from the University of Delaware who joined DuPont and then Mobil Chemicals, acquired by A&W in 1985, after which he spent time at A&W's Head Office in London as a business analyst before returning to the USA as a business manager; he became President of A&W Americas in 1993

• *Asia Pacific*: Lyell Work, aged 56, a chemical engineer from the University of Alberta, serving in Comalco from 1961 until he joined Erco in 1967; after a period at Long Harbour he worked in London as a business analyst 1976-9 before returning to North America; he became President of A&W Asia Pacific, based in Singapore, in 1991.

Management changes post-flotation

In August 1995 Ian Black and Paul Rocheleau were appointed to the Board, to increase the business representation. They retained their previous responsibilities for the Americas and Phosphates. The a move was welcomed by the stock market. Ian Black also took over responsibility for Surfactants. John Markham, initially offered the position of Operational Manager, Surfactants Europe, left the Company. John Ullmer moved from Specialities to take charge of Surfactants sales and all business groups' purchasing. Appointed as General Manager, Speciality Chemicals, based at Warley, was Mike DeRuosi, a Vice-President of A&W Americas, who was given commercial responsibility for Specialities in both Europe and the Americas. These organisational changes were in response to loss-making in Surfactants in the

UK and Spain and the wish to achieve greater coordination in Specialities developments in the UK and the USA.

In November 1995 Ken Lever (aged 42), who had become Arthur Andersen's youngest UK partner in 1985 and became Finance Director of Alfred McAlpine (construction) in 1991, joined the Board as Finance Director. He succeeded Michael Winstanley, who was to remain an executive Director until his retirement in August 1996. Ken Lever was one of the very few appointments to a senior executive position in Albright & Wilson who had not been promoted from within the Company or brought in through an acquisition (the others since 1951 being Ed Kinsley, Robin Paul and John Adsetts). As such, Ken's impressions of the Company when he joined it are of particular interest. He observed that the organisation was complex and somewhat confusing because of the inconsistent ways of managing business (Phosphates, Surfactants, Specialities) and geographical (Europe, Americas, Asia Pacific) responsibilities; the structure was to remain an incomplete matrix - not unusual in international companies with diverse operations. He was also struck by the lack of emphasis on cash, with the relatively high dividend and plans involving considerable capital expenditure but much of the cash generated not being remitted to the UK. At the time gearing was low but borrowing was likely to rise quite rapidly. The Company had a high cost structure, although much of its business was in commodity rather than speciality chemicals, and in some respects was geared to manage the more diversified operations that existed before the divestments of the latter years of Tenneco ownership.

In April 1996 there was a further step in streamlining the management of Phosphates and Surfactants, providing for common management of the functions of production, purchasing and administration and giving fuller profit accountability to the country managers in Italy, France and Spain. There was no place in the new structure for John Ullmer, who left the Company after 25 years' service.

In February 1997 it was announced that Robin Paul would be retiring at the end of July, upon reaching 62, the normal retirement age for executive Directors. He had led the Company through the final period of Tenneco's ownership and the early years of public ownership. He had promoted a much-needed strengthening of A&W's technical resources and had made a particular contribution to the elimination of environmental problems, within the Company and more widely. During the years of Tenneco ownership, the divestments (especially Paper Chemicals and Pulp Chemicals) and the background problems of Tenneco had been negative factors; there had been little real growth in sales of the continuing businesses and while profits had shown some growth there were exceptional charges for rationalisation, environmental remediation and writing down unprofitable businesses. Some of the growth in profit after the recession of 1991 was attributable to favourable economic circumstances, particularly the weakness of sterling, which were to reverse later. In summary, for a variety of reasons, Robin Paul's time was more a period of holding the fort than achieving a leap forward.

Robin's successor was Paul Rocheleau, aged 43, who came to A&W when the Mobil Chemicals operations were acquired in 1985, had become President of Albright & Wilson Americas in February 1993 and had been appointed to the main Board in August 1995. Like Robin Paul, he was a Chemical Engineer. He had been particularly responsible for building up A&W's operations in the Americas, culminating in the acquisition of an interest in Troy, in Mexico. Paul brought enthusiasm, energy and optimism but no experience of acting as chief executive of a public company. He declared that he had no plans for a radical shift in strategy, saying "I am looking for evolution rather than revolution". He went on to say: "The continuous improvement of our internal systems, as outlined in the seven core values, will provide the platform to capture new opportunities for A&W". The seven core values were defined as:

- The development of Human Resources
- The manufacture and shipment of products at the lowest possible cost
- The achievement of operational integrity with respect to safety, environmental performance and product stewardship
- The achievement of excellent Customer Service
- The rapid and effective commercialisation of new products and processes
- The formulation of innovative customer and supplier alliances
- The continuous improvement of Business Processes and Systems.

In an interview with The Birmingham Post he said that he wanted to shed A&W's image as a "146-year old Birmingham business that plods along". "We are taking a number of actions", he said, "to support more aggressive growth. Historically there has been marginal turnover growth, but we have taken out a lot of costs to drive forwards. I want to use our worldwide platform to expand geographically and into higher value downstream products". Against the background of some disappointment with A&W's recent forecasts and results, the deck-clearing that followed his appointment carried with it the risk that any further shortfalls in profits that occurred in the near future would severely dent confidence in the company. And so it proved.

In March 1997 it was announced that Gabriel Kow would become President of Albright & Wilson Asia Pacific, based in Singapore, from June 1st and would also become a Director of the main Board. Lyall Work, who had been President of Asia Pacific since 1951, succeeded Paul Rocheleau as President of Albright & Wilson Americas. Gabriel Kow, aged 48, was Managing Director and Country Manager - Greater China for Glaxo Wellcome and had a degree in Chemical Engineering from Melbourne. He had spent 22 years in Australia and had become the head of speciality chemicals for Glaxo in Asia at the age of 32. He had built up a reputation for turning round businesses.

Gabriel proceeded to make organisational changes and key new appointments in Asia Pacific, including putting the management of the two Australian companies under one chief executive, appointing new managers in the Philippines, Singapore, Thailand, Korea and Taiwan, and new finance directors for Asia Pacific and Albright & Wilson (Australia). He took action to integrate the Asia Pacific operations, clarify lines of responsibility, eliminate unprofitable activities and reduce costs. "We need to enhance our productive assets in the region", he said, "especially in India and China, and to lift capacity in derivative products throughout the region in order to widen our margins". His vision for Asia Pacific was that it would provide "a major engine for A&W's growth worldwide". Despite the economic and currency crisis in Asia from mid-1997, profits in that year (in £) were substantially higher than in 1996.

A few days after Paul Rocheleau became Chief Executive, Ian Black was appointed to the new position of Chief Operating Officer and President - Europe. The Press announcement explained the position as follows: "In his new role Mr Black will co-ordinate raw material supply, the installation of operating processes and intra group customer relationships. He will also oversee the European administrative functions". The Annual Report for 1997 clarified the position a little, describing Ian's role as "the coordination of our relationships with multinational customers and suppliers". It was never clear, however, whether the appointment was anything more than a recognition of Ian's leading position, based on a depth of experience with A&W that Paul Rocheleau did not possess. The appointment lasted for less than 18 months; Ian retired in December 1998, at the age of 58.

In September 1997 there was a realignment of the business groups through the transfer of phosphorus halides (oxychloride, trichloride) and phosphonates from the Phosphates group to Specialities, renamed Phosphorus Derivatives & Acrylics (PD&A). The new groupings were described as being based on the technologies involved. Mike DeRuosi was the general manager for PD&A for both Europe and the Americas. Separate general managers for Europe and the Americas were appointed for Phosphates and for Surfactants, while in Asia Pacific there were also individuals responsible for development in each of the groups. Paul Rocheleau published targets for return on sales for each of the three business groups: 12% for Phosphates, 8% for Surfactants and 15% for PD&A - to produce a return on sales for the Company of 11%. The actual figures achieved for 1997 and (1996) were: Phosphates 9.7 (12.5), Surfactants 5.8 (4.4), PD&A 11.1 (9.1), total 8.1 (8.2). The figures were worse in 1998.

In May 1998 the Technical Director, John Adsetts, retired and was replaced by Grey Jennings, but with the title Executive Vice-President - Technology and not a member of the main Board. Grey Jennings, a chemical engineer, came to A&W with the acquisition of Mobil Chemicals in 1985 and had become Vice President Manufacturing & Engineering for Industrial Chemicals in A&W Americas.

On the retirement of Ian Black, Gabriel Kow was appointed President of Europe and Asia. The Press release announcing his appointment included: "Over the past eighteen months he has demonstrated his capability to lead a complex organisation in a difficult economic environment. Albright & Wilson's business in Asia has grown with improved profitability despite devaluations and falling demand in many countries". In March 1999 Gabriel issued, under the title 'The Way Forward', a Company Announcement that made clear his dissatisfaction with the European organisation:

> *"When I was appointed as president of A&W Europe in addition to Asia Pacific on 1 January", he wrote, "my first task was to take a long hard look at the European organisation, the people and the systems. It soon became very clear to me that as a region we had many people with a very great depth of experience who work very hard, often for long hours and under great tension. The systems in place, both administratively and technologically are outdated, inefficient and frequently hamper rather than help the work in hand. The Technology group structure largely emphasises our loyalty to the chemistry and focuses us on asset performance and our systems encourage us to judge success as 'quantity of product' and not as 'market requirements satisfied'. Everywhere I turned I found that the current organisation created administrative duplication. 'Loyalty' to Business or Technology Groups makes cross-functional planning ineffective at a European level; impossible at a corporate level. Everyone has different priorities and their own 'unique' way of doing things. At the same time it became equally clear to me that salvation lies in responding to the market and not in asset management".*

He went on to announce changes in organisation. There were to be three marketing groups, bringing together product groups with the same customers, applications and competitors. There were three geographical management groups: North Continental Europe, South Continental Europe and the UK. A Functional Group was to provide services for the other groups. He remarked: "A&W is not a technology-rich company and to realise its full potential must exploit its technology base and product know-how anywhere in the world where we can develop markets and profitably serve customers' needs. I want you all to treat Europe and Asia/Pacific as one contiguous business".

The implementation of Gabriel Kow's strategy was to involve a severe slimming-down in the UK to turn round the losses then being made. He brought in

Cambridge Management Consultants to help in creating a new mindset and making the changes. Because of the need for a 90-day consultation period with the Unions, it was not until July 1999 that Gabriel's programme could be implemented. He identified initial savings in fixed costs of £20 million out of the £100 million cost base in the UK, with a target of £8.3 million in the first year, against which nearly £10.5 million was achieved. 550 employees were made redundant in 1999, working capital was reduced in a few months by £3.5 million and the capital expenditure programme was cut back from £27 million to £12 million, with a substantial reduction in the number of project engineers.. Through concentrating on market-driven activity it was possible to reduce the number of scientists in ITC from around 100 to 30. Improvements in plant efficiency were targeted. The cost of the 1999 programme was nearly £20 million, aimed at achieving savings of £20 million per annum eventually. It is not possible to say what the eventual outcome would have been, because when the programme started the end of Albright & Wilson's independence was already in sight and when that occurred nine months later a new strategy was brought in, with even more profound changes.

Developments

In this period there was a significant decline in the UK-based phosphates operations and increasing emphasis on expansion in the Americas, while the speciality and surfactants businesses disposed of unpromising activities and made limited progress in newer developments.

Phosphates

The European position

The core of A&W's operations continued in this period to be Phosphates, with purified wet phosphoric acid (PWA) its foundation. In the Summer 1995 issue of 'Albright World' there was a confident statement of A&W's strength including the words: "A&W is the only company in the world with a phosphates business in three continents....We are the world leader in purified wet acid (PWA)". In the Annual Report for 1998 there was a similar claim, though couched in less confident terms: "We continue to believe that we have the leading worldwide position in industrial phosphates". The position had, however, been seriously weakened by a significant change in the fundamental competitive position in PWA, caused by two factors - increasing exports of phosphorus from China and the entry of Morocco into PWA.

At the beginning of the 1990s there were several phosphorus plants in China but they were small and mostly based on technology similar to A&W's. There was one plant using Uhde technology with Soderberg electrodes, efficient, well-run and a model of cleanliness. From that point there were major developments, including the largest phosphorus installation in the world, built adjacent to a major deposit of phosphate rock and serviced by a newly-built railway giving communication with a port for exports to world markets. While there were times of scarcity for exports, because of demands within China and occasional shortages of water and power, exports of Chinese phosphorus became an increasingly important factor. Piesterritz, an East German company, made food-grade acid from Chinese phosphorus and, in order to break into the market and demonstrate to the European Commission a case for further subsidised investment, sold phosphoric acid at very low prices. Its initial output of 20,000 tpa was expanded to 60,000 tpa, which had a significant impact on the market.

Inevitably, exports of phosphates from China followed and by 1998 were affecting A&W's sales in Mexico and Brazil as well as in Europe. Although for some time the supply and price of chemicals from China fluctuated - which led A&W to take steps to reduce its dependence on Chinese phosphorus in Australia and Asia - the price of phosphorus from China fell from around $1,500 per tonne in 1995 to $1,000 in 1997 and subsequently to only $800. At that point it was highly competitive with PWA, particularly because only part of the output of PWA was of food grade acid comparable with thermal acid.

A&W had a longstanding relationship with the Moroccan phosphate rock producers, through OCP (Office Cherifien des Phosphates). Moroccan rock had been used from the start of wet phosphoric acid production at Whitehaven. In 1992, when the production of green (unpurified) phosphoric acid at Whitehaven ceased with the closure of F5, a contract was placed with OCP for the importation of green acid. In the following year A&W approached OCP with a proposal for a joint venture to build a plant for the production of 160,000 tpa phosphoric acid of salts grade (suitable for detergent phosphates but not products requiring food-grade acid). The proposal was for the output to be shipped to Whitehaven for purification and for the PWA then to be sold in Europe to companies that would otherwise produce their own PWA. OCP was not interested in a move that was essentially defensive for A&W, to prevent OCP from competing in PWA.

In 1994 the new head of OCP, previously the Moroccan Finance Minister, wanted to attract investment into Morocco, including the building of a PWA plant, and approached A&W for a joint venture. He was seeking a plant to produce 160,000 tpa of food-grade acid, at a cost of $60 million, and submitted to A&W a Letter of Intent for approval. A&W, however, was not interested because of the cost of the plant compared with the investment estimated for an equivalent expansion at Whitehaven, and the belief that there was not a market in Europe for that additional quantity. OCP suggested that acid could be sold to the Americas but A&W did not wish its position as the leading producer there to be undermined. A&W was also concerned at the political risk and apprehensive that there would not be respect for its proprietary technology.

About 6 months after discussions with A&W had been broken off, OCP announced a joint venture with Prayon (the Belgian company historically associated with the development of wet phosphoric acid) for the construction of a 160,000 tpa plant, using Prayon's own PWA technology. Although there was not an immediate market in Europe for such an additional quantity, there was one factor of which A&W was not aware. Budenheim (a German producer of food and other phosphates) had a plant producing nearly 100,000 tpa of acid by its own PWA technology, from green acid supplied by Prayon. Through environmental problems, it had been ordered by the German authorities to close its plant. It had approached OCP-Prayon but had not been willing to pay the then market price for PWA. OCP-Prayon then offered Budenheim a partnership in their joint venture (thought to be a 15% share) and a contract for supply of PWA at a price based on the cost of green acid plus conversion and a small margin, giving a total thought to be about $100 below the market price of $730. The joint venture also captured Rhone-Poulenc's requirement of about 30,000 tpa, at a price well below the market. Although outlets for the production from the plant were thereby obtained, the immediate return on investment seems likely to have been poor, especially since the plant required additional expenditure to make it operate satisfactorily.

Nevertheless, A&W had missed the opportunity to join with the world's biggest vertically-integrated producer of phosphoric acid, giving a dominant position in Europe and an advantage in sales to Arab countries. A hedge against continued strength of sterling and a better match of costs against selling-prices were foregone. The threat of stronger competition in phosphates was increased. At the beginning of 1997 there were further discussions with OCP about business opportunities but after an attempt by A&W to persuade OCP to dispose of its interests in phosphates and the rejection of a counter-proposal from OCP for a joint venture the discussions were terminated. Meanwhile BK Ladenburg, a second German competitor in food phosphates, which was struggling to compete on the basis of thermal phosphoric acid from phosphorus bought from Hoechst, was acquired by the Israeli company Negev, which already owned the third producer, Giulini. On the basis of the Israeli PWA, BK Ladenburg became a keen competitor.

A&W's preference was to invest further substantial sums at Whitehaven. Accordingly in July 1995 the Board directed that a proposal for expansion be brought forward and in November authorisation was given to spend £8.5m. to increase PWA capacity by 30,000 tpa and increase the proportion of high purity acids from the existing plant. The Annual Report for 1995 declared: "The investment will confirm the plant as the world's largest production unit for purified phosphoric acid". There were commissioning problems on the plant, which led to purchases of acid in March 1997 and an overrun of capital expenditure, and the plant did not reach its rated capacity until the end of 1997. There were also problems during 1997 with the supply of green acid from OCP, culminating in running out in December and a claim for compensation from OCP. Production of PWA in 1998 was a record but plant efficiencies were disappointing. Partly because of the strength of sterling but also because Whitehaven had inherent cost disadvantages, some sales became uneconomic. The 1998 Annual Report explained: "Aggressive import competition meant that we had to reduce margins in order to maintain market share. In some instances, where prices being quoted were uneconomic, we decided to sacrifice volume rather than match these". Actions being taken to enhance the performance of Phosphates were listed, the first being: "We will continue to drive technical improvements to our purified acid processes and in particular we will simplify the operations at Whitehaven, allowing us to take out significant cost".

The change in competitive position, including the effects of the strength of sterling, meant that in 18 months £20 million of profits and cash flow were eroded. In the absence of actions to rationalise and reduce costs (such as were introduced from mid-1999, as already described), the financial engine that the UK phosphates business had provided for many years became a loss-maker by 1999.

Both the major tonnage Phosphates products, PWA and STPP, were commodities increasingly subject to price competition. In addition to the competitors already mentioned, there was Thermphos (the name given to the former phosphorus division of Hoechst, spun off under the ownership of Hoechst-Celanese), which was prepared to cut the price of thermal phosphoric acid in order to run its three furnaces at Vlissingen and compete with Chinese phosphorus. Both Israel Chemical Industries and Haifa Chemicals expanded their capacity for PWA and added capacity for STPP and food phosphates. In STPP, there was not only competition from China and Israel but also the impact of the detergent manufacturers' switching from STPP to zeolites. Procter & Gamble reformulated Ariel, which removed 15,000 tonnes of STPP from the UK market, and then announced that it would reformulate its other powder detergents unless the price of STPP were reduced by about 20% from a level already 30% below the sterling price in 1995. A&W was not prepared to supply on those terms. Rhone-Poulenc stepped in, saying that it was its duty to protect the market for phosphates (even if at what A&W believed to be a loss). A&W thus lost the whole of 45,000 tonnes of STPP sales. Unilever continued to take A&W STPP but with diminished profits for A&W and some unreliability of supply because of the age of much of the Whitehaven plant. When Persil tablets were introduced by Unilever in 1998, A&W - which had not exploited its technology in that area - was not asked to supply STPP for them.

One area of profitable growth was food phosphates. In September 1996 the Board approved projects for a £3.5m. upgrading and 50% expansion of the food phosphates plant at Widnes, £2.9m. for a powder blending plant, to enable A&W to supply blends direct to bakery customers instead of to blenders, and £1m. for an automated packaging line. The plant was opened in September 1998. There were also profitable developments in granular STPP and electronic grade phosphoric acid. There was, however, a setback in dicalcium phosphate, used as an abrasive in toothpastes. Although Colgate had used DCP for many years and continued to do so, neither Procter & Gamble nor Unilever did so, with one exception. In 1993 Unilever Indonesia moved to DCP, requiring around 15,000 tpa, which was significant in relation to world consumption at that time of 100,000 tpa. In 1998, however, it reverted to silicates.

The Americas

This period opened with the purchase by A&W of a 50% share in Troy Industries in **Mexico** (p.304) in December 1994 . Troy had been acquired by an investment banking group when spun off by the Mexican government in 1992 as part of its privatisation programme. There was a PWA plant, built in 1969 using Israeli (Israel Mining Industries) technology, which was less capital-intensive than A&W's plants at Whitehaven and Aurora but produced technical rather than food grade acid; it had a capacity of 125,000 tons pa. Also manufactured on site were sulphuric acid, green phosphoric acid and triple superphosphate. The plant was sited on the Gulf coast, with a wharf on deep water, an attractive contract with OCP for the supply of Moroccan phosphate rock, very low cost sulphur, a large domestic market and an excellent workforce (which had been reduced from over 1,000 to around 500 by the new owners) . Sales were $115-120 million, with profits of around $12 million pa. The underflow from the PWA plant was disposed of through the triple superphosphate, so avoiding the expensive alternative of landfill as adopted at Whitehaven. The owners were concerned that Troy was essentially a one-product operation with heavy dependence on one customer (Resistol), taking phosphoric acid for STPP. They were looking for a partner with technology and access to international markets and for operational management. They had discussions with FMC and Monsanto before settling on A&W.

It became apparent that the owners were not long-term investors and so A&W moved in two further stages to acquire 100% ownership. The original 50% holding had cost USD 58.6 m. (£37.8 m.). In October 1997 a further 25% was acquired at a cost of £22.6 m.; the conversion of Troy into a subsidiary company meant, inter alia, that Troy's borrowings of £34.6m. were brought into A&W's balance sheet. A&W exercised its option to acquire the final 25% holding in March 1998 for

$35million (£22m.) plus $5.4m. (£3.3m.) related to 1998 profits. In total, therefore, the investment in Troy had directly cost £85.7m., to which might be added the borrowings assumed, bringing the total up to £120 m., not far short of 25% of the total net capital employed in the A&W group at the end of 1998. Sales of Troy in 1997 were USD138 million (£84m.) and operating profit was USD 17.9 million (£10.8m.); the figures forecast in March 1998 for the full year were sales of £92m. and operating profit of £16m. In financial terms as well as strategically, Mexico had therefore become very significant.

From the time when A&W acquired a shareholding, there was substantial expenditure by Troy on product diversification, expansion, infrastructure and the environment. In 1995 a mothballed NPK fertiliser plant, which had never been operated, was converted to make 33,000 tons pa of STPP, at a cost of $7.5m.. That reduced Troy's dependence on Resistol and enabled the company to increase its exports, from $10m. in 1995 to a target of over $20m. in 1996. In 1996 a UFEX unit was added, to upgrade the technical-grade PWA. The sulphuric acid plant was refurbished at a cost of nearly $5m. and over $3m. was spent on repairs to the pier. A setback to Troy's progress came in October 1996, when Resistol made it known that it proposed to reduce its purchases of PWA from Troy and use its own production. In the following month it ceased to take any acid. That caused Troy to seek other markets, including A&W's operations in Asia Pacific; it also led to a postponement of A&W's increasing its holding. Resistol resumed purchases from Troy in January 1997, but at only about one-third of the previous volume. In February 1997 it was decided to install a spray tower to increase the capacity for STPP to 70,000 tons pa, at a cost of $5 million, to recover the revenue lost through Resistol's move. The Latin American market for STPP was forecast to increase by 15% by 1999 and it was planned to displace imports, mainly from Europe, which accounted for 25% of supplies. Troy's product range was expanded to include monoammonium phosphate, sold for fire extinguishers and liquid fertilisers. In 1998 approval was given to the expenditure of $12m. to upgrade the sulphuric acid plant and there was also a proposal to increase the capacity for green acid.

While Troy was the focus of investment in this period, the PWA plant at **Aurora** achieved increased volumes, for supply primarily to A&W's phosphates plants at Buckingham and Port Maitland. A&W's original partner in the joint venture, Texasgulf, was bought out in 1995 by The Potash Company of Saskatchewan, which in the following year further consolidated its position by the acquisition of the US fertiliser company Arcadia.

A&W's other investment in Latin America was in **Colombia** through its 49% holding, dating from 1985, in Albright & Wilson PAAD Ltd, which had manufacturing sites at Bogota and Cartagena making phosphoric and fumaric acids. A new thermal phosphoric acid plant was opened at Cartagena, Colombia, in 1987.

In August 1998 a multipurpose plant was commissioned at Cartagena to produce calcium phosphates for foods, nutrition supplements and toothpaste. The plant cost £3.2m. and had a capacity of 14,000 tpa of food phosphates, with the ability to make sodium and potassium phosphates as well. A&W's strategy in 1998 included acquiring 100% of PAAD and concentrating operations at Cartagena; the Bogota site was closed in 1999.

The main planks in the strategy were to exploit to the full the cost advantages of Troy, supplying phosphoric acid and phosphates from there within the Americas and more widely, to build on Aurora-Port Maitland-Buckingham for US and Canadian markets, and to establish an additional base in South America. The country chosen for a base was **Brazil**, which not only was the largest of the South American economies but also had achieved an economic stability, the lack of which had deterred investment in earlier times. Brazil was part of the Mercosur, a trading bloc established by Brazil, Argentina, Paraguay and Uruguay. A&W's sales into Brazil had grown to around $30 million pa. In April 1996 discussions were opened with Copebras, a Brazilian chemical company 73% owned by Minorco, part of the Anglo American group, with the balance held by a Brazilian company under US ownership. Copebras owned a phosphate rock mine and produced green phosphoric acid for fertilisers, animal feeds and industrial phosphates, manufactured at a factory at Cubateo, on the coast near San Paolo. Employing over 1,000 people, it was also the leading producer of carbon black in the region. In December 1997 it was announced that Minorco and A&W had signed a Letter of Intent for a joint venture owned 50% by each partner to build a 90,000 tpa technical phosphates plant at Cubateo at a cost of $15m., with completion by the end of 1998. Initially PWA would be supplied from Troy. A&W was, however, concerned that it would be parting with valuable technology for a relatively low return and so formed a strategy, defined in April 1998, for the venture to include the building of a 120,000 tpa PWA plant and for A&W to acquire equity in Copebras and so participate in the company's industrial phosphates and fertiliser business. Then in July 1998 A&W decided to put the project on hold pending the outcome of discussions with Solutia (p.364). It was never proceeded with.

The acquisition of Troy, with its very favourable economics, and the prospects for development in Latin America and more widely provided the basis for a significant expansion for A&W and marked an important shift in the centre of gravity from Europe to the Americas. The investment in Mexico was used as a leverage point for purchases of phosphorus and for transactions with Potash Company of Saskatchewan. There was one negative aspect: the European producers of STPP had traditionally not expanded in developing countries that were principal markets for exports from Europe; A&W's actions in Mexico and Brazil broke with that tradition and were believed to be a contributory factor in the loss of 30,000 tpa of Whitehaven's exports, taken by its European competitors. It is, however, probable that Whitehaven's economic disadvantages would have made such exports unprofitable in any event.

Phosphorus Derivatives & Acrylics

During this period the specialities business was re-focused, to develop its strengths and divest several operations that were unprofitable, some of which had been part of 'Specialities' over a long period. Technical effort within the company was concentrated on phosphorus derivatives. Outside them there were only two operations of consequence: the acrylics plants in Australia and Thailand and the methacrylate plants for oil additives at Whitehaven.

An expansion of the **acrylics** plant at Box Hill, to more than double the capacity for acrylic resins, was announced in April 1997. In July 1996 there had been an approach for the purchase of the Australian Specialities business, which was rejected. A revised offer was received three months later. There was an offer in the region of AUD20m. from A C Hatrick, an Australian speciality chemical company, but it was withdrawn in December. In October 1997 the management of A&W Specialities and A&W Australia was combined, while the two companies retained their separate accountability. The possibility of disposing of the acrylics business was raised again in March 1998, with discussions with S C Johnson, but again came to nothing. Negotiations in September 1998 to acquire the 51% balance of AWAT Thai, whose operations included an acrylics plant in Thailand, concluded with 100% ownership in 1999. In October 1997 approval was given for £2m. to be spent at Whitehaven on the methacrylates plant, for which a profitable future was forecast. These non-phosphorus operations thus continued to be part of A&W.

Other operations were, however, disposed of during this period. In May 1995 **Rio Linda** was sold to a US company, Vulcan Materials Company for £8.5m. The interest in Rio Linda (p.289), of Sacramento, California, had been acquired in 1989, as a natural extension of A&W's interest at the time in chlorine dioxide for pulp bleaching; Rio Linda's business was the sale of small generators to produce chlorine dioxide as a bactericide. In 1991, the company made a profit of over 10% on sales of $7.5m.. When the pulp business was sold in 1992, Rio Linda was retained but its smallness, failure to sustain an adequate profitability and its remoteness from the main business of A&W made it a clear candidate for rationalisation. It made a loss of £0.6m. in 1994. **Chemrich**, of Westwego, Louisiana (p.291) had been acquired in 1986, when its business of selling chemicals and services to oil producers, particularly in the Gulf of Mexico, was supported by sales to Tenneco Oil. After the sale of Tenneco Oil, however, Chemrich lingered on, making losses until the beginning of 1997, when it was sold to Ambar Inc., a neighbouring company, for $8.7m., resulting in a small loss on its book value.

Whitehaven works 1989, showing foaming from surfactants run-off in the sea.
[photo: Airfotos Ltd]

Part of Charleston (South Carolina) plant of A & W Americas 1992.
[photo: Larry Workman Photography]

Troy phosphoric acid plant at Coatzacoalcos, Mexico.

Board of Albright & Wilson plc 1996: l. to r.back row: Nicholas Barber, John Adsetts, Ian Black, Hans Lottig, Paul Rocheleu, Michael Garner; front row: Robin Paul, Sir Christopher Benson, Michael Winstanley

A third disposal within the specialities area was the long-established **Service Chemicals** unit whose business was focused on water treatment. Its sale to Nalco Chemical Company, one of the leading US companies in service chemicals, was completed in December 1996. (Nalco was itself later acquired by Compagnie Suez de l'Eau.) Another of the original A&W specialities units, **Surface Technologies** (formerly Metal Finishing) was sold in early- 1999 to Atotech UK Ltd, part of the Elf Aquitaine group. The sale included all the chrome chemicals and pyrophosphate processes for electrodeposition but excluded the Phosbrite and aluminium auxiliaries used in chemical polishing and protective coating. The Surface Technologies had made modest profits for many years but with sales of only £4-5m. faced competition with Elf-Atochem and other companies with sales in the hundreds of $ million, full product-lines and large technical resources.

A&W's exit from **RAP** (red amorphous phosphorus) in October 1997 was portrayed as part of the divestment of non-core activities but the fundamental reason for the sale of the business to Clariant GmbH of Frankfurt was the failure of the Canadian RAP plant to perform. Clariant GmbH had been formed in July 1997 by the merger of the speciality businesses of Clariant AG and Hoechst AG and was a major manufacturer of flame retardants based on red phosphorus. All that A&W had to offer was a market position and trademarks.

A&W's specialities business was then focused primarily on phosphorus derivatives, of which the most important were chemicals developed for biocides, corrosion prevention, flame retardancy, pharmaceutical intermediates and catalysts. Changes in organisation led to increased transatlantic cooperation. Supported by a realigned International Technical Centre at Oldbury and the laboratories at Richmond and founded on a strong position in the basic phosphorus intermediates, the prospects for profitable growth were very good.

There was considerable expenditure on key plants. At Oldbury £6 million was spent on a phosphorus oxychloride plant employing new technology developed in-house, replacing a batch reactor with a computer-controlled continuous loop reactor, to produce high-quality material with improved safety and efficiency. The plant was commissioned in August 1995, raising the capacity for oxychloride to 35,000 tpa; that proved to be well ahead of demand, which did not exceed 20,000 tpa. In March 1997 an additional reactor for the trichloride plant was authorised, at a cost eventually of nearly £3 million. The main outlets for trichloride, for which A&W had a virtual monopoly, were glyphosate, the basis for herbicides manufactured by Monsanto and Zeneca, and phosphonates, which had become a major product group for A&W. Zeolite-based detergent formulations, as marketed by Procter & Gamble, incorporated phosphonates for their effectiveness. In July 1996, approval had been given for expansion of the ADPA (acetodiphosphonic acid) plant at Oldbury for £1.7m.

In July 1998 a 'Semi-Works' plant was opened at Oldbury, at a cost of £2.5m (It was a conversion of the mothballed £2m. plant built in 1987 to make ethyl PCT. With a capacity of 1,000 tpa, it provided a stage beyond pilot plant production for new products developed in the ITC. It was also to produce the high-value, low-volume pharmaceutical intermediates, catalysts, plastics additives and other chemicals invented by the customers, who were looking for a company with manufacturing expertise and facilities. At Charleston the rebuilt high-temperature unit and other plants were fulfilling a similar role, with herbicides particularly important. Over $4 million was also spent on a plant to manufacture Ethepon, a herbicide for supply primarily to Rhone-Poulenc. The phosphorus speciality capacity at Avonmouth was upgraded and steps were taken to integrate the UK and US development and marketing of flame retardant products.

The most successful of the products invented at the ITC in the 1990s was launched in 1995 with the name Bricorr 288 (see p.312). It was an organic, heavy metal and solvent free, corrosion and scale inhibitor, for use particularly in industrial water cooling systems. Launched internationally in 1997, it received two Environmentally Significant Product Awards in the USA in the following year.

With a much older origin and the most successful speciality ever developed by A&W was **THPS** (tetrakis hydroxymethyl phosphonium sulphate, see p.312). Evolving from THPC (the chloride equivalent), developed as a flame retardant for textiles, THPS became an important bactericide. It possessed advantages over other biocides, in its solubility, compatibility with other chemicals and materials, stability and effectiveness at low dosage rates. In recognition of the growing importance of THPS and other products, including Bricorr 288, the biocides unit was renamed Water Management at the end of 1995.

A significant step forward, after seven years of work, was the granting in October 1995 of registration for THPS (under the name Tolcide PS75) by the US Environmental Protection Agency as an industrial water treatment biocide, which was followed in December by the registration of some of the formulations containing THPS. In that month, the Board approved the building at Oldbury of a second THPX (THPC/S) reactor, at a cost approaching £2 million. In 1997 A&W received the 1997 US Presidential Green Chemistry Challenge Award, for the development of a biocide with a significantly improved toxicology profile relative to other biocides. Two other US awards were given in that year, for pollution prevention and chemical innovation. In October 1998, after more than two years of effort by a US chemical industry coalition led by A&W, the Antimicrobial Regulation Technical Corrections Act of 1998 was passed, which allowed the Food and Drugs Administration to approve the use of THPS by paper manufacturers for the control of micro-organisms in paper slurry. That allowed the contact of THPS-treated paper with foodstuffs, an important extension to its use.

The 1997 Annual Report stated that Tolcide sales had more than doubled in two years and that Water Management sales volume in total was up by 10%. In 1998 sales of Water Management chemicals were 35% higher than in 1997 and sales of new products continued to increase, particularly in pharmaceutical intermediates and catalysts. In total, however, the sales and profits of Phosphorus Derivatives & Acrylics were lower than in 1997 because of the direct and indirect effects of the slowdown in Asian markets, which had a substantial impact on the higher volume, less specialised, products. Nevertheless this sector of A&W's operations, which had shown an unbroken growth in profits in 1995, 1996 and 1997, remained the area of greatest potential development.

Surfactants

The flotation prospectus issued at the beginning of 1995 stated: "The margins in the Surfactants Business have been adversely affected by price competition, the high cost base at a number of the Group's European operations and the large proportion of lower margin products. The Business is now focusing on higher value added products and the Group has addressed its high European cost base by a rationalisation in 1994 designed to reduce operational costs. The Directors do not expect any further restructuring charges or asset write-downs in the Surfactants Business in the foreseeable future".

In 1994 £6.75m. was provided against profits for rationalisation costs at Whitehaven (£5.5m.) and write-offs relating to the investment in DPH (Spain). The provision covered the cost of closing the loss-making DPH plant at Sanchidrian in 1995. Further rationalisation costs of £5m. were, however, charged against profit in 1995, to cover headcount reductions and related costs in Spain and headcount reductions in Speciality and head office functions in the UK. In 1995 the bottling operation at Castiglione (Italy) was partly disposed of through transfer into a joint venture, Sintesi Srl, with the Italian company Pizzolotto. The Whitehaven and Spanish packed powder businesses were sold in April 1995 to Robert McBride, which was floated as a public company in July of that year. McBride was the largest manufacturer of private label household and personal care products, selling to most of the large supermarket chains. Also in 1995 Surphos, based in Benelux, distributing small quantities of surfactants and phosphates, was sold. Greater responsibility was given to the management of the surfactants operations in France and Italy, which were both making good returns.

In 1996, the loss-making bottling business at Alcover (Spain) was sold. Exceptional charges against profits in that year amounted to £3.2m. In 1997, there was a further charge of £8.3m. to cover the cost of redundancies at Whitehaven and in Spain and the closure of the sulphuric acid plant at Whitehaven. Spain achieved a breakeven position in 1997 and Whitehaven showed an improvement but still with inadequate profitability. The Lavera ethoxylation plant was reported to have achieved "a positive operating performance". As has been described earlier, the Lavera venture had been unprofitable from the start. Consideration was given to disposing of some or all of A&W's holding, without success, and an attempt to renegotiate with BP a revision to the contract for supply of ethylene oxide failed.

While the profit-margins on surfactants remained generally unsatisfactory, there was progress towards achieving a shift from commodity to speciality products and profits improved after 1995. In 1996 sales of products introduced within the last 5 years accounted for 20% (£61 million) of sales, of which one-third were introduced in 1996. In 1997 it was stated that "downstream value added derivatives" accounted for over 50% of European sales and in 1998 what were termed speciality products, defined as "those where the customer can discern a value difference between our product and that of our competitors" were just under 50% of surfactant sales.

The 1995 Annual Report defined the higher added value products as heavy duty liquids (HDLs), amines and derivatives and chemicals for the personal care and industrial surfactants markets. A&W had succeeded in developing super concentrated HDLs, with 70% solids but low viscosity and free of organic solvents, based on patented technology. They accounted for more than a third of HDL sales in 1995. Total UK HDL sales in 1996 were six times the sales in 1986. In October 1995, however, a 4-year patent dispute with SB Chemicals, a small detergent producer supplying liquid detergents to a retail chemist chain, ended with withdrawal by A&W as a result of failing to file papers within the time allowed in the High Court action. In practice, the damage was more to reputation than to sales. There was a further challenge to A&W's patent position at the end of 1997. More importantly, the development by the major soapers of washing powder tablets significantly affected sales of HDLs in 1998 and brought to an end the period of expansion.

Other developments were more encouraging. In 1996 the production of tertiary amines, a feedstock used in the production of speciality surfactants, increased 50%. Among the products introduced were emulsifying agents for agrochemicals, mild surfactants for personal care products and household products. Notable was the expansion in naphthalene sulphonates, used in industrial products, in concrete, plasticisers, textile and leather processing and in agrochemical formulations. A plant for naphthalene sulphonate formaldehyde condensates (NSFs) had been opened at Alcover in 1991. Sales from the plant into Australia were followed by a decision in October 1995 to build a world-scale plant at Wetherill Park (Sydney), to make 13,000 tpa of NSFs. In 1998 an agrochemical laboratory was set up at St Mihiel, to add to those in Spain and Asia.

The most significant developments in surfactants in this period were in **North America**. Reference has already been made (p.320) to the agreement with Pilot

Chemical Company for the toll manufacture of high-active surfactants, on a plant that came on stream in March 1995. In 1996 a second unit was opened at the Cincinnati site and a surfactants organisation was set up in the USA under a Vice President formerly with Henkel. Establishing a significant presence in the USA would obviously take some years and it was forecast that the Pilot operation would break even by 1998. In 1997 the US surfactants operations lost $1 million.

Towards the end of that year, a significant step was taken with the acquisition of the Witco surfactants plant at Blue Island, Chicago. Through a series of acquisitions, Witco Corporation had become a significant US producer of specialty chemicals, including surfactants and plastics additives, with sales of over $2 billion. It had earlier lost a dispute with A&W concerning HDL patents (p.260). Just before the flotation of A&W, Witco with FMC approached Tenneco concerning a possible bid for A&W but by then the course was fixed for flotation. Towards the end of 1995, Witco made an approach to buy A&W. Then in 1997 Witco enquired whether A&W's surfactants business was for sale. At the same time there were approaches for A&W's surfactants from Stepan (a leading US surfactants producer) and the German company Huls. Huls offered £120m., around ten times A&W's 1996 operating profit from surfactants, but was rebuffed by A&W, which was forecasting a profit from surfactants of £20 m.. Not long after that, Huls was taken over by Condea, the major German producer of alcohols and surfactants. Witco next attempted to merge its surfactants interests with A&W's but was again rebuffed. It then decided that it should get out of sulphonation and commodity surfactants and in mid-1997 announced that it wished to dispose of Blue Island.

In November 1997 A&W's acquisition of the Blue Island operation was completed. The price paid, including working capital taken over, was $9.2m (£5.6m.). A&W announced that it planned to spend £10 m. on the acquisition and on expanding and enhancing the acquired plant to make the same range of products as in Europe. It was expected that A&W's US sales of surfactants would rise to $50m. (£30m.) by the year 2000 and that there would be operating losses for the first two years after the acquisition. In the first year, over $1 million was spent on equipping the plant to produce three additional product ranges - amine oxides (thickeners and foam boosters, mainly for detergents), betaines (mild surfactants, mainly for shampoos and other personal care products) and lamellar blends (highly concentrated blends for personal care products). A similar sum was spent to protect health and the environment, greatly reducing air and water pollutants from the site. Sales from Blue Island were expanded to the point where the plants were effectively sold out. The next step was to bring the plant into profit. At the same time, the creation of an effective base in the USA would add to sales on a global basis to major customers. The question of whether the steps taken would have created a significant contributor to A&W's profit cannot be answered because of the acquisition then of Albright & Wilson.

The main developments in **Asia** were in India, China and Indonesia. Although in this period the recession in Asia affected exports from the UK, profits and expansion were maintained in A&W's Asian companies. In December 1996 the A&W Board resolved that the Company's strategy should include more rapid growth in Asia.

In October 1996 A&W brought its shareholding in **Albright, Morarji & Pandit** up to 73% through the purchase of the 33% holding of its partner, the Dharamsi Morarji Chemical Company (DMCC) for 145 million rupees (about £3 million). The company was renamed Albright & Wilson Chemicals India Ltd (AWCI). Surfactants operations, starting with the building of a linear alkyl benzene sulphonic acid plant at Roha in 1991 and greatly extended by the purchase of DMCC's alpha olefin sulphonates plant in 1993, were further expanded in 1997 by the manufacture of ammonium lauryl and lauryl ether sulphates. In the year to September 1997 surfactants represented 25% of AWCI's sales, which were double those of three years before. Profits grew similarly. AWCI had become one of the most profitable of A&W's operations. In 1998 the possibility arose of acquiring SMZ Chemicals, another Indian company producing surfactants, but SMZ withdrew from negotiations. In August 1998 Ishwar Khandelwal, Managing Director of AWCI, retired after 25 years' service with AMP and AWCI. He had become Chief Executive of AMP in 1983, at a time when the company was making losses because of an excess of sodium tripolyphosphate capacity in India. His departure was followed by decline: although in the two years after 1998 steps were taken to improve marketing and distribution, profitability fell and with it the price of AWCI's shares, which were quoted on the Mumbai market.

In **China**, Hunan Resun-Albright & Wilson Industrial Company, the joint venture in surfactants based at Changsha, capital of Hunan Province, had begun to operate officially from the beginning of 1995. The range of products was extended, a dioxane stripping unit (built in the UK) was installed, new offices and laboratory facilities were built and an additional sales office was opened, in Kunming, to add to those in Beijing and Shanghai and the long-established office in Hong Kong (which was to become part of China in 1997). The venture was, however, only moderately successful, in the face of competition from other manufacturers in eastern China. In 1997 there was a proposal to acquire a 50% interest in a Shanghai manufacturer of phosphorus derivatives, which did not materialise. A&W's main interests in China continued to be importing speciality products and sourcing phosphorus and phosphorus intermediates. A proposal for the acquisition of a 51% share in a phosphorus producer in Yunnan province was rejected by the A&W Board.

PT Albright & Wilson Manyar, the joint venture in Indonesia, continued to perform well. In 1995 an agrisurfactant plant was opened, to service mainly the large local market. The success of the Indonesian operation in exporting within Asia led to the closure in 1997 of the surfactants plant at Jurong (Singapore), as already mentioned. Jurong continued to be the headquarters for A&W Asia Pacific, with the main laboratories for the region and warehousing for distribution. In mid-1997 a surfactants blending facility was opened at Port Klang (Malaysia) to replace a similar facility at Jurong.

Mention has already been made (p.358) of the construction in Australia of a 13,000 tpa NSF condensates plant, to produce industrial surfactants. Commissioned in 1997, there were problems in the early stages of operation and it does not appear to have had the expected success. At the beginning of 1997, the Salim Group, A&W's partner in Australia, offered to sell its share to A&W but the terms were not acceptable to A&W. The Salim Group, with sales of chemicals of $1.3bn out of total sales of $20 bn., then raised the possibility of a wider partnership with a closer involvement in the management of the surfactant operations in Asia, other than India and China. It already had a shareholding in the Philippines surfactant and phosphate companies and in EMPL, the ethoxylation operation in Singapore. Like other discussions with the Salim Group on closer cooperation outside Asia, however, the initiative came to nothing. A&W and the Salim Group did, however, assume a more direct role in the management of the Philippine operations. In Australia, the management of Albright & Wilson (Australia) and Albright & Wilson Specialities, the acrylics business based on Box Hill, was combined in 1997 under the Specialities Managing Director, Bruce Henshaw, but A&W retained its 100% holding in Specialities.

In 1998 (the last year for which detailed information is available) surfactants sales in the Asia Pacific region (including Australia) were 13% of A&W's total surfactants sales, nearly double sales in the Americas. Total profits of the Asia Pacific region, from all operations, were higher in 1998 than in 1997 in US dollar terms, despite an average 43% fall in Asian currencies since mid-1997.

The Environment

The Annual Report for 1998 (the last published) included a policy statement that the Company recognised its duty "to protect the environment both in the vicinity of its operations and elsewhere by the responsible management of waste materials and high standards of product stewardship". In September 1999 Paul Rocheleau stated that for the first time in his 13 years with A&W it was possible to say that there were no significant environmental issues outstanding.

The main areas of concern had been the former phosphorus-producing sites and Whitehaven. Remediation work at Varennes was complete by September 1998, at a cost of $7 million, which covered demolition of the plant, building two secure containment cells for phosphorus-contaminated material and landscaping, leaving a site suitable for redevelopment. The remediation plans for Long Harbour, approved by the government in January 1996, were expected to take 4 years. Although the cost of remediation was higher than estimated at the time of flotation, the work was essentially complete within that timescale; residual phosphorus was contained within a membrane and there were plans to market some of the huge quantity of slag on the site. The digging out of the phosphorus-containing muds at Portishead was expected to be completed in the second half of 1999 but continued into 2001.

The plant at Whitehaven for the encapsulation of pollutants was doubled in 1996. In that year, the government introduced a landfill tax, to which the Whitehaven landfill operation was subject; although a reduced rate was negotiated, the charge of £2 per tonne plus the costs of operating the process meant a total burden in excess of £1 million pa. The only (and eventual) solution to the financial problem was a reduction in operations on the site.

Most of the other A&W production sites installed plant for the treatment of emissions. An 'emissions index' was created, based on the amount of each emission multiplied by published hazard factors based on the views of independent scientists. The index for the Company was set at 100 in 1993, which was down to 83.5 in 1998 and would have been much lower if it had not been for the inclusion of Troy (Mexico) from 1997 - in that year the inclusion of Mexico raised the index by more than 20%. Other marks of success in dealing with the environment were the many public awards received in America, Europe and Asia for performance at manufacturing sites and the development of environmentally-friendly products, notably Tolcide (the biocide based on THPS, as described earlier) and Bricorr (the corrosion inhibitor). Another aspect of the increased concern with the working environment was the attention paid to health and safety. The main index of performance was the Lost Time Case Rate (LTCR), the number of lost time accidents per 1,000 employees, which was reduced from 1.26 in 1993 to 0.58 in 1998, compared with the average of 0.74 reported for the members of the UK Chemical Industries Association in 1997.

So the 1998 Annual Report stated: "Whilst we are never complacent about our environmental performance and constantly aim for improvement, we firmly believe that there is no risk to the public or our employees as long as our well established procedures are adhered to".

Divestments and attempts at consolidation

The main strategies pursued after flotation were: first the elimination of non-core businesses and reductions in the cost base; next, consolidation with other producers to increase the competitive weight of a relatively small force in the international chemical industry; and finally cost reduction and re-focusing to improve profit. The introduction of new products and geographical expansion were not enough to provide the strength needed to withstand the effects of recession and adverse exchange rates.

Numerous divestments and rationalisations have already been described: Rio Linda, Chemrich, Service Chemicals, bottling operations, RAP, Surface Technologies, packed powders, plus Surfachem, Surphos and the closure of Whitehaven phosphoric acid and sulphuric acid plants and the Jurong surfactants plant. There were substantial write-offs prior to the flotation and then when Paul Rocheleau became Chief Executive and a further round of cost reductions under the direction of Gabriel Kow after he became responsible for Europe at the beginning of 1999.

Early in 1998 the possible divestment of A&W's surfactant business resurfaced (see p.359 for earlier approaches), as Ken Lever (the Finance Director), with Nigel Turner (of Lazards) and Malcolm Moir (of Cazenove) attempted to persuade Paul Rocheleau to sell it, at a time when the profits were at a peak. The intention was to use the cash for a major acquisition to consolidate A&W's position in phosphates (see later). Paul Rocheleau would not agree because he believed that surfactants could become as profitable as phosphates, through continuing the strategy of upgrading the product range and extending geographically.

When interviewed by Chemical Week in May 1998, Paul Rocheleau stated that A&W was aiming for a proactive role in the consolidation of the chemical industry. In the 1998 Annual Report he wrote: "we will continue to seek opportunities to pursue consolidation initiatives" - but by the time the report was published, in March 1999, the initiatives of the previous two years had failed and there was virtually no scope for further attempts.

Towards the end of 1996 there were suggestions that Hoechst might be considering the sale of its phosphorus operations, including the phosphorus furnaces at Vlissingen (Flushing, Holland) from which A&W's UK plants obtained much of their phosphorus requirements. Initially the possible sale was seen as a threat to the supply of phosphorus. In mid-1997 Hoechst confirmed the formation of **Thermphos** from July 1st, with the intention of divesting it. Thermphos was the last remaining phosphorus manufacturer in Europe, with furnaces at Vlissingen and Knapsack (its original phosphorus manufacturing site, in Germany). It also manufactured phosphorus halides and pentasulphide, thermal phosphoric acid and sodium tripolyphosphate. It had an STPP plant at Buenos Aires and was building a second plant in Argentina and was negotiating for a joint venture for manufacturing STPP in China. Hoechst was pursuing a strategy of exit from inorganic chemicals and had already disposed of some of its chlorine and derivative operations. In October 1997 Hoechst invited bids for Thermphos.

The A&W Board decided to make a bid . The executive management regarded the project (given the name Project Flare) as "a unique opportunity of great significance for the Company" and the Board regarded it as "of key strategic importance for the Company". Several other companies expressed interest, including Kemira (Finland), Fedmis (South Africa), Prayon (Belgium, owned by the Moroccan OCP) and Rotem (Israel). Hoechst's timing was good, since chemical assets were at a premium, and it was suggested that the price sought was in the range DM315-350 million. The A&W Board agreed in December 1997 to make a bid of DM250 million. That was not accepted by Hoechst and in March 1998 discussions were terminated because of the disagreement on valuation and some doubts by A&W on the profitability of the business. Hoechst did not receive an acceptable bid from anyone else and retained Thermphos. Its profitability subsequently declined, which perhaps showed that A&W was fortunate not to have bought it, but if A&W's bid had been accepted there would have been scope for rationalisation and the Vlissingen furnaces would have removed A&W's vulnerability to high prices for one of its principal raw materials.

The second possibility of expansion/consolidation arose with **Solutia**, which had been created in the autumn of 1997 through a spin-off by Monsanto of its basic chemicals, including phosphorus and phosphates. Disposal by Monsanto had been rumoured a year earlier and Robin Paul visited Monsanto in February 1997 but was told that divestment was not intended. The finance house Wassersteen & Perella was interested in promoting a merger of A&W and Solutia but priority was given to the spin-off. In November 1997 Solutia indicated to A&W that it regarded its phosphates operations as a non-core business but did not wish to divest it; a joint venture or merger might be possible. Doing a deal with Solutia then became a major project for A&W; action on the Copebras joint venture was suspended. Strangely enough, the project was given the name Hale-Bopp, after the comet that had recently been observed; like the comet, the possible deal approached, burned brightly for a while and eventually receded.

At the beginning of 1998 Paul Rocheleau and Ken Lever (A&W's Finance Director) had discussions with Solutia, from which Solutia decided that its preference was to find a buyer for the whole company. The size of the financial commitment that would be involved led A&W to consider an acquisition jointly with Potash Company of Saskatchewan (PCS), A&W's partner at Aurora. A&W's financial adviser, Lazards, was enthusiastic about the acquisition of Solutia, described by Nigel Turner (A&W's main contact in Lazards) in July 1998 as "a truly transforming transaction for the Company" but he was concerned at the cost, which would either involve heavy borrowing or require a call on shareholders at a time when A&W's share price was declining steeply. Hence his advocacy of the sale of A&W's surfactants business. In that he was supported by A&W's largest shareholder, Phillips & Drew, which was also concerned at the level of borrowing otherwise. In October discussions were terminated after the rejection by Solutia of a bid of $400 million, which was considered to be $100 million too low. In its 1998 accounts, A&W wrote off £1.1 million of due diligence costs for the unsuccessful Thermphos and Solutia bids.

Solutia then appointed Goldman Sachs to find a buyer for the company and A&W with PCS was accepted as a bidder. Changing market conditions and policy within Solutia led to a reduced bid, of around $300 million. That was again rejected. In March 1999 there were Press reports that A&W was planning to bid for the phosphates operations of Solutia, estimated to have a value of over $200 million. By then, however, A&W was no longer in a position to carry out such a transaction. In the end, Solutia merged its phosphates business with FMC's operations in phosphorus and derivatives. For anti-trust reasons, Solutia was forced to sell its Augusta phosphorus plant. The purchaser, OCP, thus obtained a production facility in the USA and became a new competitor there.

The third attempt at consolidation was with **Rhone Poulenc** at the beginning of 1997. The project was given the title Millennium. Rhone Poulenc (RP) had become increasingly competitive in phosphates, including taking the UK STPP business of Procter & Gamble (p.350) and entering into PWA in the USA. Discussions began in February 1997 for the merger of A&W with the relevant parts of RP. A&W's initial position was that RP would acquire shares in A&W to give it 29.9% of the equity (the maximum allowable without a full bid) but RP was initially looking for not less than 35%. As discussions and the exchange of information continued, RP revised its position to seek a majority of the shares in A&W. Discussions were terminated in July 1997, as RP concentrated on spinning off its specialty chemical operations to form Rhodia. In the light of subsequent events, the Millennium project may have influenced the course of the eventual submergence of Albright & Wilson, as described in the next section

Decline and submergence

In this period, traditional manufacturing industry was not a sector favoured by the stock market, which tended not to give the benefit of the doubt where companies described their problems and their proposals for rationalising and restructuring. In the first two and a half years after flotation A&W managed to show a rising trend of profits and the share price was at or above the price at flotation, though declining in relation to the stock market as a whole. From mid-1997, however, there were storm signals for investors and analysts, which led from mid-1998 to a collapse in the share price and then submergence.

The first period after flotation

The prospectus issued at the beginning of 1995 included the statement: "The Directors are confident that the Group has good growth prospects.....The Directors believe that the flotation will enhance Albright & Wilson's public and commercial profile and give the Company independence and greater access to the capital markets, enabling it to take full advantage of opportunities as they arise". Robin Paul, addressing the 1995 Company council meeting, said: "We have been dealt as good a hand as we could wish for in the quality of our products, processes and people". Borrowings were very low, giving considerable scope to raise funds for expansion. The £20 million charges against profits and reserves in 1994 for restructuring costs (mainly the European surfactants operations) and environmental liabilities were intended to provide a sound basis for moving forward.

The first reported results after flotation were the 6 months' figures issued in September 1995, which were generally encouraging: sales were up 15% on the first 6 months of 1994 and operating profit (before exceptional items) was £31.7m. against a comparable £28.2m. for the same period of 1994. The one weak spot was surfactants, with an operating profit of only £1.8m. against £4.1m. in the first half of 1994, despite the restructuring carried out at the end of 1994. The report accompanying the figures was cautious. Although raw material cost pressures had eased, market demand particularly for specialities in the UK and continental Europe was showing some weakness and results might be affected by further weakness in the Mexican peso. In October 1995 A&W lost a patent case, and its monopoly in heavy duty laundry liquids (p.358). The share price, which had risen post-flotation relative to the FT index and had touched 200p., fell from 179p. to 164p. when the results were announced, declining further to around 146p. in November 1995. Relative to the FT index it fell from 115 to 85.

The full year results for 1995 showed sales up nearly 10% on 1994 and operating profit (before exceptional items) up by 2%, from £62.6 m. to £64.1m. In the second half of the year, however, sales were up only 5% on the corresponding period of 1994 and operating profit was down from £33.2m. to £32.4m., even though the latter included the benefit of a cut of £3.1m. in UK pension charges (resulting from the surplus on a triennial valuation) and the release of a £1.4m. provision in Surfactants. The preliminary announcement of A&W's results for the year stated: "1995 was a difficult year for companies in intermediate and speciality chemicals" and explained that the problems were raw material price increases in the first 6 months and softening in demand in the second 6 months.

The figures highlighted in the Annual Report were the pretax profit and earnings per share, which showed a 20% increase over 1994, but the comparison was distorted by environmental charges in 1994 and profits on the sale of some operations in 1995. Also, £4.5m. of the 1995 operating profits came from the 50% holding in Troy (Mexico) acquired in December 1994. The underlying trend in profits was not obviously upwards. Nevertheless, although the results were disappointing they were in line with the general experience of the chemical industry. The share price recovered to over 180p.. Some optimistic broker's reports were issued including one from Union Bank of Switzerland in July 1996 entitled "A&W: All bright & undervalued". That was despite a Company announcement in April 1996 detailing a reorganisation in the Surfactants unit, which opened with the words: "The performance of the European Surfactants business remains unsatisfactory in terms of its profitability and the return it is generating on the substantial assets the business deploys across Europe".

The optimism was supported by the results for the first half of 1996, published in September. Although sales (including A&W's share of associated companies) were up by only 3%, operating profit was up by 12%, from £31.7m. to £36.9m.. The largest improvement was in Surfactants, up from £1.8m. to £5.6m.. Among the Press comment at that time was the following from The Daily Telegraph: "Buy…Albright & Wilson at 201p.…Interim results showed growth resulting from streamlining in the surfactants business and despite the recent run in the shares, there is room for the share price to rise further". The share price rose briefly to a peak of 207.5p. in the fourth Quarter of 1996 and to just over 100% relative to the FT index since flotation.

The results for the full year 1996 showed an advance in operating profit (before exceptional items), to £70.5m. from £64.1m.. There were further rationalisation charges for reducing the headcount in the UK and Italy, of £3.5m., after the £5m. charges in 1995; a provision of £1.1m. for the costs of closing production at Jurong (Singapore) was offset by profits on the disposal of non-core activities. The Annual Report for 1996, while recording progress in several directions, gave an indication of problems ahead: "In 1996 significant progress has been made in a number of areas to develop a strong base for the continued growth in profitability of the Group. However, in 1997 the economic effect of the recent rapid strengthening of sterling, particularly against European currencies, will mask in part the full underlying benefit of the improvements made. The immediate challenge for management is to seek ways to mitigate the impact of the currency effect to ensure cost and price competitiveness is maintained in the UK business…In Phosphates with the exception of the effect of exchange rates, the specific negative factors affecting margins in 1996 are largely over. Overall, the Group has a good foundation for further progress". Comment on the results included, from The Financial Times: "Margins fall at Albright & Wilson…The group has done well to lift its surfactants business while the market for cleaning materials is over-populated. But the lack of progress in speciality chemicals, billed as the group's greatest hope, is disappointing. More worrying still are the declining margins within the phosphates business".

The impact of exchange rates

Since the end of 1995, sterling had been strengthening against all currencies, particularly the continental European currencies and the Japanese yen: the deutschemark rate had moved from 2.22 to 2.50 and the yen from 158 to 185. Against the US dollar the rise was smaller and later, moving in the fourth Quarter of 1996 to 1.64 against 1.56 at the end of 1995. The Phosphates business was particularly threatened. It had enjoyed a boost to competitiveness since the end of 1992, when sterling weakened against the continental European currencies and it had then become possible to sell into Germany and France because of the advantage of a relatively cheap UK manufacturing base; 60% of A&W's UK production was exported in 1995. The tide turned in 1996, for Albright & Wilson as for other UK manufacturers.

In October 1996, when the A&W Board considered the Company's budget for 1997, the exchange rate against the deutschemark had moved above 2.84; the budget was based on a rate of 2.72 and Ian Black (the Director responsible for Europe) warned that profit from the European phosphates business would be £15m. worse than then budgeted if exchange rates continued at the current level. In November 1996 it was reported to the A&W Board that Phosphates were receiving extremely tough competition from the German company BK-Ladenburg and the Moroccan-Belgian company OCP-Prayon (p.349). In January 1997 Procter & Gamble reduced its purchases of surfactants from A&W because of exchange rates. There was also a growing problem of customer migration: as the strength of sterling against the Euro currencies continued, both Procter & Gamble and Unilever moved their formulation capabilities to the Continent, which particularly affected surfactant sales.

A further adverse factor was the decision in November 1996 by Resistol, the largest customer of Troy, to cease buying from the company. (There was a partial resumption in January 1997, but at a much lower level.) A&W issued a statement to the Stock Exchange at the beginning of December, reporting the deterioration in trading. The A&W share price fell almost without a break from over 200p. in November 1996 to around 145p. in March 1997 when the 1996 results were published. The price then rallied to around 170p.. One leading broker's report said "We believe that the shares are oversold but acknowledge that given the series of profit warnings since flotation it will take some time before investor confidence is restored".

In July 1996 A&W's prices were 30% higher than its continental European competitors. The impact of strong sterling and problems in achieving PWA output at Whitehaven were disclosed to a meeting with analysts. Another adverse factor was the abolition of the tax credit on dividend income, announced in the 1997 UK

Budget, which adversely affected the income of the UK pension funds, and gave rise to an increase of more than £1m. in the charge against profit in the six months. The analysts were told, however, that results in the second half of the year were expected to improve.

The results for the first 6 months of 1997, which were published in September, demonstrated that sales and profit (before exceptional items) would have been greater than in the first half of 1996 had it not been for the strengthening of sterling. Operating profit would have been £39.2m. against £33.2m. actual and £36.9m. (actual) in 1996. The adjusted figures took into account the effects of translating profits not of UK origin into sterling as well as transaction effects. What they did not take into account was the third consequence of moving exchange rates, the economic effect, causing some UK exports to be uneconomic as well as making the UK market more open to imports, especially from continental Europe.

While the stock market's reaction to the results was not unfavourable, what had not been expected was an exceptional charge of £29m. against profit, stated to have arisen as a result of "a strategic review of the organisation and performance of the Group's operations". In July Robin Paul had retired as Chief Executive and his successor, Paul Rocheleau, engaged in a deck-clearing operation "to provide a strong platform from which to accelerate growth and profitability". He drew on the chief executive's prerogative; many of the changes would not normally justify being treated as exceptional items.

The movement in exchange rates had made clear the necessity for cost reductions, particularly at Whitehaven. £12.9m. was written off the value of fixed assets, £3m. was written off the value of UK finished product stocks and £5.4m. was provided for redundancy costs. Asset rationalisation included the closure of the sulphuric acid plant at Whitehaven from the end of 1997. There were redundancy programmes for Whitehaven, Australia and Spain. It was expected that these measures plus improved raw material efficiencies and higher productivity would improve the profit from Whitehaven by at least £3m. pa over the next three years. £3m. was written off A&W's investment in the associated companies in the Philippines. There were also additional provisions of £3.5m. for environmental remediation work at the former phosphorus sites. Operations terminated (Chemrich, red amorphous phosphorus) cost a further £1.1m.

"The underlying business looks in good health", commented The Independent. "With minimum gearing and good cash flow, the company has some £200m to spend on its plans for expansion in China and Brazil". The Birmingham Post, however, wrote: "Albright & Wilson stunned the stock market yesterday when it took a £27.8 million exceptional charge against first-half results, resulting in pre-tax profits of £1.6 million against the £32 million a year ago...Shares in the company...lost over ten per cent of their value in early trading, but they recovered later on good underlying figures". The share price, however, then declined from around 165p. to 140p. at the end of 1997, when relative to the FT index it was only 60% of its standing at the time of the flotation, as the stock market remained relatively strong.

The full year results for 1997 were published in March 1998. Shortly before publication it was announced that the remaining 25% shares in Troy were to be purchased and that Troy made a profit of $18 million in 1997. A visit by investment analysts to Mexico produced favourable comment. The figures for A&W were again reported on a 'constant currency' basis as well as the actual figures. Prior to exceptional items, actual sales and profits were slightly below 1996. Operating profit was £68.4m. against £70.5m. in 1996 but would have been £80.7m. with constant currency. The 1997 profit benefited from Troy's conversion to a subsidiary company in October but contributions to the UK pension funds were £3.3m. higher. The economic turmoil in Asia Pacific caused financial disruption in the second half of the year but lower raw material costs, including PWA shipped from Troy, and increased profits in Australia led to higher sales and profits in total. After the exceptional charges, earnings per share were 4.8p. against 13.9p. in 1996. The dividend, which had been raised in 1996 from 6.5p. to 6.9p., was again increased, to 7.15p.. After payment of the dividend of £22m. and £2.5m. purchase of shares, there was a cash outflow leading to an increase of £80m. in borrowing.

The headline in The Financial Times was "Albright & Wilson hit by strength of sterling" but the comment was more optimistic: "After three disappointing years and with its shares barely above the 150p. at which they came to market in 1995, Mr Rocheleau has begun to take methodical and determined steps to turn the business round. Behind the dismal veil of sterling, there are signs of improvement - the surfactants business is becoming profitable and margins are improving. Certainly he has done enough to justify a stronger rating than the current level of 11.5 times earnings to December on pre-tax profits forecast of £65-£70m". The share price had risen strongly in 1998 since a low of 134p. in January to around 175p. at the beginning of March but that was against a background of a general rise in stock market prices to new highs; the A&W price was still not much more than 60% of its price relative to the FT index at flotation. The price fell to 168p. following publication of the 1997 results but then recovered and remained in the range 170-190p. until June. In May there was a favourable review of the Company in 'Chemical Week', following an interview with Paul Rocheleau, under the title 'A&W Reactivated'. The article, however, quoted a London investment analyst as saying: "A&W needs to meet its targets. It has disappointed in the past and needs to prove itself. It doesn't have particularly high-growth businesses".

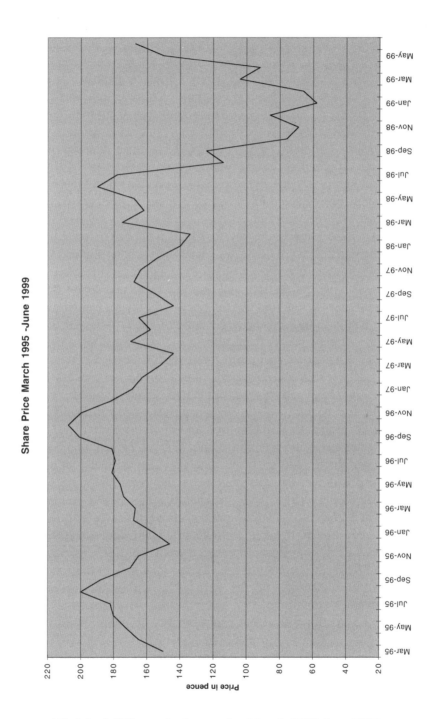

Albright & Wilson plc share price March 1995-June 1999

Decline

On 10th July 1998 A&W issued a 'Trading Update Statement'. It warned: "the impact of the weakness of continental European currencies against sterling and the US dollar continues to affect performance. Together with some slow down in activity in end markets, principally in the developing countries, this will limit the progress this year towards the margin targets which we have set for our businesses and may make it difficult to achieve progress overall for the year as a whole...Sales into continental Europe are difficult to achieve at acceptable margins and prices and volumes are under pressure in the UK from the threat of lower priced imports". The warning applied to Phosphates and to Phosphorus Derivatives & Acrylics. Although several positive points were made, the stock market latched onto the profit warning and marked the shares down. Three days later Paul Rocheleau issued a statement to the employees repeating that the European Phosphates and PD&A segments were affected by the strength of sterling and that there was also a slowdown in many developing countries. He reported that the price of the shares had fallen on the news to 121p. before recovering to 130.5 at the close of the day. He added: "During the past few weeks, virtually every chemical company on both sides of the Atlantic has issued profit warnings or has had profit forecasts downgraded". Although progress was being made towards objectives, the slowdown in the manufacturing sector would have an impact on capital expenditure and expansion plans.

The results for the first half of 1998, published early in September, showed actual operating profits of £33.6m, just ahead of the first 6 months of 1997 (excluding exceptional items) but, with higher interest charges, a fall in pretax profit and earnings per share. (Although the statement showed that profits would have been well ahead with constant exchange rates, that would not have been so if the comparison had been with the CER figures published for 1997 a year before.) While Phosphates and Surfactants achieved increases in profit, PD&A profits were down because of a reduction in demand for industrial chemicals and the slowdown in Asia. The 1998 Phosphate figures benefited from the 100% ownership of Troy, which added £3.2m. to operating profit. Borrowings rose in the six months from £116m. to £159m. because of the cost of acquiring the balance of Troy, environmental and restructuring costs and increased working capital. Gearing rose to 48%. The forecast for the second half year was for pretax profit to be slightly down on the £27.7m. reported for the first.

When the results and expectations were announced to a meeting of investment analysts, there was annoyance that only 2 months after the July statement - which pointed to a full-year pretax profit of £60m. - the forecast had been reduced to about £54m.. It was reported that the mood at the meeting was quite nasty and that the Company was criticised for consistently letting people down. The shares were immediately marked down to below 100p., to half the price in June. The price continued to fall, to 84p a few days later, when purchases were made by the Chairman and the three executive Directors. During October the price fell below 70p. and, although there was a brief rally in November, the price then dropped to around 60p. at the beginning of January 1999. At that point, the price relative to the FT index was less than a quarter of the ratio at flotation.

In December, presentations to A&W's UK employees stated: "Albright & Wilson's business performance in the UK is showing a rapid decline in profitability...Costs will continue to rise unless a series of cost management measures are introduced urgently". Revision of the non-contributory UK pension schemes (which were estimated to cost the Company £9.5m. in 1999) was proposed, to give employees the choice of contributing 4% of pensionable earnings or changing to a money purchase scheme; all new entrants would be on a money purchase basis (where benefits would be based on money contributed by the Company and employees, with accumulated investment income, rather than on a percentage of earnings at retirement). The proposal was accepted.

In January 1999 a 'Year end trading update statement' was issued, which summarised the position in 1998 as follows: "A slow down in activity in Surfactants in the UK and a continuation of aggressive competitive activity in Phosphates throughout Europe and the UK have held back progress in these businesses in the second half. With these exceptions, our businesses world-wide are progressing as expected at the time of the announcement of the Interim Results. Notably we expect the final result in the Asia Pacific region to be at a similar level to last year". The 1998 accounts would include redundancy and other remedial costs. Borrowings had been reduced in the second six months through the curtailment of capital expenditure and reduction in working capital. A simultaneous internal Company message from Paul Rocheleau said that equity markets had "run away" from chemical investments. He highlighted Chinese competition and deflation and called for a focus on margins, cost savings and cash flow. "It is unlikely", he said, "that underlying market growth or price movements will provide upside lift. Improvement in profitability will be hard fought in the face of declining prices, stronger competition and mature markets. We must find ways to reduce raw material costs and reduce fixed costs. Everyone must have the mindset that we need to compete, and make money, against new low cost competition. We cannot accept revenue stagnation, falling prices and rising costs". He went on to say: "The success stories are those companies that have an entrepreneurial culture and act like they are in a 'management buy-out'....I am confident that in 1999 we can demonstrate real progress to our shareholders".

The full year results for 1998, announced in March 1999, were worse than indicated in the September profit warning. The pretax profit was only £48.3m. against £60.6m. (before exceptional items) in 1997. Key factors affecting the results were the strength of sterling and the devaluation of Asian currencies (£7m.) and the reduction in exports to Asia Pacific (£6m.). Exceptional items balanced out: there was a windfall gain of £7.9m. from unwinding a financial arrangement but £4.6m was written off non-performing assets, £1m. was provided for the final remediation stage at Portishead, £1.2m. was provided for redundancies and £1.1m. costs of two aborted acquisitions were written off. Although there was a negative cash flow of £37m. for the year, there was an improvement in the second six months, as working capital was reduced and capital expenditure was cut back; the amount spent on discretionary growth projects was half that in the second half of 1997. Comments by Paul Rocheleau included: "There are few signs that the economic climate and market conditions existing at the end of 1998 will show any near term improvement in 1999. We are optimistic that our firm actions to reduce costs, lower raw material prices and some easing of market conditions later in the year will lead to progress for the Group in the second half". While another difficult year for UK business was expected, further progress was expected in continental Europe, Asia Pacific and Mexico. Capital expenditure would be further reduced and there would be more redundancies.

The news from the Company was by no means all bad but the stock market in the late-1990s reacted sharply to profit warnings, especially if there were more than one. In the case of Albright & Wilson, for which there were so many hopeful signs at the flotation, any disappointment tended to be all the greater. The deck-clearing at that time, including provisions for environmental liabilities, soon proved to be insufficient, while expectations of rising profits were dashed when the Company's dependence on advantageous exchange rates became clear. For the share price to be driven down to less than a quarter of its value relative to the FT index at flotation might seem to be an over-reaction to a less than calamitous fall in profits but at the beginning of 1999 it was difficult for the market to foresee an upturn in the Company's fortunes.

Submergence

At the beginning of 1998 a 'Defence Committee' was formed, to explore ways of realising greater value for the shareholders, against the background of a search for consolidation and increasingly difficult trading conditions. The Committee consisted of Sir Christopher Benson, Paul Rocheleau, Ken Lever, Andrew Cree (Company Secretary and General Counsel) and Stuart Humphreys (Treasurer) from A&W with Nigel Turner (Lazards) and Michael Moir (Cazenove). The main work was done by Ken Lever, Stuart Humphreys and Nigel Turner. One of their main recommendations was the sale of Surfactants, blocked by Paul Rocheleau. Estimates were made of the value of A&W on various bases; on a discounted cash flow basis the value per share was calculated to be 130p..

From the middle of 1998 the decline in A&W's share price brought the possibility of a hostile bid ever closer. In July Paul Rocheleau visited Charlie Walker, CEO of Albemarle, in Richmond, where Albemarle as well as A&W Americas had its headquarters, to suggest that Albemarle should acquire Albright & Wilson. That was followed in October by a visit of Albemarle to London, where there were talks with Sir Christopher, Paul Rocheleau and Ken Lever. Albemarle wanted to achieve a combination of businesses of the two companies, through acquisition of A&W or otherwise.

Albemarle was formed in February 1994 by a spin-off from Ethyl Corporation of its olefins and derivatives, bromine chemicals and specialty chemicals businesses, used in detergents, personal care products, agricultural pesticides and fertilisers, pharmaceuticals and photographic chemicals. In March 1996 it sold its olefins business to Amoco. There was not much common ground with A&W but Albemarle claimed that there were complementary interests in flame retardants, pharmaceuticals, consumer products ingredients, water treatment, agrochemicals and surfactants. Albemarle was clearly attracted by A&W's leading world position in speciality phosphates and by its cheapness, with a share price of around 80p., resulting in a market value of around £250 million. Albemarle's market value was around £700 million. Its sales were less than A&W's, a little over £500 million against nearly £800 million, but its pretax profit was about £75 million against A&W's (1998) less than £50 million. Employee numbers were 2,700 for Albemarle and over 5,000 (excluding associated companies) for A&W. Albemarle was thus more profitable than A&W and was showing a rising trend of profit while A&W's (excluding exceptional negative items) was downward. Albemarle's balance sheet indicated that it had sufficient borrowing capacity to allow a bid for A&W and facilities were offered by Credit Suisse First Boston, the finance house acting for Albermarle.

In November 1998 the A&W Board agreed not to respond to Albemarle's overture. Albemarle then indicated that it might be prepared to acquire A&W for 110p. per share, which was rejected. At about the same time, there were discussions with HSBC and Advent (a venture capital firm) on the possibility of conversion into a private company, which led to leaks to the market of such a possible move. The price required to go private was estimated at 125-130p. per share. The 'bottom fishers' then started to appear. One of the fishers was Harris Associates, a company formed to build up a portfolio of investments in chemical companies; finance was provided from the sale of Harris Chemicals by its founder. It indicated that it was prepared to pay 120-140p. per share, subject to obtaining more information. Another was Ineos, a venture-capital backed company, which indicated a price range of 125-140p., subject to information. (Ineos was to go on to acquire ICI's acrylics business and chlorchemicals, ethanolamines from Dow and Phenolchemie from Degussa, to build up what it claimed to be the second largest UK chemical company; with sales of over £2 billion pa and 6,000 employees.) Interest was also shown by Huntsman Corporation of the USA, the world's largest privately held chemical company, which had been acquiring industrial chemical businesses from ICI. In December 1998 Jean-Pierre Tirouflet, Chairman and Chief Executive of Rhodia (see p.377-379), contacted Sir Christopher Benson about reports that A&W was interested in disposal or merger; he was met with a denial but it was agreed that there would be an informal meeting in January.

The share price remained at about 65p. from mid-December for much of January but rose to 76.5p on 28th January. On February 1st A&W issued an announcement: "Albright & Wilson plc has noted the recent movement in its share price and confirms that it has had a number of tentative approaches all of which are very preliminary: these may or may not lead to an offer for the company. Contrary to press speculation, the company is not considering a management buyout. A further announcement will be made as appropriate". At the close of that day the price had risen to 104.5p.. It did not rise much further and on March 1st was 92p.

Meanwhile, Albemarle continued to pursue the possibility of acquiring A&W, eventually raising its bid to 130p.. At that point, the A&W Board decided that it could recommend the offer because it was consistent with the value calculated by the Defence Committee. An announcement was made on March 8th, under the heading "Recommended cash offer from Albemarle for Albright & Wilson plc", in terms so lukewarm as to cause Press speculation of a boardroom split (which was denied). The statement included these words:

"In considering the offer from Albemarle, the Board of Albright & Wilson has carefully reviewed the Company's prospects as an independent public company against the immediate benefits to Albright & Wilson's shareholders provided by this Offer. Although the current trading conditions of the Company are challenging, the Board believes that the medium term prospects for Albright & Wilson are good. However, the low stock market rating of the UK chemicals sector in general and of medium sized chemical companies in particular limits the Company's options to participate in the continuing consolidation of the speciality chemicals industry and consequently reduces its prospects for long-term growth. The Board believes, in the absence of any offer for the Company, the value of 130p. per share attributed to the Company's shares by the Offer will be difficult to achieve under present stock market conditions and in the foreseeable future....Against this background, the Directors of Albright & Wilson, who have been so advised by Lazard Brothers, have decided to recommend to

shareholders the terms of the Offer as being reasonable. In providing its advice to the Board Lazard Brothers has taken account of the commercial assessments of the Albright & Wilson Board".

The announcement also included a comment by Sir Christopher Benson:

"The Board of Albright & Wilson plc has for some time been seeking to pursue a strategy of participation in the consolidation of our industry which could create long term value for our shareholders. It has become increasingly apparent that our options to achieve this are limited as an independent public company in current market conditions. The combination with Albemarle will accelerate our opportunities to pursue this strategy. The integration of Albright & Wilson into Albemarle will create a leading world-wide speciality chemicals company which will provide an excellent range of products for customers and significant opportunities for employees".

The Chairman of Albemarle, Floyd Gottwald, said that he had no plans to close any of A&W's factories and that any reductions in employee numbers were more likely to be by retirements than by redundancies. He hoped that all of A&W's management would be retained.

Following the announcement Albemarle bought in the market at the offer price shares amounting to 18.6% of A&W's issued capital, costing £76 million. While several institutions sold their holdings, Phillips & Drew, the largest holder, waited. At the end of the day the price was 129.5p.. Press comment claimed that there were other bidders hovering, naming Witco, Solutia and Rhodia. Within days, Rhodia did indeed confirm that it was considering an offer for A&W. The statement caused the share price to rise to 138p., which prevented Albemarle from adding to the 18.6% it had picked up on the day of its announcement. The formal offer from Albemarle, for 130p. per share, was issued on March 12th, naming April 6th as the deadline for acceptances. On March 16th, however, A&W announced that it had received an offer from Rhodia of 145p. per share.

Rhodia was formed at the beginning of 1998 by spinning off from Rhone Poulenc its chemicals, fibres and polymer activities. In May it sold 32.4% of the equity to institutions and individuals through an initial public offering (IPO) and the stock became quoted in Paris and New York. In October 1999 the rest of the equity was sold. In March 1999 the market value of the share capital was around £1.5 billion (the share price, 140 francs for the IPO, had fallen by the end of 1998 to around 85 francs, suffering from the general fall in chemical stocks). Rhodia's sales in 1998 totalled £3.7 billion and its pretax profit £113 million. The five divisions of Rhodia were (1998 figures):

	Sales £m	no employed
Fine Organics:	**665**	**4,500**
• Life Science Chemicals: synthetising customised molecules	193	
• Pharmaceutical ingredients: e.g. paracetamol, salicylic acid	126	
• Diphenols & aromas: for flavours & fragrances & polymerisation inhibitors	146	
• Fine organics intermediates: phenol, acetone & derivatives for pharmaceuticals, fragrances, textiles, plastics, solvents, etc.	200	
Consumer Specialties:	**717**	**3,400**
• Home, Personal Care & Industrial Ingredients: surfactants, polymers, speciality phosphates, silicates, etc.	409	
• Rhodia Food: food phosphates, vanillin, xanthan gum & products for organic farming	215	
• Phosphates: manufacture of phosphates and marketing of phosphoric acid etc.	93	
Industrial Specialties:	**707**	**3,300**
• Silicones: for personal care & industrial use	255	
• Tyre & Rubber: silica for tyres, toothpaste, paint, newsprint, etc.	134	
• Paper, Paint & Construction Materials: latex & polyisocyanates	318	
Polyamide:	**725**	**4,200**
• Polyamide intermediates: polyamide 6.6 & adipic acid	160	
• Engineering plastics: for packaging, cars, household appliances, etc.	109	
• Textile yarns: for fabrics	275	
• Industrial yarns: for tyres, filters, paper making, etc.	87	
• Fibres: for carpeting, furnishing	94	
Services & Specialties:	**595**	**3,700**
• Acetow: acetate tow for cigarette filters, cellulose acetate for textiles	256	
• Eco services: water filters, soil treatment, sulphuric acid regeneration	232	
• Rare earths: for batteries, TV screens, pigments, catalytic converters, etc.	107	
Sales to affiliates etc.	**304**	

Headquartered in France, Rhodia had production facilities in 29 countries, including the USA, Canada, UK, Spain and Brazil. It claimed to be geographically complementary to A&W and that the strategic fit between the two groups would be particularly good. The offer document included the statement: "Rhodia's position as one of the world's leading specialty chemical manufacturers should benefit Albright & Wilson in terms of technology, expanded sales opportunities and greater financial resources". There were more areas of common interest with A&W than Albemarle had, which gave Rhodia more scope for savings from rationalisation and increased sales, particularly in phosphates. Its size also gave it an advantage over Albemarle. Rhodia asserted that "financial synergies...would have the effect of making the acquisition accretive to Rhodia shareholders in the first full year of ownership". Rhodia expected that A&W would become part of the Consumer Specialties division and would share in the management of the division. It was therefore likely that acquisition by Rhodia would be better for A&W's shareholders but worse for A&W's management and other employees, since total submergence was more likely with Rhodia.

Rhodia's bid was complicated by the negotiations under way with Hoechst for the merger to form Aventis. At the time, Rhone Poulenc still owned 67.4% of Rhodia's shares. The offer was therefore made by ISPG, a company incorporated in England for the purpose of the offer, owned by Danube Chemicals Acquisition Corporation, a Delaware company. Danube in turn was owned by Donauchem Handelsgesellschaft, an Austrian company, subsidiary of Donau Chemie, based in Vienna, a small chemical company with sales of £71 million in 1998. Donau Chemie was the subject of a management buy-out in April 1997 when Rhone Poulenc (the majority shareholder) and Creditanstalt-Bankverein sold their shares to Alain de Krassny (formerly part of RP's Austrian management) (holding 8%) and de Krassny Privatstiftung (92%). Upon closing of the offer, Rhodia would be granted an option to acquire 100% of Danube between 1st January and 1st April 2000. In the unlikely event of Rhodia's not exercising its option, Danube would have an option to acquire Rhodia's phosphate business between 2nd April and 1st July. Up to the exercise or expiry of Rhodia's option, ISPG would operate A&W as an independent business, subject to Rhodia's prior consent being required for the declaration and payment of dividends, the issue of any equity or debt securities or the acquisition or disposal of assets representing more than 20% of the total A&W assets. Finance for the offer was to be provided to Danube/ISPG by a bank credit plus the issue by Danube to Rhodia of a £50 million convertible bond.

PDFM (Phillips & Drew Fund Management) accepted Rhodia's offer, undertaking to take steps to procure acceptances from its clients representing 23.1% of A&W's shares. The undertaking would cease to bind if a third party made an offer of 160p. or more within 14 days of the despatch of the Rhodia's offer to shareholders. The offer was dated 13th April and the deadline for acceptances was 3rd May. The A&W share price rose above the 145p. offer, with speculation that other bidders might appear or that Albemarle would come back with a higher offer. The latter did not take long to materialise.

On 16th April Albemarle made a revised offer, of 160p. per share (which of course released PDFM from its undertaking to Rhodia). A&W's announcement noted that Albemarle had US and UK regulatory approval of its offer and recommended it to the shareholders. Sir Christopher Benson commented:

> "We welcome the higher offer from Albemarle. The global chemicals industry continues to restructure and the combination of Albright & Wilson with Albemarle will create a powerful platform, from which to grow and create value. The geographic spread, technology base and customer interface are very complimentary (sic). The Board also notes the assurances given by Albemarle in relation to existing employee rights and the value they attach to the skills and experience of our employees".

Paul Rocheleau wrote:

> "I want to highlight the value that Albemarle has placed on our business. I hope you have a sense of pride in this recognition of the value that has been created by A&W employees over many years".

The offer, like Rhodia's, was cum dividend, i.e. the declared final dividend of 4.8p. per share would not be paid to A&W's shareholders so that effectively the offer was worth not much more than the price at which the shares were floated 4 years before and certainly less in real terms.

Once again the shares rose above the value of Albemarle's offer, closing at 163p. on the day of the announcement. Not surprisingly, there were very few acceptances of the offer, for which the closing date was May 12th. On 29th April (the day after the Annual General Meeting of A&W), ISPG announced an increased offer, of 167.5p. (cum dividend) and purchased shares in the market at that price to give, with the PDFM commitment, 30.5% of A&W's shares in issue. In the next few days, before the issue of its revised offer document on May 6th, ISPG picked up a further 5.5%.

On the same day Solutia and FMC announced the merger of their phosphates operations; Rhodia said that it would probably not have been allowed by the competition authorities to acquire A&W if A&W had acquired Solutia's phosphates. The four leading companies' sales of speciality phosphates (broadly defined) in 1997 were ($ million): A&W 885, Rhodia 464, Solutia 337, FMC 332.

The A&W Board recommended the increased Rhodia offer on 5th May, saying that it had "carefully considered the terms and conditions of ISPG's increased offer, in particular, the fact that the increased offer is no longer conditional on clearances from any competition authorities (although the increased offer will lapse if, before it becomes unconditional, the competition authorities of the UK or the EC initiate an investigation) and is conditional solely on acceptances being received in respect of more than 50% of A&W's share capital". On 13th May Albemarle announced its decision not to raise its offer above 160p.; it had also sold 8% of its holding to ISPG, retaining 11.3%. By 19th May ISPG had acquired 57% of the shares and declared its bid unconditional and its wish to acquire 100%; it was still necessary to obtain US and EC clearance, which meant that A&W and Rhodia had to continue to operate independently and competitively. On 27th May Albemarle announced that its offer had lapsed and that it was accepting the ISPG offer for the whole of its remaining holding.

The European Commission approved the deal on July 13th ; it imposed some conditions, for toll manufacture of calcium and ammonium phosphates, licensing of trademarks and provision of customer lists to a third party. Shortly afterwards, the Aventis merger was approved by the shareholders of Hoechst and Rhone Poulenc. At the end of January 2000 the US Federal Trade Commission (FTC) indicated that it would approve the Rhodia/A&W deal on condition that the phosphoric acid plants at Aurora, North Carolina and Coatzacoalcos, Mexico were divested. Eventually the Mexican divestment was avoided but A&W's 50% share of Aurora was sold to its partner, Potash Company of Saskatchewan, which thereby became a major player in phosphoric acid. FTC approval was received on March 14th. On the next day, Jean-Pierre Tirouflet, Chairman and Chief Executive Officer of Rhodia, announced that the acquisition of Albright & Wilson had been completed. From March 14th the name of Albright & Wilson UK Ltd was changed to Rhodia Consumer Specialties Ltd. The move was clear and decisive.

The Aftermath

In the period between ISPG's acquisition of a majority holding in A&W and the effective extinction of Albright & Wilson 10 months later, work proceeded on plans for integration. In June 1999 a new organisational structure was announced for the Consumer Specialties Division, by the President, David Eckert, to prepare for the integration of A&W in 2000. There were to be four 'Enterprises': Specialty Phosphorus Products; Phosphate Manufacturing; Home, Personal Care & Industrial Ingredients; and Food. Teams from A&W and Rhodia were formed in July 1999 to work on management structure and on rationalisation of manufacturing, sales and administrative sites. The Deputy President of the Consumer Specialties Division and the President of Phosphates Manufacturing were relocated from France to Rhodia's office at Watford. There was an assurance from Jean-Pierre Tirouflet that appointments in the new organisation would be based on capability rather than company of origin.

Towards the end of July 1999 the non-executive Directors of Albright & Wilson plc (Sir Christopher Benson, Nicholas Barber, Michael Garner and Hans Lottig) resigned and Daniel Lebard, a Director of ISPG, became Chairman. Before long he was replaced by Alain de Krassny, the other Director of ISPG and a Director of its parent companies. Ken Lever, A&W's Finance Director, resigned at the end of October but stayed on the A&W Board as a non-executive until the acquisition was confirmed in March 2000. Paul Rocheleau retained his position until that event. Meanwhile, as already described, cutbacks were continuing under Gabriel Kow's direction and by the end of 1999 A&W UK was down to 1,500 employees against 3,000 in 1996; from 1996 to 1999, provisions against the cost of rationalisation had amounted to nearly £100 million.

Early in 2000 Jean-Pierre Tirouflet said that the "synergies" between Rhodia and A&W were expected to generate cost savings of Euro20 million (£13 million) in that year and up to Euro80 million pa by 2002. The annual report for 2000 confirmed savings of Euro20 million in 9 months in 2000 and forecast Euro90 million in 2002. Sales of Consumer Specialties in 2000 were up 95%, almost entirely because of the inclusion of A&W, and earnings (before interest, tax, depreciation and amortisation) were up 121%; on a constant structure and exchange rate basis earnings were up 68% (Euro58 million) because of the synergies and the restructuring costs incurred by A&W in 1999.

In June 2000 Rhodia outlined its plans for Specialty Phosphates. Facilities at Coatzacoalcos and Port Maitland were to be upgraded and expanded but the Buckingham phosphates site was to be closed over a 2-year period. There was to be a phased withdrawal from purified acid production at Whitehaven: the MMO (technical acid) plant was to be closed by the end of 2000 and the MOS (food grade acid) once other acceptable sources could be found. Two of the three STPP units at Whitehaven were closed and the third was to be upgraded. A year later, when reduced volumes of sales and a fall in profits because of adverse economic conditions were announced, it was stated that the restructuring programme would be accelerated, including the closure of the Buckingham phosphates site and the whole of the phosphates operations at Whitehaven.

From the beginning, Rhodia had not committed itself to retaining A&W's European (including UK) surfactants business. David Eckert said: "It does have synergies and substantial value but it remains to be seen if other companies can offer us more for the business". It was set up as a separate business managed by Gabriel Kow and continuing to have its administration centred at Warley. In April

2000 Rhodia announced its sale to Huntsman International (see p.376) "on the basis of an enterprise value of 205 million euros". Gabriel Kow and the staff reporting to him went with the business to Huntsman, which acquired the world-wide rights to the Albright & Wilson name. Another part of A&W offloaded was the methacrylate oil additives business at Whitehaven, which was stated in June 2000 to be for divestment as a non-core business and was sold a year later to a unit of Degussa, of Germany.

The senior appointments announced in March 2000 included a number of A&W managers. Two of the four 'Enterprises' within the Consumer Specialties Division were to be headed by former A&W employees: Lyall Work, President of Specialty Phosphates, and Mike DeRuosi, President of Phosphorus & Performance Derivatives. (Mike DeRuosi moved to be President of the Home, Personal Care & Industrial Ingredients Division of Rhodia, based in the USA, from the beginning of 2001. Lyall Work left Rhodia and returned to America in 2001.) In the next tier of appointments within the Enterprises there were 18 former A&W employees. The Richmond headquarters of A&W Americas was closed and staff were relocated to the Rhodia centre at Cranbury, New Jersey. The Warley headquarters premises of A&W had already been sold, with the intention of relocating within the Birmingham area. After the acquisition by Rhodia staff reductions continued; some staff were relocated to Rhodia at Watford, others to the Oldbury works site, where a new building was erected, for occupation from the end of October 2001. The A&W production sites at Oldbury, Widnes and Avonmouth continued in operation. The last companies bearing the Albright & Wilson name disappeared in 2001 when the UK pension funds became part of the Rhodia fund.

So, after nearly 150 years, Albright & Wilson ceased to be a significant presence in the chemical industry of the world. Over the half-century covered by this history the Company had grown, by a series of acquisitions and otherwise, and then shrunk by almost as many divestments. Threatened by extinction in 1969/70, it survived under the mantle of Tenneco and reached a peak of profit (in real terms) in 1977. In the 17 years of full ownership by Tenneco there was shrinkage through divestments and then in the brief 4 years of restored independence the Company was exposed to increasingly competitive circumstances and an unforgiving stock market until it became a tasty and relatively small morsel for others to swallow. How far that conclusion was inevitable is considered in the Epilogue to this history.

EPILOGUE

"I am but a gatherer and disposer of other men's stuff"
(Sir Henry Wotton, c.1610)

Epilogue

In the eight chapters of this history I have attempted to describe events objectively, with comments by many of those involved. The temptation to offer opinions and make judgments has, I hope, been generally resisted. Since I was employed by Albright & Wilson for over 40 years of the period covered (from 1952 to 1993)[1] and personally involved in a number of the events described, it is perhaps appropriate and legitimate if in this Epilogue I offer some of my views on the course of events and the management of the Company.

Hindsight usually reveals what might have been done better or differently and exposes apparent failings and mistakes. It is important to avoid being over-critical of those who acted as they deemed fit at the time and I hope that I have avoided giving offence to any who may read this history and particularly this Epilogue.

I have included an Appendix that charts the sales and profits of A&W expressed in real terms, i.e. adjusted for changes in the UK Retail Price Index from 1951 to 1998. While there are shortcomings in the application of that adjustment, I believe that it provides a perspective that the reported figures year by year do not. The chart is also based on profits after incorporating adjustments for the numerous items that in the past were treated as outside the main reported figures, e.g. the large write-downs of Canadian investments.

The financial performance of Albright & Wilson over the 50 years can be summarized by reference to the chart. Between 1951 and 1967, sales grew as a result of the major capital expenditure in the early 1950s and the acquisitions made between 1955 and 1965. There was then a period up to 1989 when sales appeared to be on a plateau because growth was offset by declining prices (in real terms) and by the sale of Midland Silicones, the former ACC industrial chemicals and BBA,

---

[1] My career with A&W can be summarised as follows. Entered in August 1952 as the first Arts Graduate recruit, spending a year in departments and locations in the UK before joining the central cost department at Oldbury (with an incidental job as speechwriter for the Chairman, Kenneth Wilson). Assigned in 1953 to investigate the economics of Thomas Tyrer and seconded for 6 months in 1954 to sort out the administration at Portishead when phosphorus production started there. From 1954-67 various financial positions, moving in 1958 with headquarters to Knightsbridge. In 1965 a member of a group set up to consider changes in organisation. In 1966-7 engaged in the USA and Canada in raising loan finance for the Belledune and Long Harbour projects. August 1967 appointed first Corporate Planner for A&W, reporting to Ed Kinsley. November 1968 a member of the 4-man 'Short Range Planning Group' set up to consider possible solutions to problems arising from Canadian difficulties and the death of Ed Kinsley. 1972 transferred to Bush, Boake, Allen as Administration Director. 1974-8 Managing Director of BBA Australia and New Zealand. June 1978 General Manager Finance based at Knightsbridge. From 1978 to 1993 frequent visits to Tenneco at Houston. 1983 Financial Director, responsible also for legal and secretarial functions. From 1990 Director in charge of Asia & Australasia. 1990/1 temporarily also responsible for Human Relations. Retired in March 1993.

only partly offset by the acquisition of paper chemicals and Mobil Chemicals. In 1990-92 there was the contraction caused by the sale of the paper chemicals and pulp chemicals businesses and then a further plateau, with falling prices and sundry disposals offsetting growth and the inclusion of Troy.

The profit history shows some very large movements. Up to 1965 there was strong growth, through expansion and acquisitions, in a relatively favourable trading environment. From 1966 to 1971 the write-downs of investments in BFL and Long Harbour caused a catastrophic collapse in profits. From then up to 1977 there was a remarkable recovery, once again in a favourable trading environment. That was followed by a second period of decline in 1978-82, which was caused by recession, industrial troubles in the UK, the cost of redundancies and the loss on disposal of BBA. Although there was some improvement after that, profits never recovered to the level of 1975-7, despite the acquisition of Mobil Chemicals and developments in PWA. Further provisions for the closure of Long Harbour and Varennes, costs associated with the Whitehaven F5 plant and environmental improvements and the removal of the paper chemicals and pulp chemicals businesses severely affected profits. From just prior to the flotation up to the loss of independence, there was a struggle to maintain profits in the face of the strength of sterling, growing competition and the costs arising from rationalisation.

Within this broadly disappointing picture, there were laudable achievements including:-

- the development of purified wet acid, the building of the plant at Aurora and the acquisition and development of Troy
- the development of phosphine and THPC/S for flame retardancy and subsequently as a biocide
- the exploitation of STPP as a detergent builder, which generated a significant part of the Company's cash flow for many years
- the development of chlorine dioxide technology, to provide a valuable source of income without major expenditure
- expansion in Asia despite financial constraints
- the acquisition of the Mobil Chemicals business and the development of phosphorus specialities in the USA and UK
- modernisation of the Oldbury and Widnes sites
- the creation of the bottled detergent & toiletry business in Continental Europe, which generated substantial profits for several years
- the achievement of high standards in health, safety and the environment in the 1990s
- the maintenance of an ethic of honesty in dealings and humanity towards employees.

I believe, however, that a wholly objective reading of the history of the past 50 years (if that is possible) must show several examples of serious failings and mistakes. Perhaps the key failing was **hubris** (defined as arrogance inviting disaster), born of the history of the previous 100 years. In the early years of this period the Albright & Wilson management was too confident in the Company's reputation as a pioneer in the manufacture of phosphorus and in its success as a family business that had become the no. 2 chemical company in the UK. The belief that A&W knew how to make phosphorus, at least as well as and probably better than anyone else, led to the disasters of Portishead and Long Harbour and the refusal of help from UHDE.

Hence also the reluctance to hire senior management from outside the Company, with very few exceptions until towards the end of the period. Also there was a lack of market orientation (in contrast to Marchon), a belief that the customer should be pleased to buy from A&W. That was encouraged by the heavy tariff protection for the UK until the advent of the European Common Market, shortages during the 1939-45 war and for some years after and a long-standing near-monopoly in the UK on phosphorus, pure phosphoric acid and phosphates. The long-term depreciation of sterling helped and when that depreciation was reversed after 1995, the impact on A&W's core profits was shattering.

Hubris may also have contributed to insufficient investment in R & D, and the readiness to make cutbacks in that area when there was financial stringency. The warning by Charles Suckling that under-investment in R & D would require many years of later enhanced investment to recover the lost ground was proved true. For a while, under the direction of Keith Piercy, licensed know-how had made up some of the lost ground but after the 1960s that activity largely ceased. The realisation that there had to be a move from commodities to specialities, and that today's speciality would be tomorrow's commodity, came late in the day. For too long there was a comfortable reliance on old products, notably STPP.

The perceptive views put forward by Sydney Barratt on growth, investment, profit margins, research and human resources did not make any appreciable impact. If they had been followed, the history of the Company might have been very different.

A&W's experience with **mergers and acquisitions** was disappointing. The Company attempted to grow and develop, beyond what was feasible organically. That was true at the beginning and at the end of the period but for the reasons given below A&W mostly did not achieve its objective.

The various attempts at merger or major acquisition (not submergence), with Fisons, Laporte, Borax in the early years and with Stauffer Chemicals, Thermphos, Solutia and Rhone Poulenc in the later years all came to nothing. The intention behind the attempts was primarily to increase the size of the Company and reduce its vulnerability. The first three companies were medium-sized, smaller than A&W

at the time, and the business fit was small. The last four had substantial business fits. The Fisons and Laporte discussions broke down on questions of relative size and managerial control, the Borax because Sir Sydney regarded the company as American-dominated. The Millennium discussions with Rhone-Poulenc also foundered on relative size and control, while the Stauffer, Thermphos and Solutia attempts failed because A&W was not willing to pay the sums sought. David Livingstone's attempt in 1976-7 to persuade Tenneco to back a move to create a second ICI (the Nemesis project) - which he referred to as "The last infirmity of noble mind" - failed to excite Sydney Ellis, the Tenneco Chairman of A&W at the time.

The three acquisitions that produced significant benefits and were retained to the end of this period were of Marchon in 1955, Mobil Chemicals thirty years later, in 1985, and Troy in 1994-8. The last was a significant success that occurred too late to bring full value for the shareholders.

Marchon brought with it the production of wet phosphoric acid, a more economic method of producing STPP and entry into surfactants. It also had a more competitive, customer-oriented business attitude. Full advantage was not taken of what Marchon had to offer because of the lack of cooperation between the Whitehaven management headed by Frank Schon and the Oldbury-originated management headed by Sydney Barratt, which ended with the resignation of Schon. The development of PWA was delayed through the decision to concentrate on phosphorus and thermal acid. While the eventual success in producing food-grade PWA was largely due to Whitehaven staff and for many years much of A&W's profits came from Whitehaven STPP, in the long run the disadvantages of the Whitehaven site - a high-cost remote site with poor communications - became apparent; it was a strategic error to continue investing heavily in the site instead of in a joint venture with the Moroccan phosphate rock producers and/or expansion in the Americas. It is doubtful whether the Whitehaven surfactant operations had ever produced an adequate return on investment.

The acquisition of the Mobil Chemicals business brought A&W back into the USA nearly 30 years after the unfortunate disposal of OECCo in 1956. The Mobil purchase was initially thought by Tenneco to be primarily for the purpose of making use of the phosphorus produced by Long Harbour. It soon became clear that phosphorus from other sources was more economic and that the benefit from the acquisition was the entry it gave to A&W in the US market, particular for speciality products backed by the technical expertise in Mobil Chemicals. That was no surprise to A&W. The re-orientation of A&W's North American interests through integrating the Canadian and US operations with headquarters in Richmond, Virginia was a good strategic move. It took time, however, for the Richmond/Charleston and Avonmouth operations to be operating fully in tandem.

The accession of the Avonmouth operations was not an acquisition in the usual sense of the word since they were passed over to A&W by Tenneco on the breakup of Tenneco Chemicals in 1983. The phosphorus chemicals part of Avonmouth brought to A&W products that Oldbury had failed to develop, as well as one of the main customers for Oldbury products. The paper chemicals side of Tenneco Chemicals, with production sites also in Holland, France, Sweden, Canada and South Africa, was an attractive addition to A&W's interests and its sale in 1990 at the command of Tenneco deprived A&W of a profitable segment.

While the move into flavours and fragrances through the acquisition of Boake Roberts was initially accidental, the acquisition then of Bush and Stafford Allen was just what was required to construct a leading world player in a field that should have been suitable for A&W. From then on, however, the initiative was mismanaged. The three companies were not integrated for years, there was a succession of managing directors, frequent changes in organisation and a loss of the motivation that had driven the three constituent companies. In the UK there was a severe erosion of market position, as there was slippage in customer relations. As recorded earlier, the combined sales of the BBA companies in 1963 had equalled those of IFF, which became the world market leader, while the poor performance of BBA in the UK and North America made it a prime candidate for the divestment forced by Tenneco.

The next acquisition, of ACC in 1965, was in response to a 'white knight' appeal from ACC rather than planned by A&W. It added some mass to A&W and broadened A&W's portfolio in metal treatment through the addition of chrome chemicals but the drawbacks probably outweighed the positive aspects. ACC was an agglomeration of many small companies with numerous locations and mostly old plants. It took A&W into fertilisers, an area that had always been shunned by the Company. The chrome chemicals operations were hazardous to employees and a great problem environmentally. Substantial capital expenditure was required for both fertilisers and chrome chemicals. Then from 1973 to 1983 all the ACC operations were disposed of, other than the metal treatment processes, which were eventually divested in 1999. So nothing remained and in real terms it is doubtful whether ACC was cash positive over the whole period.

Apart from the purchase of interests in Asian joint ventures, the smaller acquisitions brought no long-term benefits and were mostly a distraction.

The hinge-point in the history of A&W in the last 50 years occurred with the investment in **Long Harbour**. By itself, it might have been enough to bring A&W to its knees but the situation was made worse by the entirely misconceived venture in Belledune, which followed the mistaken investment in fertilisers at Port Maitland. The ambitions of the management of Erco for major expansion in Canada, prior to the appointment of Ed Kinsley as President in 1963 and then with full force after his appointment, were too easily accepted by the top management in

London. Sir Sydney Barratt was nearing retirement from the mid-1960s and his nominated successor, Sir Owen Wansbrough-Jones, had neither experience of industrial management nor the strength of purpose to contain Ed Kinsley's ambitions. The changes in organisation just before Sir Sydney's retirement in 1967, which adopted the McKinsey recommendations and centred all executive power in Ed Kinsley, proved to be disastrous. Ed Kinsley's death in the following year brought about a return to a more orthodox management structure and the emergence of David Livingstone as chief executive, without which the situation would have deteriorated further.

The decision to proceed with Long Harbour and the organisational changes precipitated the departure of Frank Schon, a deeply significant event in A&W's history. Frank's consistent opposition to the developments in Canada, to the McKinsey reorganisation (which deprived him of an executive role) and to the appointment of Ed Kinsley as chief executive proved to be fully justified. His entrepreneurial flair, which had proved successful in Marchon, was foreign to the 'Oldbury' managerial tradition. If he had become chief executive (which is inconceivable, given the weight of opposition of the other members of the A&W Board), events would almost certainly have been very different. By 1967, however, a lot of the seeds of disaster had already been sown. Also, Frank would have had to be restrained from over-investment at Whitehaven, where he had hoped to add further anhydrite kilns, which became obsolete by 1973. He would have accelerated the development of wet phosphoric acid but would have been reluctant to reduce the importance of Whitehaven.

The basic idea behind building a large phosphorus plant at Long Harbour had enough to commend it to persuade the majority of the A&W Board to approve the project, although the return forecast was not expected to be more than the minimum then regarded as acceptable. For strategic reasons, A&W believed it needed a large new plant based on cheap power and Long Harbour promised to provide that, as well as seaborne access for raw materials and finished product. The fundamental problem was that A&W had no experience of a successful plant of the kind designed beyond the size of the old Oldbury plant, which itself offered poor working conditions and an unacceptable environmental impact. The unsolved difficulties at Portishead should have prevented a further scaling-up of an old-fashioned design.

The situation was made worse by the attempt to keep down the cost of the Long Harbour plant through economies that exacerbated the problems created by the design. The rejection of the UHDE offer to provide a plant of its design was based on the supposed higher capital cost and there is no evidence that the life-time costs were examined. The very large costs involved in remedying the faults of the plant were, of course, not foreseen and the McKinsey risk analysis did not include an adequate assessment of the risk that the plant would not operate satisfactorily. It seems strange that it took some 15 years from start-up at the end of 1968 for the plant to be operating consistently at a reasonably high level. It took more than 10 years for computerised controls to be installed (a shortcoming that also applied to other plants, notably the F5 phosphoric acid plant at Whitehaven, the largest capital expenditure project since Long Harbour).

Bringing the Long Harbour plant to the point of reasonably consistent operation took a long time and involved tremendous and praiseworthy efforts by Jim Medves and others. Even then, the output was well below the designed capacity, the phosphorus produced was at an uneconomic cost and there were problems of working conditions and environmental impact. It took a long time for the decision to close the plant to be taken. In the earlier years of operation there was over-optimism that solutions to problems of operation such as broken electrodes were just around the corner; later, until PWA was well-established, keeping the plant open was considered to be preferable to closure.

The consequences of the troubles at Long Harbour, coming on top of the cash drain caused by Belledune, were momentous but not fully realised for some time. When the sale of A&W's holding in Midland Silicones was under consideration, Hill Samuel agreed in January 1969 that it was not necessary on cash grounds. Two years later, the severe cash shortage caused Hill Samuel to recommend sale, although for only £3.5 million, compared with the £10 million offered by Dow Corning two years earlier.

Once it had become apparent that there was no quick or easy solution to the crippling Long Harbour situation, the A&W share price fell to the point where acquisition of the company, whether solicited or unsolicited, became likely. Was it avoidable? It is possible to argue that the recovery in profits and the accumulation of funds from 1971 to 1977 were not due to Tenneco's acquisition of a controlling interest, so that A&W could have survived as a fully independent company. Against that, under the Tenneco protectorate A&W was effectively insulated from acquisition by anyone else and the bankers were more accommodating. The balance of argument is probably that A&W would not have survived as a fully independent company.

The continuation of Albright & Wilson as an identifiable (although not fully independent) entity for nearly twenty-four years after Tenneco acquired a potentially controlling interest must be counted as fairly unusual. From 1978 (when A&W became wholly-owned by Tenneco) to 1986, A&W under David Livingstone was left by Tenneco to manage itself, with few exceptions. For two years only, from March 1979 to March 1981, Gene Anderson was joint Deputy Managing Director, with circumscribed powers. Otherwise Tenneco did not impose anyone on the management of A&W. There were regular reviews of budgets, plans and results but shortfalls (which were all too usual) were accepted without insistence on remedial action. With hindsight, the Tenneco management tended to believe that there should have been more intervention to improve profits and develop strategy (but the subsequent history of Tenneco suggests that that may not have been beneficial).

The one exception in that period was the enforced sale of BBA in 1982. The other divestments at that time were decided by the A&W management rather than dictated by Tenneco. The disposal in 1983 of the aryl phosphates business, originally part of Boake Roberts, recognised the over-capacity in the UK and A&W's regrettable loss of market share. The divestment of the former ACC agricultural operations in the same year was a well-timed and executed withdrawal from an area of inadequate profitability; the purchaser, ICI, was itself to withdraw from fertilisers later. The third divestment in 1983, of the toluene derivatives operations at West Bank, was seen by the A&W management as a sensible rationalisation move, although at the time there were signs that the operations could be made profitable. In total, these divestments produced cash, helped management to concentrate on core business and did not unduly prejudice the Company's future development.

From 1986 until the flotation in 1995, there was more significant intervention by Tenneco. It started with the removal of David Livingstone in November 1986. Tenneco (Jim Ketelsen) had finally decided that A&W's failure to meet its profit forecasts needed strong action. The move was understandable. A&W's senior management had been in place for too long without fresh input and a term of 15 years is unusually long for a chief executive. Although the way in which the change was managed was more abrupt than might reasonably have been expected and a grievous blow for David Livingstone, the introduction of Robin Paul as chief executive was accepted as a positive move.

These were years of crisis for Tenneco, leading to divestments not of A&W's choosing, which A&W was unable to prevent. Although Paper Chemicals accounted for less than 10% of A&W's total sales and less than 5% of profits, they were an expanding speciality business. The sale of the Pulp Chemicals business removed about 12% of group sales and no less than 40% of profits in 1990 (the last full year of ownership). While it is possible that A&W would have concluded that Pulp Chemicals should be divested at an appropriate time, because of its capital requirements and increasing competition, the pity was that Tenneco forced a fire-sale at a price below book value. Moreover, there was no recognition of the important, growing and assured profits from the supply of patented chlorine dioxide systems to pulp mills. If the sale had been made by A&W, the proceeds should have been much greater and could have been invested in an acquisition to strengthen A&W's core business. As it was, A&W was weakened and its potential market value substantially reduced.

In its last period as a public company, A&W had opportunities to strengthen its position in its core business. The first of these was to link with OCP, but it was preferred to continue to invest in Whitehaven (which Rhodia was later to abandon). The second was a purchase of Solutia, which did not happen because the cost was deemed to be beyond A&W's resources. It is not clear whether the only way to finance an acquisition of Solutia was to sell A&W's surfactants business, or whether the surfactants business should have been sold anyhow. Steps of that magnitude might have persuaded the stock market that the shares did not merit the downgrading in the latter part of 1998. The resistance to such changes perhaps came from too much faith that the Company could make its way without major change - another symptom of latter-day hubris?

It would be wrong, however, to suggest that Albright & Wilson had not changed substantially in its last twenty years. The development of Albright & Wilson Americas, the move into Mexico, the appointment of Paul Rocheleau, a US citizen, as chief executive in 1997, the diminution of importance of the UK as generator of profits, expansion in Asia, the appointment of Gabriel Kow - they amounted to significant changes. Yet the company still had a mainly UK orientation, with its headquarters in England and a London stock market quotation. Given more time, there would have been a bolder outlook, but time ran out.

The management practices introduced by Tenneco after Mike Walsh became its chief executive, although having merits, were increasingly complex. It is arguable that they detracted from a more direct approach to cost savings, which became increasingly important as competition intensified after 1995 - A&W had been slow to implement cost savings involving compulsory redundancy and to bring its overheads into line with the operations remaining after major disposals. The failure to be bolder in reducing costs in the end undermined Albright & Wilson's profits. The actions taken by Gabriel Kow first in Asia Pacific and then in Europe indicated what might have been done to strengthen the company and make it less likely to attract predators. If Gabriel had succeeded Robin Paul as Chief Executive, there might have been time to prevent the final submergence.

A further factor was the practice for many years to write down investments in unsuccessful plants, generally treated as extraordinary items rather than as operating costs. Statements at the time of flotation indicated that the decks had been well swept and when provisions nevertheless continued to be made in 1995-8 there were sharply negative reactions in the stock market.

Was the final submergence inevitable?

The answer to this question is perhaps that it was inevitable but not unavoidable (the two words are *not* synonymous). Many medium-sized chemical companies have proved vulnerable to absorption, particularly in recent years when rationalisation within the industry has been rife. Moreover, since the mid-1960s Albright & Wilson had become smaller relative to the rest of the chemical industry: much larger than Laporte (for example) in 1960, A&W's market value in the later 1990s was only a fraction of Laporte's. A&W's attempts at merger all failed and there was shrinkage through divestments, not fully balanced by surviving acquisitions. The Long Harbour problem imposed cash constraints on expansion and that was followed by Tenneco's problems.

At the same time, A&W's strong position in PWA and speciality phosphates and phosphorus derivatives made the Company attractive to other companies in the same field. Other small to medium chemical companies remain because either they are insufficiently attractive to potential predators or they have succeeded in making themselves too expensive to be worth bidding for. A&W was not highly profitable and offered to acquirors scope for rationalisation and significant cost savings.

In the end, bidding started from the point where A&W's share price was only half the flotation price - which itself had been driven down by the knowledge that Tenneco was committed to divestment - and so A&W's shareholders could be expected to accept an offer that was low in relation to potential earnings. A&W's survived as an identifiable entity within Tenneco for 17 years but then for only 4 years as an independent public company. It was a sad end for a company with nearly 150 years of existence, but not wholly unexpected. It was inevitable because of a long history of failings but in my judgment avoidable if at several points a different course of action had been chosen, from known alternatives. But that would have required a supply of foresight that is very much rarer than the hindsight of historians.

15th April 2002

APPENDIX I -
INFLATION-ADJUSTED FIGURES

The Chart shows sales and pretax profits for the Albright & Wilson group from 1951 to 1998. Caution needs to be exercised in drawing conclusions from the figures because:

- the use of the UK Retail Price Index as a deflator probably gives a reasonable indication of how the results might have been viewed by an economically well-informed UK shareholder but will not give a good indication of the volume of sales, since selling-prices tend to increase at less than the rate of inflation and in many instances fall over the life of a product;
- there were many adjustments to profits for asset write-downs, rationalisation costs, surpluses on disposals, etc. which fell in the year of adjustment rather than the year(s) causing the adjustment; profits are as far as possible shown on a consistent basis after all such adjustments, rather than as reported (when for much of the period they were treated as extraordinary);
- acquisitions and divestments had a significant effect on the figures, particularly the divestments after 1978
- sales by associated companies (where A&W's holding was 50% or less) are excluded;
- profits are shown before tax because of the variability of tax charges; extraordinary charges are usually shown in the accounts net of tax reliefs and where possible they have been grossed up for pretax figures.

The main events affecting the results are shown on the page following the chart.

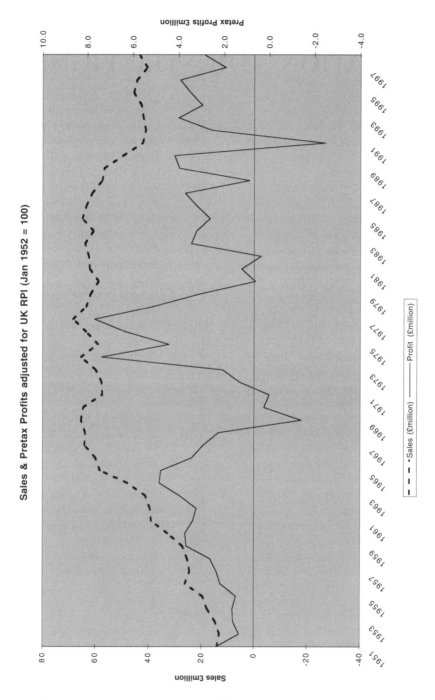

Inflation-adjusted sales & pretax profits 1951-1998

The significant special factors affecting the results year by year are shown below.

1954 - Kirkby, Varennes & Portishead opened

1955 - Barry opened, Marchon acquired (Dec.)

1956 - OECCo sold

1957 - Vancouver opened

1959 - Dominion Fertilisers acquired

1960 - Boake Roberts acquired

1961 - Bush acquired

1964 - Stafford Allen acquired

1965 - ACC acquired, Ireland became a subsidiary

1966 - BFL plant built

1967 - Potter & Moore pharmaceuticals sold

1968 - Potter & Moore toiletries sold. Portishead closed, Long Harbour opened

1969 - Temporary closure of Long Harbour

1970 - BFL write-down

1971 - Tenneco £17.5m. investment. BFL written off Midland Silicones sold

1973 - Bromborough & chrome chemicals sold. Long Harbour write-down. Whitehaven kilns closed. PWA plant opened. Tenneco 49.8% holding

1974 - Special contribution to UK pension funds

1976 - Second Long Harbour furnace reopened

1978 - Tenneco 100%. Monroe & Thunder Bay opened. Wetherill Park opened. Service Products sold

1979 - F5 opened. 40% of PPL acquired

1980 - 100% of UIC Singapore acquired

1981 - Thai Polyphosphates formed

1982 - BBA sold

1983 - Tenneco Chemicals Europe transferred to A&W West Bank & UK agricultural sold

1985 - Monroe closed. Mobil Chemicals acquired. Tensia Surfac acquired

1986 - Chemrich acquired

1988 - Provision for closure of Long Harbour Ireland & Butler sold. Colas Bewoid acquired

1989 - Aurora opened. Rio Linda & Pine Chemicals NZ acquired. Long Harbour closed. S. African companies sold

1990 - Paper Chemicals sold. Sulphonation in Indonesia & Philippines.

1991 - Provisions for phosphorus rationalisation & Whitehaven environmental costs. Lavera opened. Australia no longer a subsidiary. Explosion at Charleston

1992 - Pulp Chemicals sold. F5 closed

1993 - Sale of Buckingham hydroelectric plant

1994 - Share in Troy acquired, charges for phosphorus sites, European surfactants & Mexican currency devaluation

1995 - Flotation. Sale of Rio Linda, packed powders, etc.. Headcount reductions in Spain & Whitehaven

1996 - Headcount reductions in Italy & Whitehaven. India a subsidiary. Service Chemicals & Surfachem holding sold.

1997 - Troy a subsidiary. Charges for asset impairment, stock valuations, further headcount reductions & environment

1998 - Troy owned 100%. Further charges offset by profit on financing.

APPENDIX 2 - CONTRIBUTORS

This book would not have been possible, nor as complete as it is, without the factual and personal accounts from the following people. Except where stated otherwise, they have been interviewed.

Dr J.R. Adsetts (John):
Technical Director of Albright & Wilson October 1987-May 1998; in charge of Specialities Group 1990-95

C. E. Anderson (Gene):
seconded from Tenneco to A&W December 1972, Director of Operations January 1974-December 1975, Joint Deputy Managing Director March 1979-June 1981

G.I. Black (Ian):
joined Marchon as an accountant in August 1967, Chief Accountant of Detergents & Chemicals Group 1976, Sales Director of Surfactants Division 1979, Commercial Director of Phosphates Division 1983, Division Managing Director of Phosphates 1986, Detergents 1987, Phosphates 1991, Director 1995, Chief Operating Officer 1997, retired 1998

R.T. Blakely (Bob):
Chief Financial Officer of Tenneco 1981, Vice-President until 1999

E.R. Brazier (Ernest):
joined A&W as an Engineer in 1937, involved with phosphorus furnaces at Oldbury, Portishead and particularly at Long Harbour; consultant for Long Harbour 1980

R. Bristoe (Ron):
joined Marchon 1944, working in laboratories, production plants and customer services and for 5 years running the Kells school for young trainees; retired in 1990

D. Bucks (David):
Director of Hill Samuel, advising A&W, particularly over Tenneco bid in 1978

R.F. Chalmers (Bob):
Canadian, going to Long Harbour in 1966, then to Buckingham and Vancouver, operations manager at Long Harbour 1979-84; 1987 General Manager, Resins & Organics, 1988 Quality Manager.

J.C. Christopherson (John):
joined A&W in 1933, Sales Director 1942, retired 1969

Sir Robert Clark (Bob):
Director of Hill Samuel most concerned with A&W's affairs up to the takeover by Tenneco

M.J. Clay (Mike):
joined Marchon 1961; after production planning, from 1976 handling PR, concerned particularly with Greenpeace 1989-91.

W.H. Coates (Bill):
(written account)
joined British Chrome Chemicals (later part of ACC) in 1957, became concerned with engineering and production for ACC and then in 1975 head of the Agricultural Sector until retirement in 1977

R. Cranke (Ray):
joined the Whitehaven laboratories in 1967, moving from organics to development of PWA, becoming site manager in 1995 and then moving to Singapore

J.C. Crawford (Jim):
joined Ag. Division in 1979, moved to Warley 1983, Central Personnel Manager 1986, retired 1999

R. Croft (Bob):
worked on phosphorus furnaces at Oldbury and Portishead before going to Long Harbour in 1977, until 1983; introduced computer controls at Long Harbour and then in UK plants up to 1995

P.G. Cumming (Pat):
(written account)
joined Robt Stephenson & Son, a fertiliser company (later an ACC company) in 1946, MD of Farm Protection, formed 1947 for crop-spraying, obtained DuPont agency in 1959 and became a marketing company for pesticides in 1963; retired 1976

J. Dawson (Jonathan):
a Director of Lazard Bros, hired by Tenneco in 1992 to work on flotation of A&W, which was aborted but then accomplished in 1995

J.A. Dean (John):
joined Boake Roberts in 1946 as a chemist and worked on the construction of plasticiser and synthetic aromatic plants, then in research; production director of BBA in 1968 and later head of chemicals sector; when BBA was acquired by Union Camp in 1982, John Dean was put in charge

R.C. Edquist (Dick):
(written account)
joined A&W (Australia) in 1945, Technical Director 1954, Managing Director 1960, retired 1974

S.T. Ellis (Sydney):
joined Petro-Tex (a joint Tenneco-FMC company) in 1959 as President and CEO; moved to Tenneco Chemicals as President 1969, becoming Chairman until 1975; Executive Vice-President and Director of Tenneco 1969-78; Director of A&W 1971 and Chairman from 1972 until his retirement in 78

Dr D.A.A. Fagandini (Danny):
joined Marchon 1951, becoming Export Manager before moving to found Marchon Italiana 1960; returned to Whitehaven 1965; resigned 1967 after resignation of Frank Schon but returned 1970 as deputy to Otto Secher and then Divisional Managing Director; went to BBA as MD 1973 until May 1976, when he became Director of Corporate Development; retired 1983

K. Gregory (Keith):
(written account)
started with Boake Roberts, serving in India and moving to London 1961; moved to A&W Development Department 1965 and then to a newly-formed Overseas Department , responsible for setting up Overseas Marketing Companies; joined the marketing department of Industrial Chemicals 1970 and left 1974

P.E. Greville (Peter):
joined A&W Ireland in 1955, became a Director in 1958 and Managing Director in 1965 until 1971, when he moved to the A&W Development Department; in Specialities Group 1974 and retired 1976

P. Hughes (Pat):
an engineer in production development at Whitehaven from 1944 to 1955, working on the early sulphuric acid, sulphonation, hydrogenation and firelighters plants

G.R. James (George):
(written account)
from 1962 General Manager of Gardinol, acquired by A&W (Australia) in 1966; seconded to London 1974, MD of A&W (Australia) 1976-1978, Detergents Division MD 1979, Phosphates Division MD 1980, Technical Director of A&W 1983, retired 1987

D. Johnson (Derek):
(written account)
Technical Director of Midland Silicones, then of ACC; appointed to the New Ventures Division of A&W in 1972 and MD in 1973; NVD absorbed into Specialities Division 1976; left A&W 1978

J.L. Ketelsen (Jim):
Chief Accountant of JI Case, acquired by Tenneco 1967; became President of Tenneco and then Chairman 1978; ceased to be Chief Executive 1991 and to be Chairman 1992

I.P. Khandelwal (Ishwar):
joined Albright, Morarji & Pandit 1973, became Managing Director 1983 and retired in 1998

G. Kow (Gabriel):
became President of A&W Asia Pacific (from Glaxo) in June 1997 and a Director of A&W plc; became President also of A&W Europe in January 1999; remained with European (including the UK) surfactants when sold to Huntsman in April 2001

K. Lever (Ken):
joined A&W as Finance Director in November 1995, ceased in October 1999, after Rhodia takeover, remaining on the A&W Board until May 2000

L.G. Lillico (Lloyd):
(written account)
joined Erco in 1939 as a laboratory technician at Buckingham, moving over to production; transferred to Varennes in 1957; Production Manager at Toronto 1959, General Manager - Industrial Phosphates 1965; Vice President 1965, President 1967, retired 1983

E.J. Lowe (Ted):
joined A&W at Oldbury 1946 as a junior laboratory assistant, becoming a section

head; PA to Alf Loveless (Phosphates Technical Director) 1965-7; Technical Manager of Phosphates and member of Long Harbour Technical Committee 1974; later also in charge of production; General Manager, Phosphates 1990, retired 1991

A.T. McInnes (Allen):
joined Tenneco 1960 in budget department, becoming head of the Financial Evaluation and Development department and then a Vice President; head of Tenneco West 1975; in charge of Tenneco's international development programme 1981; Executive Vice President 1982, responsible for 4 Tenneco divisions, including A&W, and a Director of Tenneco; Chairman of A&W 1988 to 1992, when he left Tenneco

G.H. Meason (George):
joined Tenneco 1956, becoming Chief Engineer and Vice President of Bay Petroleum; then in charge of commercial functions of Tenneco Oil, becoming Executive Vice President of the oil company in 1971 and President 1973; Executive Vice President of Tenneco 1974; Chairman of A&W 1978; retired 1981

J. Medves (Jim):
(written account)
joined Erco at Buckingham 1959 as a plant superintendent; Varennes 1963-1965, Port Maitland 1965-8; in charge of team commissioning Long Harbour furnaces 1968, later in charge of production and maintenance; returned to Varennes 1971-3; manager of Long Harbour 1973-79; manager of Buckingham 1979-87

E. Messenger (Ed):
worked on developing HDLs (heavy duty liquid detergents) at Whitehaven from 1978 to about the end of the 1990s

Dr R.C. Paul, CBE (Robin):
joined A&W as Managing Director in 1986 after career in ICI (ending as Deputy Chairman of Mond Division); a chemical engineer; retired July 1997

Dr M.G. Peard (Michael):
came to Oldbury as a research chemist in 1952; 1957 transferred to London to head a newly-formed development department; 1957-8 seconded to joint A&W-Fisons team to make a survey of world phosphate deposits; 1969 a member of the Short Range Planning Group; Director of A&W 1969, in charge of planning and with responsibilities for BBA and A&W Ireland; resigned 1973

G.W. Pekarek, OBE (George):

joined Marchon at Whitehaven 1953, in sales department; became Sales Director and then Commercial Director of Marchon; Commercial Director of the Detergents & Chemicals Group 1975; A&W International Marketing Manager 1977, responsible for development of OMCs (overseas marketing companies) and involved in developments in Asia; retired 1989

W.E.K. Piercy (Keith):

(written account)

after securing rights to market Calgon in 1933, set up a company, which became a subsidiary of A&W in 1934; set up a Market Research Department in 1951 and appointed David Livingstone to head it; joined the A&W Board in 1953 as Development Director; became the Director responsible for BBA; retired 1969

Sir Richard Powell, GCB, KBE, CMG (Richard):

former Permanent Secretary of the Board of Trade, in 1968 became a Director of Hill Samuel, which persuaded A&W to appoint him a Director in 1968; succeeded Sir Owen Wansbrough Jones as Chairman of A&W in 1969; retired 1972 after Tenneco's acquisition of a controlling interest

T.S.E. Powell (Trevor):

joined Stafford Allen in 1959 as manager for Saromex (spice flavouring); 1966 Sales Director (Stafford Allen); then successively Marketing Director for BBA, Sector Chairman for Flavours and then Fragrances; resigned 1980

P.F. Rocheleau (Paul):

a chemical engineer, who came to A&W when Mobil Chemicals was acquired in 1985; to London in 1986 as an analyst in the Strategic Planning department under Peter Salmon; returned to A&W Americas and became VP - Industrial Chemicals; President of A&W Americas 1993; succeeded Robin Paul as Chief Executive of A&W in 1997, until March 2000, when the acquisition by Rhodia was completed

P.F. Salmon (Peter):

joined A&W 1955 as a trainee cost accountant; 1965 a member of the planning team for Long Harbour; became Finance Director for A&W (Mfg)/Oldbury Division; moved to Whitehaven as Finance Director for Detergents; FD for Detergents & Chemicals 1975; General Manager - Economic Analysis in London 1978, Strategic Planning Manager 1986; added Commercial Department 1987; principal person involved in most acquisitions and disposals, also in PWA in USA; retired 1992

W.W. Sapp (Walter):
joined Tenneco 1976 as General Counsel and Senior VP, remaining until Mike Walsh replaced Jim Ketelsen in 1991. Involved in acquisition of A&W by Tenneco.

W.E. Scott (Wilton):
President of Tenneco Oil 1969, Executive VP 1971, Chairman of Tenneco 1975 until retirement in 1978

O. Secher (Otto):
(from taped interview with Mike Clay)
joined Frank Schon (brother-in-law) 1941; moved to Whitehaven and became a Director of Marchon in 1952 with joint responsibility for sales; became MD and Chairman of Marchon in 1969 (after Frank Schon's resignation in 1967 and Peter Baines's appointment to the A&W Board); retired 1972

W. Shillaker (Wilf):
joined A&W 1952 as a cost accountant at Oldbury; became Group Cost Accountant and then General Manager, Finance; member of Short Range Planning Group 1969; seconded to Long Harbour for 3 months 1973; Finance Director of BBA 1978, remained with BBA after sale to Union Camp 1982

J.G. Strong (Jerry):
began with Mobil Chemical Co. before its acquisition by A&W in 1985; became Technical manager at Richmond; 1988 moved to Oldbury to help set up ITC; head of R & D for A&W 1990

Dr C.W. Suckling (Charles):
General Manager - Research & Technology for ICI, became a non-executive Director of A&W 1982, on retirement from ICI, with special responsibility for technical affairs; resigned 1989

J.T. Symonds (Taft):
son of Gardiner Symonds, who contributed recollections and written material on his father

A Taylor (Alan):
joined Solway in 1960, in laboratories and then production and training; to safety department at Whitehaven 1973; periods in Ag. Division, Knightsbridge and Oldbury before return to Whitehaven 1981 as personnel manager until the end of the 1990s

K.A. Ward (Tony):
joined A&W 1953 as Financial Accountant, at Oldbury; became Group Financial Accountant 1957, then Assistant Treasurer and Treasurer 1964; member of Short Range Planning Group 1969; appointed Finance Director 1969; Joint Deputy Managing Director (Finance & Administration) 1979; retired 1983

T.A. Williams, MBE (Alan):
joined A&W 1960; became involved in PWA 1965, in the UK and then at Aurora; appointed Senior Scientist and awarded MBE for his work 1997

J.R. Wills, OBE (John):
joined Marchon in 1961, Chief Accountant 1966, Division Finance Director 1969, Division Commercial Director 1971, Division MD 1973, MD of Detergents & Chemicals 1975, A&W Commercial Director 1977; responsible for expansion in Asia; retired 1987

C.N. Wilson (Nevil):
son of J.C. Wilson, joined A&W 1954; Company Secretary 1955, retired December 1988, the last member of the founding families to work in A&W

W.M. Winstanley (Michael):
joined the cost department at Oldbury 1959; moved to buying department 1963 and became Chief Buyer 1967; General Marketing Manager, Industrial Chemicals Division 1971; Analyst at Knightsbridge 1974; Deputy Chairman, Phosphates Sector 1975; VP of Erco Industrial Chemicals 1977; Sales Director of Phosphates Division 1980, Phosphates General Manager 1986; President of A&W Americas and member of A&W Board 1990; Finance Director 1983; retired 1995 (after flotation)

C.R. Woods (Timber):
joined W.J. Bush 1914, General Sales Manager 1951; retired 1966

L.C. Work (Lyall):
joined Erco 1967 as technical superintendent of Port Maitland fertiliser plant; Long Harbour Technical Manager April-August 1969 & 1974-6; Analyst at Knightsbridge 1976; Erco Industrial Relations Manager 1979, Technical VP 1985; VP Industrial Chemicals for USA 1987; Industrial Chemicals President for A&W Americas 1988; President of A&W Asia 1991; President of A&W Americas 1997; after Rhodia takeover, became President of Specialty Phosphates within Consumer Specialities Division.

INDEX